YEARS OF PROTEST

A Collection of American Writings of the 1930's

edited by Jack Salzman

BARRY WALLENSTEIN, ASSISTANT EDITOR

PEGASUS NEW YORK

LIBRARY OF CONGRESS CATALOG CARD NUMBER: 67-13489

©COPYRIGHT 1967 BY WESTERN PUBLISHING COMPANY, INC.
ALL RIGHTS RESERVED, INCLUDING THE RIGHT OF REPRODUCTION IN WHOLE OR IN PART IN ANY FORM.
DESIGNED AND PRODUCED BY ARTISTS AND WRITERS PRESS, INC.
PRINTED IN THE U.S.A. BY WESTERN PRINTING AND LITHOGRAPHING CO.
PUBLISHED BY PEGASUS, A DIVISION OF WESTERN PUBLISHING COMPANY, INC.

ACKNOWLEDGEMENTS

"The Hard Winter," from THE DISINHERITED by Jack Conroy, Copyright 1933 by Jack Conroy, Copyright © 1963 by Hill and Wang, Inc., is reprinted by permission of Hill and Wang, Inc. ● The selection from UNION SQUARE, Copyright 1933, 1961 by Albert Halper, is reprinted by permission of Albert Halper. ● "The Happiest Man on Earth," Copyright 1938 by Albert Maltz, is reprinted from BEST SHORT STORIES OF 1939 by permission of Albert Maltz. ● The selection from WAITING FOR NOTHING by Thomas Kromer, Copyright 1935 by Alfred A. Knopf, Inc., is reprinted by permission of the publisher. ● "Masses of Men," from THE COMPLETE STORIES OF ERSKINE CALDWELL by Erskine Caldwell, Copyright 1933, © 1961 by Erskine Caldwell, is reprinted by permission of the author; Little, Brown and Co.; and Laurence Pollinger, Ltd. ● The selection from LET US NOW PRAISE FAMOUS MEN by James Agee and Walker Evans, Copyright 1941 by James Agee and Walker Evans, Copyright © 1960 by Walker Evans, is reprinted by permission of Houghton Mifflin Company. ● "A Union Meeting" is reprinted from PUZZLED AMERICA by Sherwood Anderson, Copyright 1935 by Charles Scribner's Sons, Copyright renewed by Eleanor C. Anderson, reprinted by permission of Harold Ober Associates Inc. ● Excerpts from the opening of PINS AND NEEDLES, Music by Harold Rome, Lyrics by Harold Rome and Charles Friedman, is used by permission of the authors. "Sing Me A Song With Social Significance," and "Back To Work," Music and Lyrics by Harold Rome, are used by permission of Harold Rome and Florence Music Company, Inc. ● The selection from THE LAND OF PLENTY by Robert Cantwell, Copyright 1934, © 1962 by Robert Cantwell, is reprinted by permission of Holt, Rinehart and Winston, Inc. ● "The Earth Does Move," from ROPE OF GOLD by Josephine Herbst, Copyright 1939 by Harcourt, Brace & World, Inc., is used by permission. ● "Cops Are Funny People—If At All" is reprinted from REDDER THAN THE ROSE by Robert Forsythe. Copyright 1935 by Covici Friede, Inc., renewed 1963 by Mrs. Kyle Samuel Crichton, reprinted by permission of Robert Crichton. ● "Communists and Cops," from THE AMERICAN EARTHQUAKE by Edmund Wilson, Copyright 1959 by the author, is reprinted by permission. ● "Denoument," from NEW AND SELECTED POEMS by Kenneth Fearing, Copyright 1956 by the author, is reprinted by permission of Indiana University Press. ● "The Unknown Soldier," from COMPANY K by William March, Copyright 1933 by William March, Copyright renewed, is reprinted by permission of Harold Ober Associates Incorporated ● Dispatch from Spain, datelined April 24, 1937, by Ernest Hemingway, was written for North American Newspaper Alliance. Reprinted by permission. ● "Say That We Saw Spain Die" is reprinted from COLLECTED POEMS, by Edna St. Vincent Millay, Harper & Row, Copyright 1939, 1966 by Edna St. Vincent Millay and Norma Millay Ellis. Reprinted by permission. ● "Litany for Dictatorships" is from SELECTED WORKS OF STEPHEN VINCENT BENET, Copyright 1935 by Stephen Vincent Benet, Copyright renewed 1963 by Thomas C. Benet, Stephanie B. Mahin and Rachel Benet Lewis. Reprinted by permission of Brandt & Brandt. ● The selection from YOU CAN'T GO HOME AGAIN by Thomas Wolfe, Copyright 1940 by Maxwell Perkins as Executor, is reprinted by permission of Harper & Row, Publishers, and William Heinemann, Ltd. ● The selection from THOSE WHO PERISH by Edward Dahlberg, Copyright © 1934, 1962 by Edward Dahlberg, is reprinted by permission of the John Day Company, Inc., publisher. ● The selection from JEFFERSON AND/OR MUSSOLINI by Ezra Pound, Copyright 1935, 1936 by Ezra Pound, is reprinted by permission of New Directions Publishing Corporation, agents for the Committee for Ezra Pound. ● "September 1, 1939," by W. H. Auden, Copyright 1940 by W. H. Auden, is reprinted from THE COLLECTED POETRY OF W. H. AUDEN by permission of Random House, Inc., and Faber & Faber, Ltd. ● "Wilder: Prophet of The Genteel Christ," by Michael Gold, is reprinted by permission of the author. ● "Invocation To The Social Muse" by Archibald MacLeish, from COLLECTED POEMS 1917-1952, is reprinted by permission of Houghton Mifflin Company. ● "Mr. Burnshaw and the Statue," by Wallace Stevens, Copyright 1936 by Wallace Stevens, is reprinted from OPUS POSTHUMOUS by permission of Alfred A. Knopf, Inc., and Faber & Faber, Ltd. ● "Bankruptcy of Southern Culture," by V. F. Calverton, from Scribner's Magazine, May, 1936, Copyright 1936, 1963, is reprinted by permission of the author. ● The selection from A NOTE ON LITERARY CRITICISM by James T. Farrell is reprinted by permission of The Vanguard Press. Copyright, 1936, by The Vanguard Press; Copyright, 1963, by James T. Farrell. ● "The Temptation of Dr. Williams," by the editors of Partisan Review, Copyright 1938 by Partisan Review, is reprinted by permission. ● "Partisan Review," by Malcolm Cowley, from The New Republic, Vol. 96, October 19, 1938, renewal Copyright 1966 by Malcolm Cowley, is reprinted by permission of the author. ● "A Letter To The New Republic" by the editors of Partisan Review, Copyright 1938 by Partisan Review, is reprinted by permission. ● "Red Ivory Tower" by Malcolm Cowley, from The New Republic, Vol. 97, November 9, 1938, renewal Copyright 1966 by Malcolm Cowley, is reprinted by permission of the author. ● "Cow" by Ben Field is reprinted from PROLETARIAN LITERATURE IN THE UNITED STATES by permission of International Publishers Co., Inc. ● "Did God Make Bedbugs?" by Michael Gold, is from JEWS WITHOUT MONEY, Copyright 1930 by Horace Liveright, Inc., Copyright renewed 1958 by Michael Gold. Reprinted by permission of Evelyn Singer Agency. ● "I Have Seen Black Hands" by Richard Wright is reprinted by permission of Paul R. Reynolds, Inc. ● "What The Thunder Said, A Fire Sermon" by Sol Funaroff is reprinted from PROLETARIAN LITERATURE IN THE UNITED STATES by permission of International Publishers Co., Inc. ● "New York, Cassandra," reprinted from NO RETREAT by Horace Gregory, Copyright 1933 by the author, is used by permission of the author. ● "Joe Hill Listens to the Praying" by Kenneth Patchen is reprinted from PROLETARIAN LITERATURE IN THE UNITED STATES by permission of International Publishers Co., Inc. ● "August 22, 1927" by David Wolff is reprinted from PROLETARIAN LITERATURE IN THE UNITED STATES by permission of International Publishers Co., Inc. ● "The Trial," from THEORY OF FLIGHT by Muriel Rukeyser, Copyright © 1935, 1962 by Muriel Rukeyser, is reprinted by permission of Monica McCall, Inc. ● "Peace! It's Wonderful!" by Henry Miller, from THE COSMOLOGICAL EYE, Copyright 1939 by New Directions, is reprinted by permission of the publisher, New Directions Publishing Corporation, and Laurence Pollinger, Ltd. ● "Speech from a Forthcoming Play: I" by e. e. cummings, Copyright, 1936 by e. e. cummings, reprinted from E. E. CUMMINGS, A MISCELLANY edited by George J. Furmage, by permission of Harcourt, Brace and World, Inc. ● "Speech from a Forthcoming Play: II" by e. e. cummings, Copyright, 1946 by e. e. cummings, reprinted from E. E. CUMMINGS, A MISCELLANY edited by George J. Furmage, by permission of Harcourt, Brace and World, Inc. ● "Night Without Sleep" by Robinson Jeffers, Copyright 1937 and renewed 1964 by Donnan Jeffers and Garth Jeffers, is reprinted from SELECTED POETRY OF ROBINSON JEFFERS by permission of Random House, Inc. ● "The Dawn of Another Day" from THE FARMER'S DAUGHTERS by William Carlos Williams, Copyright 1938 by William Carlos Williams, © 1961 by New Directions, is reprinted by permission of the publisher, New Directions Publishing Corporation. ● "Aspirin Is a Member of the N.R.A." by William Saroyan is reprinted from THE DARING YOUNG MAN ON THE FLYING TRAPEZE, Copyright 1934, 1962 by William Saroyan. Reprinted by permission of the author. ● "Miss Lonelyhearts and the Dead Pan" is reprinted by permission of the estate of Nathanael West. ● The selection from CALL IT SLEEP by Henry Roth is reprinted by permission of Cooper Square Publishers, Inc.

For Cecily and Patricia

CONTENTS

Preface 7

PART I

NO ONE HAS STARVED 11
    In a Coffee Pot *by Alfred Hayes* 15
    The Hard Winter *by Jack Conroy* 19
    From Union Square *by Albert Halper* 22
    The Happiest Man on Earth *by Albert Maltz* 29
    School for Bums *by Mary Heaton Vorse* 39
    From Waiting for Nothing *by Tom Kromer* 45
    Masses of Men *by Erskine Caldwell* 50
    Cows and Horses Are Hungry *by Meridel Le Sueur* 60
    Dubious Battle in California *by John Steinbeck* 66
    Talking Dust Bowl *by Woody Guthrie* 72
    I Ain't Got No Home *by Woody Guthrie* 74
    From Let Us Now Praise Famous Men *by James Agee* 76

A LACK OF CONFIDENCE 85
    Harlan: Working under the Gun *by John Dos Passos* 89
    Which Side Are You On? *by Florence Reece* 100
    A Union Meeting *by Sherwood Anderson* 102
    From Pins and Needles *by Harold Rome* 108
    From The Land of Plenty *by Robert Cantwell* 113
    From To Make My Bread *by Grace Lumpkin* 123
    The Earth Does Move *by Josephine Herbst* 131
    The Strike *by Tillie Lerner* 138
    Cops Are Funny People—If at All *by Robert Forsythe* 145
    Communists and Cops *by Edmund Wilson* 149
    Waiting for Lefty *by Clifford Odets* 156

LET US HAVE MADNESS 179
    Denouement *by Kenneth Fearing* 182
    The Unknown Soldier *by William March* 187
    Dispatch from Spain *by Ernest Hemingway* 191
    Dispatch from Spain *by Herbert L. Matthews* 196
    Say That We Saw Spain Die *by Edna St. Vincent Millay* 199
    Litany for Dictatorships *by Stephen Vincent Benet* 201
    From You Can't Go Home Again *by Thomas Wolfe* 205
    From Those Who Perish *by Edward Dahlberg* 212
    From Jefferson and/or Mussolini *by Ezra Pound* 221
    September 1, 1939 *by W. H. Auden* 226

PART II

THE SOCIAL MUSE 231

    MICHAEL GOLD AND THE GENTEEL SPIRIT
    Wilder: Prophet of the Genteel Christ *by Michael Gold* 233

ARCHIBALD MACLEISH AND THE SOCIAL MUSE
Invocation to the Social Muse *by Archibald MacLeish* 239
The Social Muse Replies: Letters to The New Republic
   *by Allen Tate, John Peale Bishop, Rolfe Humphries, Yvor
   Winters* 241

THE WRITER ON MIDDLE GROUND
Turmoil in the Middle Ground *by Stanley Burnshaw* 245
Mr. Burnshaw and the Statue *by Wallace Stevens* 248

ON SOUTHERN CULTURE
The Bankruptcy of Southern Culture *by V. F. Calverton* 253
The South Is a Bulwark *by John Crowe Ransom* 264

JAMES T. FARRELL AND THE LITERARY LEFT
From A Note on Literary Criticism *by James T. Farrell* 277
Sectarianism on the Right *by Isidor Schneider* 279
In Defense of James Farrell *by Granville Hicks* 285
Rebuttal *by James T. Farrell* 288

WAS "PARTISAN" TOO PARTISAN?
The Temptation of Dr. Williams *by the Editors of* Partisan Review 295
Partisan Review *by Malcolm Cowley* 297
A Letter to The New Republic *by the Editors of* Partisan Review 300
Red Ivory Tower *by Malcolm Cowley* 304

A WORLD TO WIN 309
Cow *by Ben Field* 311
Did God Make Bedbugs? *by Michael Gold* 320
Can You Hear Their Voices? *by Whittaker Chambers* 327
A Place to Lie Down *by Nelson Algren* 347
I Have Seen Black Hands *by Richard Wright* 354
Four Poems *by Joseph Freeman* 356
What the Thunder Said: A Fire Sermon *by Sol Funaroff* 359
New York, Cassandra *by Horace Gregory* 363

FOUR MARTYRS
Joe Hill Listens to the Praying *by Kenneth Patchen* 367
Stone Face *by Lola Ridge* 371
August 22, 1927 *by David Wolff* 372
The Trial *by Muriel Rukeyser* 373

A BLAZING SUN 377
Peace! It's Wonderful! *by Henry Miller* 379
Two Speeches *by e. e. cummings* 384
Night Without Sleep *by Robinson Jeffers* 387
The Dawn of Another Day *by William Carlos Williams* 389
Aspirin is a Member of the N.R.A. *by William Saroyan* 400
Miss Lonelyhearts and the Dead Pan *by Nathanael West* 406
Pioneers! O Pioneers! *by Daniel Fuchs* 413
From Call It Sleep *by Henry Roth* 425

Selected Bibliography 447

PREFACE

YEARS OF PROTEST is the first of what we hope will be a continuing series of anthologies devoted to representing the literature of the recent past in the light of the conditions under which it was produced. It is thus an historical anthology rather than a critical one, and its purpose is both to survey the literature of a decade, and to capture a sense of the times through that literature. To aid in the realization of this second aim we have augmented the literary selections with numerous illustrations, as well as songs, newspaper articles, and other non-literary documents. In the choice of our literary selections, our double purpose meant that each piece not only had to be interesting and significant in its own right, but also in some way representative of the events or attitudes important to the period in question.

The thirties became the subject of the first of these projects because we felt the decade to be particularly misunderstood, and undeservedly ignored. The time now seems ripe for a general reassessment of its concerns, and we hope our collection will prove useful in this endeavor. We have tried to subvert the clichè that all the writers of the thirties were involved in writing Communist-inspired propaganda, and have not only included many of the decidedly non-proletarian writers active during the decade, but have tried to supply evidence that even among writers of avowedly proletarian works, honesty and talent were not unheard of. Above all, we found the thirties a time of intense, exciting, and significant ferment, and it is a sense of this ferment, as much as an understanding of the issues that went to make it up, that we would like to convey in this collection.

*   *   *

Many people have been generous with their time and suggestions, and we would like to thank them. First and foremost, our thanks must go to James T. Farrell, under whose guidance this book was first conceived. In 1962, Mr. Farrell was asked to compile an anthology of writings which would reflect his personal view of the 1930's; however, other commitments became pressing and it was suggested that we take over the project. The direction of the book has ultimately changed from its original plan, but Mr. Farrell's influence is still felt.

Professors T. B. Strandness of Michigan State University, M. L. Rosenthal and Maurice Baudin of New York University, Randolph Goodman of Brooklyn College, and Arthur Zeiger of City College looked at our outline in various stages of finality, and for their many valuable suggestions we are most grateful. Louise Heinze, Eileen Penn, Margaret Skaggs, and Robin Greene were of particular help in research and the preparation of the manuscript, while Mrs. Joseph Freeman kindly gave us access to her late husband's unpublished manuscripts.

Special acknowledgements must go to Leo Zanderer of Brooklyn College and to R. Tinker Greene, our editor, whose influence on the shape of the book has been decisive. To whatever degree this is a useful and interesting collection, it is due in large part to their encouragement and enthusiastic efforts on its behalf.

J. S.
B. W.

PART ONE

Washington, D.C., 1930.

No One Has Starved

Nobody is actually starving. The hoboes, for
example, are better fed than they have ever been.
—HERBERT HOOVER *(February 1931)*

IN his final message to Congress, delivered on December 4, 1928, Calvin Coolidge spoke in glowing terms of the state of the nation. He told Congress that the country could "regard the present with satisfaction and anticipate the future with optimism. . . ." At home there was tranquility and contentment; abroad there was peace and the good-will which comes from mutual understanding. As was so often the case, Coolidge was wrong.

The Great Depression, of course, did not begin with the collapse of the stock market in October 1929. For one thing, the prosperity enjoyed by many Americans in the twenties was not shared by Europeans. Europe spent the twenties first trying to restore the losses suffered as a result of World War I, and then trying to maintain the fiscal balance; it was a futile attempt. Europe was unable to cope with the financial strains which continued to plague it; and, as a result, its stock prices began to decline months before the great crash. But the unrest and financial instability which permeated Europe seemingly had no more effect upon the optimism of America's leaders than did the cries of discontent which had for years been coming from rural America. America was prospering, and Europe was at peace; it was easy to ignore the signs of trouble.

The election of Herbert Hoover in 1928 was a foregone conclusion. He offered the American people dreams of a great society and they applauded him. In accepting the Republican nomination Hoover told his audience that unemployment, "in the sense of distress," was widely disappearing and that America was nearer to the final triumph over poverty "than ever before in the history of the land." And in the early months of his administration it might well have seemed that poverty was indeed soon to be banished from the nation. For until June of 1929 the American economy continued to boom, the high point being reached in April, May, and June. Then, suddenly, the economy began to decline, and continued to do so until October. Hoover was apparently distressed. He had watched the decline with care since the early summer, but, afraid to jar the confidence of the business world, he refused to admit publicly the gravity of the situation. When the New York *Herald Tribune* reported on October 24 that "Stocks Off 5 Billion in Severest Break of Wall Street History," Hoover would only say that "The fundamental business of the country . . . is on a sound and prosperous basis."

Just how sound the American economy really was soon became all too clear. The day after Black Thursday (October 24) the New York *Times* told the story: "The most disastrous decline in the biggest and broadest stock market of history rocked the financial district yesterday." Despite the fact that five of the country's leading financiers hastily issued a statement of confidence in the soundness of the market (the crash, they claimed, had been caused "by technical rather than fundamental considerations"), the situation got worse. Tuesday, October 29, was to be the worst day in the market's history; an estimated 880 issues lost between eight and nine billion dollars.

Despite the obvious, attempts to give business confidence by decrying the facts continued. John D. Rockefeller expressed his belief in the soundness of the fundamental conditions of the country; Secretary of the Treasury Andrew W. Mellon could "see nothing . . . in the present situation that is either menacing or warrants pessimism"; and Arthur Brisbane, in his syndicated column, offered the following advice: "If every man would learn to talk about the country's progress and future as a young mother talks about her new baby, there would be no danger of hard times." President Hoover, meanwhile, managed to find a scapegoat for the country's problems and in a radio address informed the American people: "The depression has been deepened by events from abroad which are beyond the control either of our citizens or our government."

For some, the depression was seen as a definite good; it would enable the nation to be saved from the evils of false prosperity. "The average man won't really do a day's work unless he cannot get out of it," Henry Ford told the press with all his self-made-man arrogance. "I'll say this about these so-called hard times, more character is being built than ever before. People are thinking more and more about helping themselves. When they get to that condition, they will find more people willing to give them help." On August 12, 1931 *The Nation* printed the following item: "Henry Ford has shut down his Detroit automobile factories almost completely. At least 75,000 men have been thrown out of work."

The Ford Motor Company, in fact, serves as a good example of the devastating effect the crash had upon employment. In March of 1929, more than 128,000 people were on the Ford payroll. Two years later the number of employees had dropped to 84,000; by August of 1931 only 37,000 were employed by Ford. Throughout the country the situation was equally distressing; with only a few temporary setbacks, the rate of unemployment increased steadily until the spring of 1933. In March of 1930 the number of unemployed had reached about 3,500,-000. Within two years the number had jumped to almost 12,000,000; and, by March 1933 the estimates of the number of persons unemployed ranged from 14,000,000 to 16,000,000. For the next four years the effects of the New Deal were felt and by 1936 the number of jobless workers had been just about halved. But then the depression of 1937-38 caused the number of unemployed to once again reach the area of 10,000,000. And, although the next two years saw a gradual decrease in the number of men who were without work, it was not until 1941, when the war effort sufficiently stimulated the economy, that the Great Depression finally came to an end.

"No one has starved," said the complacent and the comfortable. But the fact is that people did starve. If most Americans in the early years of the depression were unaware of the gravity of the situation, to others it was a nightmare. The Hall of Jurors became packed on court days; jury duty, after all, paid $4 a day. Apple sellers abounded, but so did shoe shine boys; a shine kit was less expensive than a box of apples. Unemployed men arrested for vagrancy were thankful for the opportunity to get a free meal and shelter. In Chicago, the Commissioner of Public Welfare reported that several hundred unemployed women were sleeping nightly in Chicago's parks. And there were, of course, the seemingly endless breadlines, which, in Heywood Broun's phrase, "tangles itself around a man's ankles and then it knots." The men who would stand in line for hours to get a chance to fill their stomachs were not the men who were waiting for Clifford Odets' Lefty or, years later, would wait for Samuel Beckett's Godot. Together with Tom Kromer, who dedicated his book "To Jolene, who turned off the gas," they were waiting for nothing.

If, as Edmund Wilson says in *The American Earthquake,* "between 1929 and 1933 the whole structure of American society seemed actually to be going to pieces," the psychological shock was much greater for the urban worker than it was for the farmer. The farmer did not share in the prosperity of the twenties and so had no dreams to lose. For him, the crash simply made worse an already intolerable situation.

In the years after World War I the farmer found himself in an economic trap from which he could not escape. His problem was not one of production, but one of price control. Total farm production in 1929, for example, dropped by only six percent; prices fell by sixty-three percent. By 1932 the purchasing power of the farmer was exactly one-half of what it had been ten years earlier.

The problems created by an overabundance of farms, farmers, and staple crops were compounded by the draught and dust storms which began to devastate the mid-West in 1933. The dust began blowing on November 12, 1933, and huge clouds covered an area from Texas to South Dakota. In the next few years, thousands of families were desolated; the topsoil was stripped, homes and machines were buried beneath huge drifts of soil. So severe were some of the storms that one seven-year-old child, who wandered from his home, was suffocated before he could be found. During March and April 1936 there were forty-seven days on which visibility in Amarillo, Texas was six miles or less; during six storms the visibility was less than five hundred feet. The cost was enormous. The *New York Times* reported on April 20, 1935 that within a month more than a million dollars worth of damage had been done by the ceaselessly blowing dust. And, between 1934 and 1938, the destruction of crops by grasshoppers alone—who hatch readily during droughts—was estimated at $315,753,000.

So when, as Woody Guthrie wrote in "Talkin' Dustbowl Blues," "the rain quit and th' wind got high,/ Black old dust storm filled th' sky," more than 350,000 farmers set out northward in search of work. The California ranch owners, hoping to attract enough workers to make jobs scarce and thus keep the working wage to a minimum, had handbills distributed to inform the dust bowl victims of the opportunities which awaited them in California. But the fruitgrowers had no real sense of the plight of the mid-Western farmer, and were not prepared to cope with the hordes of migrants who traded their farm "for a Ford-machine/ Poured it full of this gasoline./ And started . . . rockin' and a-rollin'/ Out to the California . . . the old fruit bowl." It wasn't long before the handbills proclaiming California a garden of plenty began to read: "Warning! Come to California for a vacation. Advise anyone not to come seeking employment." The garden was indeed filled with grapes of wrath; the dust bowl refugee became the despised Oakie, who once again was forced to fight for his survival.

Yet as bad as the situation was for the Oakies (and their neighbors, the Arkies and Texicans), the plight of the Southern sharecropper was even worse. The South had twenty-one percent of the country's total population and the highest birth rate in the nation; its share of the national income, however, was only nine percent. For years, her natural resources had been corroded. The sickness and death rates were one of the highest in the country; more persons died in the South without medical attention than in any other part of the country. The ability of the tenant farmer to survive depended almost solely upon the landlord's ability to provide him with the necessary goods. But as the depression worsened, many of the landlords were unable to finance the tenants for another year. The situation was perhaps best summed up by Alabama Congressman George Huddleston, who told the LaFollette-Costigan committee in 1932 that "any thought that there has been no starvation, that no man has starved, and no man will starve, is the rankest nonsense."

In a Coffee Pot

BY ALFRED HAYES

Tonight, like every night, you see me here
Drinking my coffee slowly, absorbed, alone.
A quiet creature at a table in the rear
Familiar at this evening hour and quite unknown.
The coffee steams. The Greek who runs the joint
Leans on the counter, sucks a dead cigar.
His eyes are meditative, sad, lost in what it is
Greeks think about the kind of Greeks they are.

I brood upon myself. I rot
Night after night in this cheap coffee pot.
I am twenty-two I shave each day
I was educated at a public school
They taught me what to read and what to say
The nobility of man my country's pride
How Nathan Hale died
And Grant took Richmond.
Was it on a summer or a winter's day?
Was it Sherman burned the Southland to the sea?
The men the names the dates have worn away
The classes words the books commencement prize
Here bitter with myself I sit
Holding the ashes of their prompted lies.

"In a Coffee Pot" originally appeared in the first issue of *Partisan Review* (February-March 1934), and was highly regarded for its sensitive portrayal of "the depression generation." Alan Calmer, for example, praised the mood and material which enabled the poem "to catch the typical reactions of unemployed white collar workers in the great economic crisis." * * * A member of the John Reed Club and the Young Communist League, Alfred Hayes was on the editorial board of *Partisan Review,* to which he contributed regularly in the mid-thirties.

The bright boys, where are they now?
Fernando, handsome wop who led us all
The orator in the assembly hall
Arista man the school's big brain.
He's bus boy in an eat-quick joint
At seven per week twelve hours a day.
His eyes are filled with my own pain
His life like mine is thrown away.
Big Jorgensen the honest, blonde, six feet,
And Daniels, cunning, sly,—all, all—
You'll find them reading Sunday's want ad sheet.
Our old man didn't know someone
Our mother gave no social teas
You'll find us any morning now
Sitting in the agencies.

You'll find us there before the office opens
Crowding the vestibule before the day begins
The secretary yawns from last night's date
The elevator boy's black face looks out and grins.
We push we crack our bitter jokes we wait
These mornings always find us waiting there
Each one of us has shined his broken shoes
Has brushed his coat and combed his careful hair
Dance hall boys pool parlor kids wise guys
The earnest son the college grad all, all
Each hides the question twitching in his eyes
And smokes and spits and leans against the wall.

We meet each other sometimes on the street
Sixth Avenue's high L bursts overhead
Freak shows whore gypsies hotdog stands
Cajole our penniless eyes our bankrupt hands.
"Working yet?" "The job aint come
Got promised but a runaround."
The L shakes building store and ground
"What's become of Harry? and what's become
Of Charley? Martinelli? Brooklyn Jones?"
"He's married—got a kid—and broke."
And Charley's on Blackwell's, Martinelli's through—
Met him in Grand Central—he's on the bum—
We're all of us on the bum—"

A freak show midget's pounding on a drum
The high L thunders redflag auctioneers
Are selling out a bankrupt world—
The hammer falls—a bid! a bid!—and no one hears . . .

The afternoon will see us in the park
With pigeons and our feet in peanut shells.
We pick a bench apart. We brood
And count the twelve and thirteen tower bells.
What shall we do? Turn on the gas?
Jump a bridge? Boxcar west?
It's all the same there's nothing anywhere
A million guys are sitting on their ass
We always land
Back where we started from—a parkbench,
Cold, and spitting in the sand.

Who's handing us a runaround?
We hold our hands for sale arms brain
Eyes taught to figure accurate ears
We're salesmen clerks and civil engineers
We hang diplomas over kitchen sinks
Our toilet walls are stuck with our degrees
The old man's home no work and we—
Shall we squat out our days in agencies?
Or peddling socks shoelaces ties?
We wrench green grassblades up with sudden hands
The falling sun is doubled in our asking eyes . . .

And evening comes upon us there
Fingering in the torn pocket of our coat
The one cold nickel of our subway fare . . .

Night after night in this cheap coffee pot
I brood upon our lives. I rot. They rot.
The Greek's awakened from his dream. The dead cigar
Drops ash. He wipes the coffee bar.
He goes to fill the boiler once again.
The clock hand moves. A fly soars down
And stalks the sugar bowl's bright rim.
And I compare myself with him—this fly and I—
He crawls head downwards down a peeling wall

And I crawl after him.
You ask "Tomorrow?" . . . Go ask Fernando in the eatquick joint.
Ask Jorgensen pounding Sixth Avenue. Ask Martinelli too,
Watching the hole enlarging in his shoe.
And ask me here—alone with the crawling flies—
And I . . . I have seen the pain there in their eyes.
We shall not sit forever here and wait.
We shall not sit forever here and rot.
The agencies are filing cards of hate.

And I have seen how men lift up their hands
And turn them so and pause—
And so the slow brain moves and understands—
And so with million hands.

Waiting for relief checks. Dorothea Lange for the Farm Security Administration.

The Hard Winter

BY JACK CONROY

AUTUMN was sharpening the air and the Jackson street crowd had thinned out. The Market had just crashed to the cellar, leaving a sick and empty feeling in the stomachs of cockroach capitalists, rolling in unaccustomed wealth and firm in the conviction that a perpetual saturnalia was written in America's destiny. Now they were scurrying to cover, perishing beneath the wreckage or jumping from eighteenth story windows. Titanic earthquakes rocked the marble fronts of the street; shattering lightnings played about hitherto impregnable heads. It was the end of an epoch to some, the stormy sunset of the Hoover Prosperity. To us it meant nothing—yet. The manipulations of the bulls and bears, wedged between the screaming headlines of the front pages and the antics of Mutt and Jeff, ordinarily escape the attention of the working stiff. Ed was not perturbed by the soap-boxer's prophecy of the wrath to come.

That battle-scarred veteran of many panics had been shouting "Wolf! Wolf!" too often. Ten years, almost, since 1921, so long that the younger workers had forgotten it. But the oldsters remembered.

"The Money Power is clampin' down again," concluded the prophet. "I've seen it too often. Just as soon as some of you fellas get the wrinkles outen your bellies you forget. Before two weeks the Inland works will close down tight as a drum. My advice is to get out of town while you can. Ride a freight, thumb, walk—or crawl! But get out. Do like me. I'm goin' to California, if I can make it. I ain't so fast

---

Jack Conroy was born in a coal mining town in northern Missouri in 1899 and as a boy he experienced many of the events in *The Disinherited,* from which we have taken this brief selection. A sketch Conroy did of the depression's effect on Toledo, Ohio was published in H. L. Mencken's *American Mercury* in 1930. With Mencken's encouragement, Conroy wrote his autobiography; but he was unable to find a publisher for it until Covici-Friede convinced him to turn it into a novel. *The Disinherited* (1933) was dedicated to "the disinherited and the dispossessed of the world"; it was regarded by William Phillips and Philip Rahv, editors of *Partisan Review,* as one of the few revoluntionary novels in which "we get a sense of thematic exploration that suggests the immense possibilities ahead of us."

at naggin' a Red Ball as I usta be, but the bulls sometimes respecks my white beard—not often, though. Go to California, comrades, where you won't starve and freeze both—only starve. If you stay here you'll starve and freeze, too. This is gonna be a hard Winter like you've heard the old folks talk about. You'll tell your kids about it—if you live through it."

A hush fell on the street. Hambone, the mad Negro evangelist, ceased his lurid description of the hell-fire sizzling for this iniquitous generation; the militant atheist forgot the knotty problem of where Cain got his wife; the throbbing of the Salvation Army tom-tom died away, and tinkling tambourines jingled to silence. It seemed as if the prophet's upraised bony finger has written *mene, mene, mene, tekel, upharsin* across the dull brick wall opposite.

"Christ, they're always bellyachin', ain't they," reassured Ed. "What t'ell does the Stock Market have to do with Inland hunkies? I ain't buyin' no General Motors Common or Willys-Overland Preferred, are you? Let's go over to Adolf's and lap up a few cold ones."

Adolf was a Russian who had been a brewer in the Old Country. He never seemed to understand why he couldn't, without violating the laws of the Refuge of the Oppressed, make beer for his family and his friends, just as he had under the Czar. He never learned concealment, so he was frequently hailed into court, fined, and sent home without comprehending what it was all about. His mild blue eyes lit up when he opened the door for us. I often visited him to talk about Russia. Soon the beer loosened his tongue and he spoke of his native village.

"I could see the tax collectors coming through the wheat. It was higher than their shoulders and heavy-headed. They were good men— it was the nobles that ground us down. My mother set out black bread, salt pork, vodka, hot pickles. One of them he geev me a kopek, called me Yellow Hair. A long time ago—long, long ago now—Say! You like black bread, salt pork, and hot pickles?"

Several steins had reduced us to the state in which anything seems good. Adolf produced an immense flitch of bacon, a jar of pickles, and a long flat loaf of bread, as heavy as lead.

"This pork," he said proudly. "I have heem two years already."

The pork had been embalmed by some occult process, but it was rancid, and repellant to an American palate. But the beer lent piquancy to it. We gulped down greasy morsels of pork, hunks of black bread. Tears streamed from our eyes as we mouthed the fiery hot pickles.

The furniture and corners of the room were hazy when an accordion began whining old folk songs. One in a minor key sounded like "The Prisoner's Song" and we wept into the beer.

"The Czar!" Adolf's voice broke through the fog like a trumpet. "He burns in Hell! I spit on him and his nobles! Their throats are all slit now; no more I raise my cap and step off the road in the mud when their coaches pass by!"

The plaintive accordion rose to a passionate crescendo, crashed into the stirring thunder of the Internationale. We cheered like mad, and fell into happy slumber.

But Adolf's face was dead when he bade us goodbye, and we were half-drunk and more than half-sick.

"Paper says it's goin' to be a hard Winter," he said as he closed the door.

Hooverville.

UPI: Courtesy FDR Library, Hyde Park, N. Y.

From **Union Square**

BY ALBERT HALPER

OVER the iron-hooved town the day was marching. Clear and cold it came. Folks flowed by in a heavy, Monday-morning tide, going toward the stores, the subway entrances, or merely killing time by walking to and fro. The dime movies had not yet thrown open their proud portals to the eager patrons, the five-and-ten-cent stores were not yet due to welcome the mob until nine-thirty. Up and down the crowds went, tramp, tramp, tramp. Every time a subway train came to a halt below, you could hear the roar of wheels coming through the iron grating of the sidewalk. Porters were washing the windows of Luchow's, the refuse trucks were hoisting up big cans of garbage from the restaurants. On Third Avenue, Pete was just about to paste up a very important announcement against the front windows, informing the gentry that for 30¢ a veal cutlet and two vegetables could be had, served in that famous Crystal Lunchroom manner with plenty of gravy seething all over the plate and maybe some of it overflowing onto your pants; be careful.

Smoke from big buildings hung above the rooftops. Over the town rolled the roar and petty strife of millions. Merchants slashed their prices for the trade, workers took cuts in wages to hold onto their jobs, girls without families who had to meet their room rent or get thrown out upon the street stayed a little later in the offices if the bosses demanded it, stayed to take "dictation" and swallowed hard, and made no outcry, there in the darkness, when the boss clicked the lights out. There was stiff competition on all fronts, selling out below cost, come in and look around, last few days, please let me go, Mr. Goldman, please, please, please, oh, I got to go home now . . . The neon lights flashed on and off. The flavor lasts. In the square, at the orange-juice stand, the attendant, casting a sharp glance around, bent over and poured a gallon of pure cold water into the hold, then stirred the con-

---

Albert Halper published *Union Square* in 1933, and followed it with *The Foundry* in 1934 and *The Chute* in 1937. The two latter books were sympathetic toward the radical movement, but *Union Square* tended to satirize it; Halper's sympathy in his first novel was for the individual rather than the Party. Hank, the central figure in our selection, is eventually beaten to death by mounted police when he is innocently caught up in a Communist demonstration. As he falls to the ground under the blows of the police, he cries hopelessly: "I'm no commoonist, I ain't a Red, I'm an Amerikin!"

tents with a wooden ladle; a few wisps of orange peel, like small, dead
fishes, floated slowly to the surface. Putting on an honest look, the attendant wiped his hands, drew a deep breath and shouted: "Orange
drink, orandri', or-range, fi-ive cents here, hot frank on a ro-oll, fi-ive
cents here, gettum while they're hot, or-range, orange!"

The clock in the tall tower of the public utilities building struck
eight times, *bong, bong, bong, bong, bong, bong, bong, bong.* Officer
Terence McGuffy, his mind alert, counted. Eight times it was. Tighten-
ing his belt, he swung across the street, free from duty now, an easy,
off-duty smile on his faithful, beefsteak face. Feeling pretty good, he
opened the little iron phone box near the bank, knocked off work,
called up, and, waving his hand leisurely at another cop coming from
the opposite corner, turned his broad, smooth back and sauntered from
the square, the blare and noise striking the rear of his head like little,
playful, cotton balls.

At eight-thirty Hank Austin, discharged from duty Saturday last, was
still walking aimlessly around the square, a hollow, beaten feeling in
his Yankee bones.

He had said good-bye to his wife and kids in the customary manner, as if leaving for work, and by the time he was going down the
stairs of the tenement he himself half-believed that he still had a job,
that he was due to punch IN soon, due to slam and expertly dump the
boxes around, due to say hello to the boys and maybe catch a look of
Old Running Water coming in, trailed by a curl of thin, blue cigar
smoke like a thinnish piece of silk over those fat, plump shoulders of
the boss. Hank clumped down the tenement stairs and began walking
up the street, half-believing he still had a job. Millions were out of
work, but he still had a job. He swung along. But by the time he covered a full block he knew damn well he couldn't fool himself any
longer, and, his chest growing suddenly heavy, his great legs started
dragging, his shoulders sank. People walked by, heading for the
square. Some were in a hurry, a lot had plenty of time. The heaviness
crept up his limbs like a chill, as if he were wading in some kind of
deepening water and pretty soon the cold feeling was in his thighs and
climbed on higher. Shoving his hands deep into his pockets, Hank
walked along.

Over the iron-hooved town the day was marching. The square now
swarmed with people, every sidewalk was crowded. Women, on their
way to the big East Side markets, carried shopping bags, salesmen held
briefcases under their arms, affecting a jaunty pre-depression, American manner, and waitresses going on duty at Child's turned smartly up
the street and entered the tiled doorway. A big special was running to-

day, roast turkey sandwich with cranberry sauce, accompanied by our famous chick-peas. In the window a neat jane was neatly flapping flapjacks.

Hank Austin, waiting for the traffic lights like the others, crossed over with the flowing tide and surged high and dry upon the other sidewalk. The early morning sunlight struck the forehead of George Washington's powerful charger with a sharp shaft of golden light. A white-wing, using his brush energetically (it was Monday morning and the supervisor was due to come coasting along in his Ford any minute now), sent a cloud of dust rolling toward the horse's eyeballs, but the steed didn't bat a lash. "Come what may," he seemed to say, this charger with the swelling buttocks.

Again the big clock in the tower bonged, a solemn tone. Time and tide wait for no man, the traffic lights changed once more, the big thick minute hand clicked forward. Never put off today what you can do tomorrow. Hank Austin, raised in the public schools, felt the heavy flow now well up into his chest, and crossed over and, aimlessly, began following the low, thick wall. Sunlight struck the back of his leather jacket; the cloud of dust had settled long ago. With a roar, a big Mack truck went tearing up the street. In the windows of the Manufacturer's Trust Company Bank was a new poster, a polite sign which arrested the roving eye: "Are you going abroad? Please step inside and inquire about our check service."

When he had walked around the square twice, following the wall, Hank saw the bootblacks arriving; they came hurrying into position and by some mutual unspoken law took their posts about ten feet apart; and there was no crowding, either. Some of the "boys" were old and gray, and had shapeless faces, as if hammer blows had been struck them, right between the eyes, on the nose, all over. That's the way they looked. Their knees were ragged from kneeling on the sidewalk while they gave you shines, s'r, shines, s'r, only 5¢.

Time and tide. By ten o'clock Hank was sick and tired of walking around the square. There were crowds crossing all the while, and new faces, but he got tired looking at them and also tired of counting sidewalk cracks. In the center of the square a gang of men were standing around a big, empty ash-can because a fire was going there, and the men were chilly and shabby, and Hank saw an old geezer taking off his hat, hold it over the blaze, then clamp it onto his dome quickly. The man was old, was bald, and did this many times, then rubbed his hands with a sort of glee.

Hank struck west. He walked westward on Fourteenth Street, but when he saw the swank of Fifth Avenue, the long cool flanks of gray buildings on each side of the street, he turned back and headed east.

He came up to Third Avenue after blocks of more walking, noted the brand of gentry ambling by with creased faces, and felt more at home. Walking south, he soon passed Eleventh Street and went briskly, in case his missus was out shopping; he passed pawn-shops, barber colleges, hash-houses, Gus Abrams' Store For Fat Men (get your over-size underwear here!), the famous Crystal Lunchroom, "cider" stores, Italian groceries, and a dim doorway where a gypsy woman of gener-ous build, who was giving her small child the breast, went "tsk, tsk, tsk" to the men passing by, yearning to read their palms; and pretty soon Hank reached the Bowery. Here he took his time, he was a man among men here; the heavy flow was still in his chest now, but because it had been there for some time it did not feel so cold.

The bums and unemployed stood on the west side of the street, standing in the sun. The east side was cool and shady, no one walked there at all. The elevated roared overhead. Hank took his time.

By noon he had an unemployed feeling in his bones. He passed a few soup-lines and saw men shoving and arguing to keep their places. The line went raggedly around two corners, like a long, disjointed tape-worm. All was meekness, all was humbleness. The sign, JESUS SAVES, was not lit up, it was daylight now. Those who came out of the soup-kitchen walked smartly for a half a dozen paces or so, then slouched along, their eyes sniffing at the curbing hungrily for cigarette butts.

In so short a time Hank became educated in the humanities, in all the social sciences; he knew what he was up against. A walk through the illustrated corridors of Bowery University was a mighty instructive course. Exhibit A and B and also C were on view, guys in varied stages of decay, illuminating matter on the situation of our times.

Noon arrived over the iron-hooved town, the sun hung brightly bril-liant over the rooftops; a wintry day. Hank's legs grew tired from walk-ing, his mind grew tired out from thinking. He turned west again, taking slow, sluggish breaths, and made for home. There was no other place to go; he couldn't run away from it, sooner or later there must be a showdown. Bending his head, staring at sidewalk cracks again, he walked west.

It was ten after twelve when he entered the doorway of Twenty-Door City, ten minutes after twelve by all the correct clocks in town. In the flat his kids were already eating, their heads bent over, their mouths close to the spoons, while Hank's missus was dishing out the food. The oldest tried to get a bigger helping and got slapped over the wrist sharply; and after that the lad was quiet. In the other room the youngest, the infant (nine months old now), was gurgling in his little bed, an old silver spoon clutched in his hands, gurgling to the walls. In the kitchen steam rose from the pot.

Outside, in the hallway, Hank stood there. His breathing was labored, his broad chest rose and fell unevenly, as if he had just unloaded an extra heavy hand-truck piled with pig-iron. He stood there, no thoughts at all in his head. At last, placing a heavy fist on the doorknob, he went inside.

His wife gave a little cry, a startled half-scream, as if she had just seen a ghost or something. The kids, their spoons midway to their mouths, turned gapingly, but didn't take it in such a spectacular manner, Hank's dramatic entrance. There he stood, at the threshold, in the center of the Austin stage. He came inside with averted eyes. There was a good, rosy color in his cheeks from walking all morning in the cold air, he looked healthy all right, but oh Christ, how heavy his legs felt, especially up in the thighs. He was fagged out, his eyes were dead. Missus Austin, squat, faithful, sturdy, loyal Missus Austin, couldn't get it through her head that her man Hank was home at noon. She stood there like a statue, a dipper in her hand, her eyes fixed, all her robust body hard and firm as wood, her brain stopped short like a stationary train on a railroad track.

"Hank," she said at last, clear and cold like pure ice-water.

And Hank stood dumb, stood dumbly in all his powerful Yankee frame. He took his cap off, and his dry hair rose slowly upward like needles on a porcupine's back.

"Hank," his missus said again, her brain coming alive, the hard wood feeling melting from her flesh, leaving it weak as water. The kids, thinking their old man had a bit of a vacation, turned to their bowls and went on eating, shoveling the food in.

Hank went slowly to the sink and washed his hands. The hot water felt strange and scalding against the chilled flesh. He wiped each mitt carefully, there was no sense getting his skin chapped this time of the year. His wife, her forehead wrinkled between her brows, grew so nervous she almost dropped the dipper loaded with hot soup over the eldest's head.

Hank pulled up a chair and sat down. He set his elbows on the edge of the kitchen table and stared vacantly ahead. One of the kids kicked his shin playfully under the table, grinned, and waved his spoon, but Hank didn't notice, didn't even feel the blow at all. The kid, disappointed, sniffled, then dug into the bowl again with the shovel of his big tablespoon. The missus put down another plate.

After a few hot gulps of pea soup Hank said, his voice dead, that he had no job. The kids stared pop-eyed. No job? That meant that papa would have something else to do then, that's what it meant.

Little by little, as the soup went down hotly, as the boiled beef was crushed to a dampish, softish mush between his jaws, it all came out. "I was laid off Saturday," Hank told his missus simply. "There were four of us."

Missus Austin sat there with hard, frightened, startled body, every muscle set. "For good? Is the lay-off for good?"

"Don't know," said Hank, the meat-mush warm and tasteless in his mouth. The kids got excited and pounded him with questions but received no answers. The sight of him in the flat when there was school, when they were due back to the classes soon, sent them up in the air. Pa's home, he's sitting right with us now, right in the middle of the day. One of them, going back into the smaller room to get a good start, rushed growling forward at his father's knees, snapping like a bulldog; the impact almost threw Hank off his chair. He sat dead, not speaking. Then the kids grew silent, and hung around like old-faced, little men, like mournful Jews praying in a synagogue, their little faces sagging.

"Pa ain't got a job," they said solemnly to each other as they went out the door, as they went toward school again. "He ain't working any more, he ain't got a job." Missus Austin, her eyes wet and glassy, buttoned their coats with fumbling fingers. As soon as they were gone, she closed the door and started crying quietly. In the other room the infant gurgled to the walls.

Hank sat on in silence, staring at the floor. After a while his missus' tears started gushing more freely and she had to blow her nose often. She started asking questions but the way she bawled he couldn't understand half of them. His answers were dead and hollow.

He got up and washed his hands at the sink again and dried them carefully, no sense getting them chapped in this kind of weather. And hours later, when the kids came home, they found him there, and they jumped upon him, and pulled his long arms, pinched his back, and forced him to crawl on the floor. They did not see their father's face, they didn't see his eyes. In the other room near the sleeping infant Hank's missus was weeping quietly. She was standing in a dark corner, away from the kitchen light, her hands half hiding her face; and both her palms were wet and sticky from her tears.

Darkness came on, a cold blue frost. Over the iron-hooved town the last part of the day went marching, tramping up the cold, gray streets. Please step inside and inquire about our check service.

In a flat next door a young couple were getting ready to take in a Broadway show.

Above, New York breadline, 1931. Below, New York breadline, 1933.

The Happiest Man on Earth

BY ALBERT MALTZ

JESSE felt ready to weep. He had been sitting in the shanty waiting for Tom to appear, grateful for the chance to rest his injured foot, quietly, joyously anticipating the moment when Tom would say, "Why, of course, Jesse, you can start whenever you're ready!"

For two weeks he had been pushing himself, from Kansas City, Missouri, to Tulsa, Oklahoma, through nights of rain and a week of scorching sun, without sleep or a decent meal, sustained by the vision of that one moment. And then Tom had come into the office. He had come in quickly, holding a sheaf of papers in his hand; he had glanced at Jesse only casually, it was true—but long enough. He had not known him. He had turned away. . . . And Tom Brackett was his brother-in-law.

Was it his clothes? Jesse knew he looked terrible. He had tried to spruce up at a drinking fountain in the park, but even that had gone badly; in his excitement he had cut himself shaving, an ugly gash down the side of his cheek. And nothing could get the red gumbo dust out of his suit even though he had slapped himself till both arms were worn out. . . . Or was it just that he *had* changed so much?

True, they hadn't seen each other for five years; but Tom looked five years older, that was all. He was still Tom. God! was *he* so different?

Albert Maltz has gained renown as a playwright, novelist, and short story writer. After attending the Yale School of Drama, he collaborated with George Sklar on the play *Merry-Go-Round* (1932), which was followed in 1933 by *Peace on Earth* (also in collaboration with Sklar) and in 1935 by *The Black Pit*. Three years later Maltz published his first collection of short stories, *The Way Things Are*; the same year he was given the O. Henry Memorial Award for "The Happiest Man on Earth," which first appeared in *Harper's Magazine* in June, 1938. * * * Since 1940 Maltz has devoted most of his talent to writing novels and filmscripts. In 1947, along with nine other Hollywood writers, he was indicted for contempt of Congress for refusing to tell the House Un-American Activities Committee whether he was a Communist; he served a prison term from June 28, 1950 to April 3, 1951. In 1949, Maltz was awarded a silver medal by the Commonwealth Club for his novel *The Journey of Simon McKeever*.

Brackett finished his telephone call. He leaned back in his swivel chair and glanced over at Jesse with small, clear blue eyes that were suspicious and unfriendly. He was a heavy, paunchy man of forty-five, auburn-haired, rather dour-looking; his face was meaty, his features pronounced and fearful, his nose somewhat bulbous and reddish-hued at the tip. He looked like a solid, decent, capable businessman who was commander of his local branch of the American Legion—which he was. He surveyed Jesse with cold indifference, manifestly unwilling to spend time on him. Even the way he chewed his toothpick seemed contemptuous to Jesse.

"Yes?" Brackett said suddenly. "What do you want?"

His voice was decent enough, Jesse admitted. He had expected it to be worse. He moved up to the wooden counter that partitioned the shanty. He thrust a hand nervously through his tangled hair.

"I guess you don't recognize me, Tom," he said falteringly, "I'm Jesse Fulton."

"Huh?" Brackett said. That was all.

"Yes, I am, and Ella sends you her love."

Brackett rose and walked over to the counter until they were face to face. He surveyed Fulton incredulously, trying to measure the resemblance to his brother-in-law as he remembered him. This man was tall, about thirty. That fitted! He had straight good features and a lank erect body. That was right too. But the face was too gaunt, the body too spiny under the baggy clothes for him to be sure. His brother-in-law had been a solid, strong young man with muscle and beef to him. It was like looking at a faded, badly taken photograph and trying to recognize the subject: the resemblance was there but the difference was tremendous. He searched the eyes. They at least seemed definitely familiar, gray, with a curiously shy but decent look in them. He had liked that about Fulton.

Jesse stood quiet. Inside he was seething. Brackett was like a man examining a piece of broken-down horseflesh; there was a look of pure pity in his eyes. It made Jesse furious. He knew he wasn't as far gone as all that.

"Yes, I believe you are," Brackett said finally, "but you sure have changed."

"By God, it's five years, ain't it?" Jesse said resentfully. "You only saw me a couple of times anyway." Then, to himself, with his lips locked together, in mingled vehemence and shame, What if I have changed? Don't everybody? I ain't no corpse.

"You was solid-looking," Brackett continued softly, in the same tone of incredulous wonder. "You lost weight, I guess?"

Jesse kept silent. He needed Brackett too much to risk antagonizing him. But it was only by deliberate effort that he could keep from boiling over. The pause lengthened, became painful. Brackett flushed. "Jiminy Christmas, excuse me," he burst out in apology. He jerked the counter up. "Come in. Take a seat. Good God, boy"—he grasped Jesse's hand and shook it—"I *am* glad to see you; don't think anything else! You just looked so peaked."

"It's all right," Jesse murmured. He sat down, thrusting his hand through his curly, tangled hair.

"Why are you limping?"

"I stepped on a stone; it jagged a hole through my shoe." Jesse pulled his feet back under the chair. He was ashamed of his shoes. They had come from the relief originally, and two weeks on the road had about finished them. All morning, with a kind of delicious, foolish solemnity, he had been vowing to himself that before anything else, before even a suit of clothes, he was going to buy himself a brand-new strong pair of shoes.

Brackett kept his eyes off Jesse's feet. He knew what was bothering the boy and it filled his heart with pity. The whole thing was appalling. He had never seen anyone who looked more down and out. His sister had been writing to him every week, but she hadn't told him they were as badly off as this.

"Well now, listen," Brackett began, "tell me things. How's Ella?"

"Oh, she's pretty good," Jesse replied absently. He had a soft, pleasing, rather shy voice that went with his soft gray eyes. He was worrying over how to get started.

"And the kids?"

"Oh, they're fine. . . . Well, you know," Jesse added, becoming more attentive, "the young one has to wear a brace. He can't run around, you know. But he's smart. He draws pictures and he does things, you know."

"Yes," Brackett said. "That's good." He hesitated. There was a moment's silence. Jesse fidgeted in his chair. Now that the time had arrived, he felt awkward. Brackett leaned forward and put his hand on Jesse's knee. "Ella didn't tell me things were so bad for you, Jesse. I might have helped."

"Well, goodness," Jesse returned softly, "you been having your own troubles, ain't you?"

"Yes." Brackett leaned back. His ruddy face became mournful and darkly bitter. "You know I lost my hardware shop?"

"Well sure, of course," Jesse answered, surprised. "You wrote us. That's what I mean."

"I forgot," Brackett said. "I keep on being surprised over it myself. Not that it was worth much," he added bitterly. "It was running downhill for three years. I guess I just wanted it because it was mine." He laughed pointlessly, without mirth. "Well, tell me about yourself," he asked. "What happened to the job you had?"

Jesse burst out abruptly, with agitation, "Let it wait, Tom, I got something on my mind."

"It ain't you and Ella?" Brackett interrupted anxiously.

"Why no!" Jesse sat back. "Why however did you come to think that? Why Ella and me—" He stopped, laughing. "Why, Tom, I'm just crazy about Ella. Why she's just wonderful. She's just my whole life, Tom."

"Excuse me. Forget it." Brackett chuckled uncomfortably, turned away. The naked intensity of the youth's burst of love had upset him. It made him wish savagely that he could do something for them. They were both too decent to have had it so hard. Ella was like this boy too, shy and a little soft.

"Tom, listen," Jesse said, "I come here on purpose." He thrust his hand through his hair. "I want you to help me."

"Damn it, boy," Brackett groaned. He had been expecting this. "I can't much. I only get thirty-five a week and I'm damn grateful for it."

"Sure, I know," Jesse emphasized excitedly. He was feeling once again the wild, delicious agitation that had possessed him in the early hours of the morning. "I know you can't help us with money! But we met a man who works for you! He was in our city! He said you could give me a job!"

"Who said?"

"Oh, why didn't you tell me?" Jesse burst out reproachfully. "Why as soon as I heard it I started out. For two weeks now I been pushing ahead like crazy."

Brackett groaned aloud. "You come walking from Kansas City in two weeks so I could give you a job?"

"Sure, Tom, of course. What else could I do?"

"God Almighty, there ain't no jobs, Jesse! It's a slack season. And you don't know this oil business. It's special. I got my Legion friends here but they couldn't do nothing now. Don't you think I'd ask for you as soon as there was a chance?"

Jesse felt stunned. The hope of the last two weeks seemed rolling up into a ball of agony in his stomach. Then, frantically, he cried, "But listen, this man said *you* could hire! He *told* me! He drives trucks for you! He said you *always* need men!"

"Oh! . . . You mean *my* department?" Brackett said in a low voice.

"*Yes*, Tom. That's it!"

"Oh no, you don't want to work in my department," Brackett told him in the same low voice. "You don't know what it is."

"Yes, I do," Jesse insisted. "He told me all about it, Tom. You're a dispatcher, ain't you? You send the dynamite trucks out?"

"Who was the man, Jesse?"

"Everett, Everett, I think."

"Egbert? Man about my size?" Brackett asked slowly.

"Yes, Egbert. He wasn't a phony, was he?"

Brackett laughed. For the second time his laughter was curiously without mirth. "No, he wasn't a phony." Then, in a changed voice: "Jiminy, boy, you should have asked me before you trekked all the way down here."

"Oh, I didn't want to," Jesse explained with naïve cunning. "I knew you'd say no. He told me it was risky work, Tom. But I don't care."

Brackett locked his fingers together. His solid, meaty face became very hard. "I'm going to say no anyway, Jesse."

Jesse cried out. It had not occurred to him that Brackett would not agree. It had seemed as though reaching Tulsa were the only problem he had to face. "Oh no," he begged, "you can't. Ain't there any jobs, Tom?"

"Sure, there's jobs. There's even Egbert's job if you want it."

"He's quit?"

"He's dead!"

"Oh!"

"On the job, Jesse. Last night if you want to know."

"Oh!" . . . Then, "I don't care!"

"Now you listen to me," Brackett said. "I'll tell you a few things that you should have asked before you started out. It ain't dynamite you drive. They don't use anything as safe as dynamite in drilling oil wells. They wish they could, but they can't. It's nitroglycerin! Soup!"

"But I know," Jesse told him reassuringly. "He advised me, Tom. You don't have to think I don't know."

"Shut up a minute," Brackett ordered angrily. "Listen! You just have to *look* at this soup, see? You just *cough* loud and it blows! You know how they transport it? In a can that's shaped like this, see, like a fan? That's to give room for compartments, because each compartment has to be lined with rubber. That's the only way you can even *think* of handling it."

"Listen, Tom—"

"Now wait a minute, Jesse. For God's sake just put your mind to this. I know you had your heart set on a job, but you've got to understand. This stuff goes only in special trucks! At night! They got to follow a special route. They can't go through any city! If they lay over, it's got to be in a special garage! Don't you see what that means? Don't that tell you how dangerous it is?"

"I'll drive careful," Jesse said. "I know how to handle a truck. I'll drive slow."

Brackett groaned. "Do you think Egbert didn't drive careful or know how to handle a truck?"

"Tom," Jesse said earnestly, "you can't scare me. I got my mind fixed on only one thing: Egbert said he was getting a dollar a mile. He was making five to six hundred dollars a month for half a month's work, he said. Can I get the same?"

"Sure, you can get the same," Brackett told him savagely. "A dollar a mile. It's easy. But why do you think the company has to pay so much? It's easy—until you run over a stone that your headlights didn't pick out, like Egbert did. Or get a blowout! Or get something in your eye, so the wheel twists and you jar the truck! Or any other God damn thing that nobody ever knows! We can't ask Egbert what happened to him. There's no truck to give any evidence. There's no corpse. There's nothing! Maybe tomorrow somebody'll find a piece of twisted steel way off in a cornfield. But we never find the driver. Not even a fingernail. All we know is that he don't come in on schedule. Then we wait for the police to call us. You know what happened last night? Something went wrong on a bridge. Maybe Egbert was nervous. Maybe he brushed the side with his fender. Only there's no bridge any more. No truck. No Egbert. Do you understand now? That's what you get for your God damn dollar a mile!"

There was a moment of silence. Jesse sat twisting his long thin hands. His mouth was sagging open, his face was agonized. Then he shut his eyes and spoke softly. "I don't care about that, Tom. You told me. Now you got to be good to me and give me the job."

Brackett slapped the palm of his hand down on his desk. "No!"

"Listen, Tom," Jesse said softly, "you just don't understand." He opened his eyes. They were filled with tears. They made Brackett turn away. "Just look at me, Tom. Don't that tell you enough? What did you think of me when you first saw me? You thought: 'Why don't that bum go away and stop panhandling?' Didn't you, Tom? Tom, I just can't live like this any more. I got to be able to walk down the street with my head up."

"You're crazy," Brackett muttered. "Every year there's one out of five drivers gets killed. That's the average. What's worth that?"

"Is my life worth anything now? We're just starving at home, Tom. They ain't put us back on relief yet."

"Then you should have told me," Brackett exclaimed harshly. "It's your own damn fault. A man has no right to have false pride when his family ain't eating. I'll borrow some money and we'll telegraph it to Ella. Then you go home and get back on relief."

"And then what?"

"And then wait, God damn it! You're no old man. You got no right to throw your life away. Sometime you'll get a job."

"No!" Jesse jumped up. "No. I believed that too. But I don't now," he cried passionately. "I ain't getting a job no more than you're getting your hardware store back. I lost my skill, Tom. Linotyping is skilled work. I'm rusty now. I've been six years on relief. The only work I've had is pick and shovel. When I got that job this spring I was supposed to be an A-1 man. But I wasn't. And they got new machines now. As soon as the slack started they let me out."

"So what?" Brackett said harshly. "Ain't there other jobs?"

"How do I know?" Jesse replied. "There ain't been one for six years. I'd even be afraid to take one now. It's been too hard waiting so many weeks to get back on relief."

"Well you got to have some courage," Brackett shouted. "You've got to keep up hope."

"I got all the courage you want," Jesse retorted vehemently, "but no, I ain't got no hope. The hope was dried up in me in six years' waiting. You're the only hope I got."

"You're crazy," Brackett muttered. "I won't do it. For God's sake think of Ella for a minute."

"Don't you *know* I'm thinking about her?" Jesse asked softly. He plucked at Brackett's sleeve. "That's what decided me, Tom." His voice became muted into a hushed, pained whisper. "The night Egbert was at our house I looked at Ella like I'd seen her for the first time. *She ain't pretty any more, Tom!*" Brackett jerked his head and moved away. Jesse followed him, taking a deep, sobbing breath. "Don't that tell you, Tom? Ella was like a little doll or something, you remember. I couldn't walk down the street without somebody turning to look at her. She ain't twenty-nine yet, Tom, and she ain't pretty no more."

Brackett sat down with his shoulders hunched up wearily. He gripped his hands together and sat leaning forward, staring at the floor.

Jesse stood over him, his gaunt face flushed with emotion, almost unpleasant in its look of pleading and bitter humility. "I ain't done right for Ella, Tom. Ella deserved better. This is the only chance I see in my whole life to do something for her. I've just been a failure."

"Don't talk nonsense," Brackett commented without rancor. "You ain't a failure. No more than me. There's millions of men in the identical situation. It's just the depression, or the recession, or the God damn New Deal, or . . . !" He swore and lapsed into silence.

"Oh no," Jesse corrected him in a knowing, sorrowful tone, "those things maybe excuse other men. But not me. It was up to me to do better. This is my own fault!"

"Oh, beans!" Brackett said. "It's more sun spots than it's you!"

Jesse's face turned an unhealthy mottled red. It looked swollen. "Well I don't care," he cried wildly. "I don't care! You got to give me this! I got to lift my head up. I went through one stretch of hell but I can't go through another. You want me to keep looking at my little boy's legs and tell myself if I had a job he wouldn't be like that? Every time he walks he says to me, 'I got soft bones from the rickets and you give it to me because you didn't feed me right,' Jesus Christ, Tom, you think I'm going to sit there and watch him like that another six years?"

Brackett leaped to his feet. "So what if you do?" he shouted. "You say you're thinking about Ella. How's she going to like it when you get killed?"

"Maybe I won't," Jesse pleaded. "I've got to have some luck sometime."

"That's what they all think," Brackett replied scornfully. "When you take this job your luck is a question mark. The only thing certain is that sooner or later you get killed."

"Okay then," Jesse shouted back. "Then I do! But meanwhile I got something, don't I? I can buy a pair of shoes. Look at me! I can buy a suit that don't say 'Relief' by the way it fits. I can smoke cigarettes. I can buy some candy for the kids. I can eat some myself. Yes, by God, I want to eat some candy. I want a glass of beer once a day. I want Ella dressed up. I want her to eat meat three times a week, four times maybe. I want to take my family to the movies."

Brackett sat down. "Oh shut up," he said wearily.

"No," Jesse told him softly, passionately, "you can't get rid of me. Listen, Tom," he pleaded, "I got it all figured out. On six hundred a month look how much I can save! If I last only three months, look how much it is—a thousand dollars—more! And maybe I'll last longer. Maybe a couple years. I can fix Ella up for life!"

"You said it," Brackett interposed. "I suppose you think she'll enjoy living when you're on a job like that?"

"I got it all figured out," Jesse answered excitedly. "She don't know, see? I tell her I make only forty. You put the rest in a bank account for her, Tom."

"Oh, shut up," Brackett said. "You think you'll be happy? Every minute, waking and sleeping, you'll be wondering if tomorrow you'll be dead. And the worst days will be your days off, when you're not driving. They have to give you every other day free to get your nerve back. And you lay around the house eating your heart out. That's how happy you'll be."

Jesse laughed. "I'll be happy! Don't you worry, I'll be so happy, I'll be singing. Lord God, Tom, I'm going to feel *proud* of myself for the first time in seven years!"

"Oh, shut up, shut up," Brackett said.

The little shanty became silent. After a moment Jesse whispered: "You got to, Tom. You got to. You got to."

Again there was silence. Brackett raised both hands to his head, pressing the palms against his temples.

"Tom, Tom—" Jesse said.

Brackett sighed. "Oh, God damn it," he said finally, "all right, I'll take you on, God help me." His voice was low, hoarse, infinitely weary. "If you're ready to drive tonight, you can drive tonight."

Jesse didn't answer. He couldn't. Brackett looked up. The tears were running down Jesse's face. He was swallowing and trying to speak, but only making an absurd, gasping noise.

"I'll send a wire to Ella," Brackett said in the same hoarse, weary voice. "I'll tell her you got a job, and you'll send her fare in a couple of days. You'll have some money then—that is, if you last the week out, you jackass!"

Jesse only nodded. His heart felt so close to bursting that he pressed both hands against it, as though to hold it locked within his breast.

"Come back here at six o'clock," Brackett said. "Here's some money. Eat a good meal."

"Thanks," Jesse whispered.

"Wait a minute," Brackett said. "Here's my address." He wrote it on a piece of paper. "Take any car going that way. Ask the conductor where to get off. Take a bath and get some sleep."

"Thanks," Jesse said. "Thanks, Tom."

"Oh, get out of here," Brackett said.

"Tom."

"What?"

"I just—" Jesse stopped. Brackett saw his face. The eyes were still glistening with tears, but the gaunt face was shining now with a kind of fierce radiance.

Brackett turned away. "I'm busy," he said.

Jesse went out. The wet film blinded him but the whole world seemed to have turned golden. He limped slowly, with the blood pounding his temples and a wild, incommunicable joy in his heart. "I'm the happiest man in the world," he whispered to himself. "I'm the happiest man on the whole earth."

Brackett sat watching till finally Jesse turned the corner of the alley and disappeared. Then he hunched himself over, with his head in his hands. His heart was beating painfully, like something old and clogged. He listened to it as it beat. He sat in desperate tranquillity, gripping his head in his hands.

"Employment Agency" by Isaac Soyer.

School for Bums

BY MARY HEATON VORSE

THEY took a census of the floating unemployed on the East Side, which covered the homeless men. In the Municipal Lodging House, in the missions and shelters, in flop-houses and speakeasies where a man can stay all night, sleeping on sawdust, if he buys a drink, they took a census.

The regular salaried census takers had a force of between two and three hundred volunteers, divided up into teams. Each captain had working under him a team of six or more people, flung across the Bowery, down Doyers Street, through Christie Street, on to the waterfront.

They are rounding up the misery of the East Side. Doing it "intensively" as one census taker puts it. This is a queer census. It is a census of misery. It is the count of despair. In New York City for future reference they will tabulate the hopeless and put between covers of books how many men are wandering around shelterless, no prospect of jobs, no place to stay in the daytime, no place to sleep at night. How many are there—the wanderers from Municipal Lodging House to Salvation Army shelter, to flop-house, to speakeasy? How many are there sleeping in the subway or under the bridge at One Hundred and Eighty-fourth Street?

Well, at this writing the figures are being compiled. They are not yet accurate, but it looks as if there are about fifteen thousand homeless men in New York—which would include a couple of hundred homeless women.

The unemployed homeless do not take so kindly to the count. Social

---

Mary Heaton Vorse was one of the country's leading authorities on the labor movement in America. She reported on almost every major strike since 1912; in 1950, at the age of seventy-six, she left her home in Provincetown, Mass. to report a textile strike in Tennessee. She was a war correspondent during both world wars, and wrote a series of pamphlets on the rights of such small nations as Poland and Czechoslovakia. Her concern for the underdog has been summed up by Murray Kempton, in his affectionate tribute to Miss Vorse in *Part of Our Time:* "In all her life," Kempton wrote, "Mary Heaton Vorse has had no involvements which did not lie upon the outermost extremities of love." "School for Bums" originally appeared in *The New Republic* on April 29, 1931.

workers reported that in the flop-houses and twenty-five-cent-a-bed hotels they were hard to talk to—different from what they had been two years before when a similar count had been taken. Some men did not answer at all. Nor did the social workers wonder at this.

Everyone said the missions were the easiest places in which to take the unemployed census. Take the mission in Doyers Street. It is where the Chinese Theatre used to be. You come into a large irregular room. They hold the mission service where the Chinese actors used to play their interminable plays. Go down a flight of stairs. Here is an underground place. Toward one end, a counter, men in aprons behind it. This is where the men get their food. After that, after they have praised God with hymns, after the prayers, the beds stacked up high against bricked-in arches will be spread down in his space, which holds perhaps three hundred.

The line, before the men are fed, shuffles patiently in front of the census takers. One is a young girl in a raccoon coat, with a clear-cut profile. Her eyes are open with surprise. She has never seen anything like this before. She is embarrassed asking questions—name, age, where born, what trade? They file along, the men in the mission, a long shuffling line. A patient line. Weary feet, broken shoes, worn clothes, unshaven faces.

Very few young men in the missions now. The young men don't go in so much for religion. Many of them over forty, comparatively few under thirty. They crawl along, glad enough to answer the questions and get on. They shuffle along like men already accustomed to waiting, easing themselves on one foot, then on the other. After a couple of hours they get their handout.

A queer census. What happened to John Bentley, 29, house painter, born in Kansas of American parents, union member? Well, there was this depression in the building trades, and he heard of a job farther east. He had a job for a short time. Now here he is in the line. His face is clear-cut, English, with a long upper lip. The type of man who should be upstanding and brisk. His shoulders sag, his shoes are broken. Defeat and bitterness are in his expression. The slight defiance in his answers is of the man who dares you to ask him how he happened to come on a breadline. There are hundreds more with his story.

The beds are being spread out. The girl in the raccoon coat cries out, "My God, they're lying on the floor!" There are not beds enough for everyone. Enough handouts, enough free food of a kind "that don't stand by you," all the drifters will tell you. But not enough flops.

A group of some twenty well dressed people suddenly appears on the stairs. "Ladies and gentlemen," chants a guide, "this was one of the underground resorts of old Chinatown. This used to be the place where Chinatown came to hit the pipe. You would find white people and Chinese together sodden in opium dreams. Behind those bricked-in arches was where the plutocrats and the society people used to come to smoke their pipes in privacy. . . ."

"My Lord!" says the girl in the raccoon coat. *"Tourists!"*

The people from the sightseeing bus peer at the men rolling themselves in blankets. They peer at the bricked-in archways behind which in the old days "plutocrats and society women" supposedly came for an opium debauch. Then they go on.

The census is over. No one else will be allowed in tonight. They are taking care of all they can.

The groups of census takers go on from the mission to the speakeasies. In some of these there is a free lunch. Here, if you buy a drink, they let you stay and sleep on the sawdust or on a chair. In some of them there is a drink of free whiskey all around at midnight.

It is not hard to understand why a man would rather sleep in the filthy sawdust than at a mission or in that place of massed misery, the Municipal Lodging House—where there is a somewhat ghastly moment after a man has given up his clothes to be sterilized. After his shower, he stands naked, with all his other naked and miserable comrades, waiting for a nightshirt. The speakeasy, after all, has a touch of home about it, a place where a man can keep his personality, what there is of it.

A group of volunteer census takers meet, men and women. They have together accumulated a series of nightmare pictures of our civilization. They have seen where the men sleep and how inadequate the beds of New York are for the homeless. One social worker sums it up as he exclaims:

"It's a school for bums."

It is a school for bums—crawling breadlines—81,000 free meals daily. No certain place to sleep, no organized shelter.

If you want to know how to make a bum out of a workingman who has had trade, home, security and ambition taken from him, talk to any of the young fellows on the breadline who have been in town long enough to have become experienced in misery. Say a man in this town goes to the Municipal Lodging House for his first night. Until lately, he would have been routed out at five in the morning. Now he can stay until six. He is given breakfast, then he must leave, blizzard or rain. He can go next to a Salvation Army shelter for a handout, and get down to the City Free Employment Bureau before it opens. Or he can find shelter in subways and mark the Want Ads in a morning paper.

If he decides on the Employment Bureau, he is wise to arrive there before the doors open. He will find himself in the midst of a huge company which augments all the time until the opening of the doors. He may have spent two hours there—from nine to eleven. After that, he will not have eaten since his handout at seven at the Salvation Army, and he will have walked quite a lot. The next thing to do will be to put himself on some other breadline. It will take him one and a half or two hours to get his noonday meal.

In the afternoon there isn't very much use hunting jobs; yet there may be a chance at something; at some of the agencies, or perhaps by looking through the scanty Want Ads in the afternoon papers. There is a question then as to how and where to spend the rest of the time. If he has good enough clothes he can kill some time in the library. With discretion, hours can be spent in the terminals of stations. He can go to a museum. If he has a nickel, he can "ride the subways." But if he can panhandle some money, he can at least stay indoors in a speak-easy or Bowery hotel.

It will take him an hour and a half or two hours for his evening meal, and if he is going to the Municipal Lodging House again, he had best be early on the line.

Until recently the Municipal Lodging House was open only one night a month to non-residents and five nights to residents of New York. This restriction has now been removed. There are 3,300 people sleeping at the Municipal Lodging House, of which one hundred are women. The beds are full, and they are sleeping on benches, on the floor.

In the life of this drifting worker there is never any security. He is never sure where he is going to sleep. It is easy to learn to panhandle twenty-five or fifty cents for a night's flop. Between the agencies who help homeless men—the Salvation Army, Municipal lodging houses, the Y. M. C. A. and missions—there are not enough beds. Make a count of all the agencies, even including the new pier, which furnishes shelter for seven hundred more, and the Salvation Army boat that gives lodging to six hundred seamen, besides its other shelters. There is still a slack of thousands for whom there is no free accommodation at present in the city.

The present situation is indeed a school for bums. A thing to sap moral and physical strength. A situation which in a few weeks would make most employable men unemployable, and which puts a premium upon panhandling. It is the deadly frustration of each unsuccessful day of job hunting when, tired and footsore, a man again stands in the long gray queue of the breadline only to seek an uncertain shelter. It is astonishing how soon a newcomer learns the ropes, how quickly it spreads from mouth to mouth where food is better, where flops are to be had.

Usually when times are hard and people are out of work, Fifth Avenue and Broadway know nothing about it. This is the first time these streets have lost their glittering shine. The shabby, shifting, ebbing men out of work have taken it from them.

On a street corner near Fiftieth Street was a store which had been turned into a free restaurant for the unemployed. Well dressed young ladies were cutting sandwiches for all who wanted to come in and get one. In the middle of each table stood a pot of mustard. There were men with well brushed clothes, men who looked like old bums, young white-collar men, all engulfing enormous sandwiches, cheese spread with mustard—three sandwiches to a person and coffee.

There were men whose faces made a spot of yellow, famine color. They had been starving. The men eating behind the plate-glass windows of the corner store were being gaped at by a crowd. Outside two men discussed them.

"That's to keep 'em from riotin'; it's to keep 'em quiet that they're feedin' 'em," said a man who talked like a play by Upton Sinclair.

"Har! Ye talk like a radical," said a man with an English accent. "That's fir hadvertising that they're feedin' 'em, them's society girls in there."

"It's to keep 'em quiet, I say. If they didn't feed 'em, they'd come marchin' down to the markets. They'd break the windows and loot 'em and help 'emselves. An' what's to prevent 'em from takin' what they want? They's a million of 'em in the city; if they was to march they'd make a procession!"

What if they should march, one wonders—all of them. What if having had their census taken and their misery compiled, they should give an exhibition of their numbers? What then? Tear gas and clubs and arrests, no doubt.

There are other sides to the avalanche of despair. As a part of the widespread slump, the people who thought themselves secure have been thrown into it. The people who have been able to have a college education suddenly find themselves out of a job. No one can take the census of this misery. It doesn't walk the street. It sits and shivers in cold houses. It hides itself.

They hunt in vain for jobs. Or, if they have homes to go to, they return, defeated, to be dependent. Or perhaps, having no home to go to, these people, too, may slip gradually downhill where they must apply for charity.

And what about such people as a friend of mine told me of recently? She was working in one of the emergency employment bureaus on the East Side where daily men came to get the Prosser jobs which are now nonexistent. Daily the little crowd of people gathers outside and waits in vain.

I watched this flood of people who had been once well-to-do, judging by their clothing. People used to steady work, coming in vain with their stories of five children, no work, savings gone.

"It's not nearly as hard as the employment agency I used to work with in Queens," my friend told me. The first day she worked there, she went to nine houses, which had in each case been lost by the young people who were in the process of buying them. Here was a little suburban community where young people, many of them with college educations, had come to found homes, to live where their children could be brought up healthfully.

"There was something more desperate in Queens," my friend told me, "than there is on the East Side, where people are used to the idea of insecurity. The car goes first: the furniture goes; then the house goes; confidence in life goes."

Of the number of people losing their all, because they cannot raise a few dollars, there is no record as yet. Maybe there will never be. One can only generalize and say that the white-collar class is suffering today with the mechanic. The man who has spent thousands upon his education is no more secure than a laborer. The misery, doubt and defeat piles up, an incalculable mountain. There is no census yet of these.

"The Mission" by Raphael Soyer.

From **Waiting for Nothing**

BY TOM KROMER

I WAIT, and, Christ, but the hour goes slow. I stand in this soup-line. Back of me and before me stretch men. Hundreds of men. I huddle in the middle of the line. For two hours I have stood here. It is night, and ten minutes before they start to feed. The wind whistles round the corners and cuts me like a knife. I have only been here for two hours. Some of these stiffs have been here for four. Across the street people line the curb. They are watching us. We are a good show to them. A soup-line two blocks long is something to watch. These guys on the curb are not in any soup-line. They have good jobs. They have nothing to worry about. It must be pretty soft not to have anything to worry about.

Sixty seconds in a minute, I think, and ten minutes. That makes six hundred seconds. If I count up to six hundred, slow, they will be started when I finish. I began to count. I count to a hundred, but I can get no further. I have to stop. I am too cold to count. I stomp my feet on the concrete walk. I swing my arms high over my head. It is a damn shame to stand in this line as cold as I am, but I have to stay. I am hungry. I have to get a little something in my belly. I wait. We stiffs in the soup-lines are always waiting. Waiting for the line to start moving. The bastards. They keep us standing out in the cold for advertisement. If they let us in and fed us, where would the advertisement be? There wouldn't be any. They know that. So they keep us out in the cold so these people on the curb can have their show.

Tom Kromer is one of the most mysterious figures in American letters. He was born of poor West Virginian parents in 1906, but managed to get an education and became a teacher for a short time. Eventually, however, he wound up on Skid Row. Barely surviving the experience, he put together *Waiting for Nothing*, which was published in 1935. A year later, Kromer reviewed William Cunningham's *Pretty Boy* for *New Masses* and then moved to New Mexico, where he and his wife published a little magazine. Shortly after he disappeared from sight.

There is a commotion up in front of me. Stiffs bunch around in a knot. A cop pushes them back in line. There is a stiff stretched out on the ground. He is an old stiff with gray hair. His eyes are wide open, but he does not move a lick. He is tired of waiting for this line to start moving. He is stretched out on the concrete, and dead as four o'clock. I can see that this stiff is lucky. There will be no more waiting for him. They cover him up with a sheet and load him in the mission truck. He is off to the morgue. There is no fuss when a stiff kicks off in a soup-line. There is no bother. They throw a sheet over him and haul him away. All he needs now is a hearse and six feet of ground, and they will have to give him that. That is one thing they will have to give him. And it will not make any difference to him how long he has to wait for it. It must burn them up plenty to have to give a stiff six feet of ground for nothing.

This old stiff croaking like this out in the cold puts this bunch in a bad humor. They shove and cuss at these guys in the mission who make us stand in the cold. They can see that we mean business. They open the doors and let us in. A mission stiff hands us a pie pan, a tin cup, and a spoon. We carry them up to where these guys are standing over these tubs of stew. It is scorching hot in here. These mission stiffs that are ladling out the stew are sweating. The sweat drips from their faces and falls in the stew. But that is nothing. What is a little sweat to a stiff? What can a stiff do about it if it maybe turns his stomach?

We get our pan of stew and our cup of water and sit down at the table. The room is filled with these tables. A mission stiff walks along the aisles with a basketful of stale bread. He throws it to us like a guy throwing slop to hogs, and we catch it. This stew is made of carrots that were rotten when they were cooked, but we eat it. We have to. A stiff can't stand the cold outside unless he has a little something in his belly. I bolt down this stew and get out. The smell of this place will turn a guy's stomach. It smells like a slop-jar.

Now for a smoke. I am dying for a smoke, but I am not holding any smoking. I keep my eye peeled over the curb. A guy will throw a snipe on the walk, and a wind will come along and blow it over the curb. You will find your biggest snipes over the curb. I spot one in front of this drug store. It is a big one. It is not half smoked. I can see that the guy who threw this butt away was in the big dough. I slouch up to this snipe and stop. I put my feet between it and the store. I lean down to tie my shoe. I am not tying my shoe. I am picking up this snipe. What these guys in the drug store don't know won't hurt them.

I walk back to this mission and stop by this stiff who leans up against the telephone pole. He is sporting a pretty good front. He carries a roll of chicken wire under his arm. You can hardly tell this guy is a stiff.

"That was awful stew," I say.

"What was?" he says.

"That slop they feed you in the mission."

"You eat that slop?"

"What else is a guy going to eat?" I say. "A guy can't starve."

"A stiff with brains don't need to eat slop, and he don't need to starve," this guy says.

"Sez you," I say.

"Sez me," he says. "I have got a ten-cent piece." He pulls this ten-cent piece out of his pocket. "What would you buy if you had a ten-cent piece?"

I think. What can a stiff buy with a ten-cent piece when he is half starved? Well, a good cup of coffee will hit the spot right now. A good cup of warm coffee will go a long way when you are hungry.

"Coffee and sinkers is what I would buy if I had a ten-cent piece," I say.

"And that is just why you have to eat slop," he says.

"What has that got to do with me eating slop?" I say.

"You do not use your brains," he says. "Why do you think I lug a roll of chicken wire under my arm?"

"I have been wondering about that ever since I see you on the corner," I say. "Why do you lug it?"

"The coppers," he says, "that's why."

"What do coppers have to do with chicken wire?" I say.

"When you walk up the main stem," he says, "how do you go, fast or slow?"

"Any stiff knows that," I say. "I go as fast as hell. If you do not go fast, the goddam coppers will stop you and frisk you on the street."

"You are right," he says. "But I don't walk fast on the main stem or anywhere else, and the coppers don't bother me."

"They don't bother you?" I say.

"They do not," he says. "They don't think I am a stiff. What would a stiff be doin' with a roll of chicken wire under his arm?"

"You are a smart stiff," I say. "I have never tried that."

"It's just as easy to be a smart stiff as a dumb stiff," he says. "All coppers are dumb. A smart stiff will fool a copper every time."

"You didn't say what you were going to do with your ten-cent piece," I say.

"I will show you some brains that are real brains and not imitations," he says. "We blow this dough for two doughnuts, see? Then we hot-foot it to a corner where a bunch of dames is waitin' for a street-car. We plant one of these doughnuts on the curb and go across the street. When enough dames is waitin' there, I duck across the street, dive at this sinker, and down it like I ain't et for a week. Dames is soft, see. This racket is good for a buck and sometimes two bucks."

I can see that this stiff has got brains, and what is more, he has got imagination.

"How long have you been working this little trick?" I say.

"Since I have been on the fritz," he says.

"And the bulls, don't the bulls ever break up your racket?" I say.

"Bulls!" he says. "I am too smart for the bulls. Come on, and I will show you why I don't eat the slop they throw out in the mission."

We go into this bakery and buy two doughnuts. They are no ordinary doughnuts. They are big and honey-dipped. I have never seen a prettier picture than these two doughnuts. That is because I am damn near starved. I want to sink my teeth into one of them, but I know that that is foolishness. After I was through eating it, I would be hungrier than ever. When you are starved and get a little something to eat, you are hungrier than ever. We can't waste any time eating one of these doughnuts. We are on our way to try out a little scheme that took lots of brains to think up.

We slouch down the street until we spot a good corner. There are a bunch of women waiting there for a street-car. When it comes along and they get on, we take this chance to lay one of our doughnuts on the curb. We put it in plain sight. Anyone waiting for a car can see it. I carry the other one, and we walk across the street and wait. In a little while there is another bunch of women on this corner. There are some men too, but we are not interested in the men. Men are hard, but women are soft. A woman does not like to see a hungry stiff starve to death. A man does not care if a stiff starves to death or not.

"Now is my chance," this stiff says.

He slouches across the street. I stand here and watch him. He has got the guts, all right. There is no doubt that this guy has got the guts. I can see now why this guy does not need to eat mission slop. A stiff with this much guts can live like a king. He stops across the street and lets his eyes fall on this doughnut on the curb. It is a picture sitting there. I expect to see him make a dive for it, but he does not. This stiff is deeper than that. He knows how to do it. He just stands there and watches it. These women see him looking. I can see they are thinking why will a guy stand on the street and watch a doughnut? He walks on by and stops a little ways up the street. Pretty soon he comes back. He walks far over to the curb and snatches it up on the fly. He hits it over behind a telephone pole. By the way he acts, you would think this was the first doughnut this stiff ever snatched off the curb. You would not think this guy has been pulling this gag for years. He downs this doughnut almost whole. It looks as though this stiff is plenty starved. You would think he has not eaten in a month of Sundays. That is what these women think. That is what he wants them to think.

This big fat woman in the brown coat reaches down in her pocketbook and fishes out some change. She walks over behind the post and hands it to this stiff. He shakes his head no, but he holds out his hand yes. This guy wants it to look as though it hurts his pride to take dough from this woman. I can see that this guy will never need to swill slop in a mission. If one person is going to be big-hearted, everybody wants to be big-hearted. Four or five of these women fish around in their pocketbooks and walk over to this stiff who hides behind the post. This is real money. This is not chicken-feed that this guy is taking in. One of these women shells out a buck. I can see the green of it from across the street. If I had the guts, I can see that there would be one more dummy-chucker in this town tomorrow than there is today. You just dive down on a doughnut, and these women do the rest.

He thanks these women and walks up the street. In a little while I walk after him. I do not want these women to think I am with him.

"You are the stuff," I say. "That is the prettiest little trick I have seen in a long time."

"You will go a long way before you find a prettier little racket than dummy-chucking," he says. "How much do you think I cleaned up on that doughnut?"

"I don't know," I say, "but I saw you get a buck."

"Two bucks and sixty-five cents," he says. "That is how much I made on one doughnut, and you wanted to spend that ten-cent piece on a cup of lousy coffee. You have got to have brains and imagination to get along on the fritz."

Me and this stiff hot-foot it to a restaurant and order up a good meal. This guy is all right. When he leaves he slips me a four-bit piece.

"Any stiff that eats mission slop ought to have his fanny kicked," he says. "There is too many doughnuts in this world for a stiff to eat mission slop."

I sit here in this restaurant and think. Why can't I do what this stiff does? I have as much brains as he has. I have the imagination, too. But I cannot do it. It is the guts. I do not have the guts to dive down on a doughnut in front of a bunch of women. There is no use talking. I will never have the guts to do that.

Masses of Men

BY ERSKINE CALDWELL

HUGH MILLER worked for the street-railway company. Hugh had a silver button, a gold button, a bronze watch fob made like a trolley car, and a small tin disk with the numeral 7 almost worn off. He had worked for the company for twenty-six years repairing tracks, and the company had once told him that some day he would be retired with a comfortable pension.

After all those years, Hugh was still trying to get along in the world. He still hoped to be made superintendent of construction. For some reason, though, he had never got far. He was still repairing tracks, replacing switch frogs, and jacking up the rails to put in new crossties.

Even though there were other men who were stepped ahead when the time came to fill up the ranks, Hugh kept his job as a laborer, repairing the tracks year after year, and hoped he would be made superintendent of construction before he got too old to work any longer.

"I'll get it yet," he told himself. "I'll get it as sure as shooting. They've got to promote me some day, and I've been working long enough now to get it. I'll get it as sure as shooting."

Hugh had put off marrying Cora until he was promoted. Cora told him that she did not mind waiting a little longer, because she was working herself then in a store in town and earning as much as Hugh himself was. But after the twelfth year, Hugh decided that if he ever was going to get married, he ought to do it without further delay. He was growing old and though Cora was still as youthful in appearance as she was when they became engaged, she was beginning to complain of the long hours she had to stand on her feet behind the counter in the variety store.

Erskine Caldwell gained his literary reputation at the height of the depression, publishing seven books between 1931-1935. At first, he concentrated almost solely upon the "poor whites." His enormous commercial success has obscured his importance as one of the most sympathetic spokesman not only for the "poor whites," but, with the publication in 1935 of *Journeyman* and *Kneel to the Rising Sun,* for the Negro as well. It is from this latter volume that "Masses of Men" is reprinted.

"We'll get married right now," Hugh told her one Saturday night while they were riding home from downtown on his company pass. "There's no sense in waiting any longer. If you are ready, we'll be married next week. I've been thinking about it a long time, and there's no sense in waiting till I get promoted."

"I'd love to, Hugh," she said, clutching his arm in the crowded car. "I think it's silly to put it off any longer. I've been hoping for it to happen for I don't know how long. We don't have to wait until you get promoted. It would be all the nicer to have the promotion come while we are married."

They got off the car at the boulevard stop and walked home slowly. They lived next door to each other, in boardinghouses, and there was no hurry since it was Saturday night.

That was the beginning. They walked slowly down the dark street talking about next week, and Hugh kept saying to himself under his breath that he would surely get promoted the next time the company filled up the ranks. He was certain of it. He told Cora he was. She believed him.

After they were married, Hugh rented a five-room house not far from the carbarn. It was just a step down the alley from the tree-lined street where the trolleys passed all day and most of the night. It was a good house, for the money, and it was comfortable. Having their doorstep in an alley did not really matter much after all. They did not mind that. The house was almost on the corner, and the upstairs windows looked out over the tree-lined street. They could step out the front door, walk a few steps, and be in the street. It was not a bad place to live, and Cora liked it.

First there was a girl; they named her Pearl. Later there was a boy, John; after another year there was another girl, and they named her Ruby.

Hugh still looked forward to the time when he would be made superintendent of construction for the street-railway company, but after Ruby was born, he did not think about it any more. He somehow got out of the habit of thinking about it. Cora had stopped working in the variety store downtown; she stayed at home and attended to the house and cared for the children. She was beginning to wonder what she could do to her skin to keep it from turning so dark; in the meantime she hid her face when people came to the door for some reason or other. She knew there was nothing wrong with her skin; it was merely becoming darker and darker every day. But she wished she knew what to do about it. Her hair already had a wide streak of gray in it.

She never mentioned it to Hugh, but Hugh never talked any more, anyway. When he came home from work, he ate his supper and went to bed. She did not have a chance to tell Hugh anything like that. He was too tired to listen to her.

When Pearl, the oldest girl, was nine, Hugh was knocked down by an automobile one day, while he was jacking up a rail to replace a rotten crosstie, and run over and killed. The company sent his body home that evening, when the rest of the workers got off at five o'clock, and Cora did not know what to do. After she had put the children to bed, she went out and walked down the street until she met a policeman. She told him what had happened to Hugh, and he said he would have the body taken away early the next morning. She went back home and looked at Hugh, but she could not notice any difference in him; at home, Hugh was always asleep.

Cora knew there would be a little money coming in from the company. She was certain there would be something, but she was afraid it would not be enough for them to live on until she could find work of some kind. When she thought about it more, she was afraid there would not even be enough to pay for Hugh's funeral and burial.

The policeman had the body taken away the next morning, and it was buried somewhere. Cora did not know where, but she did know there was nothing else to do about it. The children had to have food, and they had to have a little heat in the house.

She waited a month for the money to come from the street-railway company, and it still did not come. After that she went to the office and asked for it. There was no one there who seemed to know anything about the matter. Nobody in the big brick building had ever heard of Hugh Miller, and when they looked up the name in their records, no one was certain which Hugh Miller she was inquiring about. Cora stayed there all day, but when the people in the building went home at dark, she did not know what else to do except to go home, too.

After that she did not bother the people at the street-railway company any more. She did not have time to go there, for one thing, and she had a lot to do at home. The three children had to be taken care of, and she had to go out every day and find enough food to keep them from being hungry. Sometimes it took her all day long to get enough to feed them for just one small meal; other times she could find nothing at all for them to eat, but she kept on walking because the children had to be fed.

Pearl was going on ten. She was the oldest, and Ruby was still just a baby. But Pearl was growing up. She had long yellow hair and a blue gingham dress, and she tried to help her mother all she could. She cared for the other children while Cora was out trying to get some food, and at night she helped her mother put them to bed. After they were asleep, Cora would tell her about her father, Hugh.

"Your father worked for the street-railway company," she told Pearl. "The company would help us out, but they are so busy up there they can't seem to find time to do anything about it now. They would help us if they could get all the Hugh Millers who have worked for them straight in their minds. Your father was just one of them, and it's hard for the company to tell them apart."

"I can work," Pearl told her mother. "I'm old enough now. I'll see if I can find something to do. You take me with you, Mamma, and I'll ask about it. John and Ruby can take care of each other if we lock them in a room before we go out."

"You're not very big for your age," Cora said. "People wouldn't believe you when you told them you were going on ten."

"But I can work. I'll show them how much I can do."

"Hugh worked for the street-railway company, Pearl. He was your father. Some day the company will help us out. They're busy right now. I don't like to bother them so much when they act like they are so busy."

Pearl went to bed telling her mother that she was old enough to work. Cora did not say anything else to her, but she could not think of any kind of work that Pearl was capable of doing.

The next morning John and Ruby went out early to bring back some wood for the stove. They had no shoes to wear, and their coats were not warm enough. It was midwinter, but the ground was bare of snow. When they came back that afternoon their feet were bleeding around the toes and their heels had cracked open in several places.

"Where's the firewood, John?" Cora asked him.

"We couldn't find any."

Cora put on her cloak, pulling it up around her head and shoulders, and went out into the alley. There was no wood of any kind there, but up at the other end there was a coal bin that sometimes overflowed into the narrow way. She filled her apron with coal and ran back to the house. The children huddled around the stove, shivering and whimpering, while she kindled the fire.

"I'm hungry, Mamma," Ruby said.

"I'll get you something to eat," Cora promised her.

"When are we going to have something to eat again?" John asked her.

"I'll bring you something when I come back."

Cora put on her cloak and went out into the alley. She ran to the street and stood there indecisively for several moments until she could make up her mind which direction she would take. She turned down the street this time, instead of going up it.

After she had run and walked for five or six blocks, she came to a cluster of one-story suburban stores. There were several men standing at the curb in front of the buildings. They were waiting for a streetcar to take them downtown. The men turned and looked at Cora when they saw that she was running towards them.

"Mister, give me half a dollar for my children," she pleaded.

The men turned all the way around and looked her up and down. One of them laughed at her.

"Sister," one of them said, "I wouldn't give a dime for you and a dozen more like you."

The others laughed at what he had said. The trolley was coming down the street, its bell clanging. The men stepped out into the street and stood beside the tracks waiting for it to stop and take them aboard. Cora followed them into the middle of the street.

"Mister," she said to the man who had spoken to her, "Mister, what would you—"

"Don't call me 'Mister,' " he said angrily. "I don't like it. My name's Johnson."

The others laughed at her again. Johnson stepped forward and looked down at her while his friends continued laughing at her.

"Mr. Johnson," Cora said, "what would you give me half a dollar for?"

"What would I give you half a dollar for?" he asked.

"Yes, Mr. Johnson. What would you give it to me for?"

He turned around and winked at the other men before answering her. They urged him on.

"Have you got a girl at home?" he asked her.

"Yes, sir. I've got Pearl, and Ruby, too."

"Well, I couldn't give you half a dollar, but I might be able to give you a quarter."

The streetcar stopped and the door sprang open. The motorman had a tin disk pinned to his coat that looked just like the one Hugh had.

The other two men hopped on, calling to Johnson to hurry. He looked at Cora for a moment longer, his hand on the streetcar, but when she continued to stand there with her mouth open, unable to say anything, he turned and jumped aboard.

Cora was left standing beside the tracks. When the car started, she stood on her toes and tried to see the man inside who had spoken to her. She called to him frantically, trying to make him understand her, and she waved her arms excitedly, attempting to attract his attention.

All three of them ran to the rear end of the car and pressed their faces against the glass to see her better. Cora ran down the middle of the street, between the streetcar rails, calling to them and trying to stop them, but the car was soon out of sight and she was left standing in the car tracks. She went to the sidewalk and walked back up the street until she had reached the corner in front of the stores where the men had been standing when she first saw them. When she got to the corner, she sat down on the curb to wait.

Cora did not know how long she had waited, but she had promised the children she would bring back some food when she returned, and she had to wait no matter how long the time was. But Johnson finally came back. He got off the streetcar and walked towards her at the curb. He was surprised to see her there, and he stopped before her and looked down at her in amazement. Cora was glad the other men had not come back with him.

She led him up the street, running ahead and urging him to hurry. Even though he followed her without protest, he did not walk fast enough to please Cora, and she was continually asking him to hurry. He stopped once and struck a match for his cigarette against an iron street-light pole, and Cora ran back and pulled at his coat, begging him to follow her as fast as he could.

When they got to the house, Cora awakened Pearl. The man stood close to the door, debating with himself whether to remain and see what happened or whether to leave before something did happen. Cora got behind him and held the door shut so he could not leave.

"How old is she?" he asked Cora.

"She's almost ten now."

"It's cold as hell in this house. Why don't you have some heat in here? You've got a stove there."

"Give me a quarter, and I'll try to get some coal somewhere," Cora said.

"Tell her to stand up."

"Stand up, Pearl," Cora told her.

Pearl shrank against the foot of the bed; she was bewildered and frightened. She wished to run to her mother, but the strange man was between them. She was afraid he would catch her before she could reach the door where Cora stood.

"You're lying to me," Johnson said. "She's nowhere near ten."

"I swear to God, Mr. Johnson, she's almost ten," Cora said. "Please, Mr. Johnson, don't go off now."

"Christ, how do I know this's not a shakedown?" he said, shivering and shaking.

"I swear before God, Mr. Johnson!"

Johnson looked around the room and saw John and Ruby asleep under the quilts on the bed.

"How old is the other girl?"

"She's going on eight."

"Christ!" he said.

"What's the matter, Mr. Johnson?"

"I don't believe you. You're lying to me. Neither one of them is over seven or eight."

"Pearl's almost ten, Mr. Johnson. I swear before God, she is. Please give me the quarter."

He walked across the room towards Pearl. She tried to run away, but Cora caught her and made her stand still beside the foot of the bed. Cora waited behind Johnson.

"Tell her to turn around," he said.

"Turn around, Pearl," Cora told her.

"Christ!" Johnson said, rubbing his face and neck with both hands.

"What's the matter?" Cora asked him.

"It's too damn cold in here," he said, his hands trembling. "My feet are frozen already. Why don't you build a fire in the stove?"

"If you'll give me the quarter, I'll try to get a little coal somewhere."

"How do I know you're on the level?" he asked her. "How do I know this is not a shakedown? I'm afraid of you. You don't look right to me. How do I know you won't go yelling for a cop the first thing?"

"I wouldn't do that. Give me the quarter."

"I'd be in a pretty fix, caught like that. They'd give me twenty years at hard labor. I'd never get out alive."

"I won't tell anybody, Mr. Johnson. I swear before God, I won't. Just give me the quarter."

Johnson pushed his hands into his pockets and looked at Pearl again. His hands were cold; his feet were, too. His breath looked like smoke in the cold house.

"Tell her to let me see her," he said.

"Let him see you, Pearl," Cora said.

Johnson waited, looking at her and at Cora. He could not stand there freezing to death while waiting for Cora to make her obey.

"Hurry up, Pearl, and let him see you," Cora urged.

Pearl began to cry.

"They'd give me life for that," Johnson said, backing towards the door. "You'd get a cop after me before I could get out of the house. I don't like the way you look. Why don't you have some heat in here? You've got a stove."

"Honest to God, Mr. Johnson, I wouldn't tell on you," Cora pleaded. "Give me the quarter, and you can trust me."

"Get some heat in here first," he said. "My feet are freezing solid."

"I can't get any coal until you give me the quarter."

"You can go steal some, can't you?"

"Give me the quarter first, Mr. Johnson."

"How do I know you're on the level? I don't like the way you look. How do I know this's not a shakedown?"

"I swear to God, I won't tell on you, Mr. Johnson."

Johnson lit a cigarette and inhaled the smoke in the manner of a man gasping for breath. With his lungs and mouth and nostrils dense with smoke, he dropped the cigarette into the stove and thrust both hands back into his pants pockets.

"Tell her to come over here," he said.

"Go over there, Pearl."

Johnson bent down and looked at Pearl in the dim light. He straightened up once for a moment, and bent down again and looked at her more closely.

"They'd hang me before tomorrow night if they caught me," he said unevenly.

"Give me the quarter, Mr. Johnson, and I swear before God I won't tell anybody."

"Tell her to stand still."

"Stand still, Pearl."

"For God's sake get some heat in here."

"Give me the quarter first, Mr. Johnson," Cora begged.

"And then go out and tell a cop?" he said shrilly.

"Just give me the quarter first."

"You're crazy," he shouted at her. "I don't like the looks of you. How do I know what you'll do? You might run out of here the first thing yelling for a cop."

"Give me the quarter, and I'll get a little coal."

"And tell a cop."

"I swear I won't do that, Mr. Johnson. Give me the quarter, and I'll get some coal."

Johnson turned his back on Cora and went closer to Pearl. He took his hands out of his pants pockets and blew into them.

"Tell her to stop that crying."

"Stop crying, Pearl."

Johnson reached down and put his hands under Pearl's thick yellow hair, but the moment he touched her, she whirled around and ran to Cora.

"They'd screw my head off my neck so quick I wouldn't have a chance to think about it."

"Give me the quarter, Mr. Johnson, and I swear to God I won't tell on you."

He hesitated a moment; looking at Pearl, he shoved his hand into his pants pocket and brought out a twenty-five-cent piece. Cora grabbed it from his hand and bolted for the door.

"Wait a minute!" he shouted, running and catching her. "Come back here and tell her to keep still before you go."

"Keep still, Pearl," her mother told her.

"Hurry up and get some coal before I freeze to death in this place. And if you tell a policeman, I'll kill the last one of you before they take me. I ought to have better sense than to let you go out of here before I do. I don't like the way you look."

Cora ran to the door and into the alley before he could say anything more to her. She slammed the door and ran with all her might to the end of the alley. Without losing a moment, she raced down the street towards the one-story stores.

After she had gone a block, she stopped and carefully placed the quarter on her tongue and closed her lips tightly so she would be sure not to drop it or lose it on the dark street.

One of the grocery stores was still open. She took the coin out of her mouth, pointing at the bread and pressed meat, and placed the money in the clerk's hand. He dropped the wet silver piece as though it were white-hot steel and wiped his hands on his apron.

"What's this?" he said. "What did you do to it?"

"Nothing," Cora said. "Hurry up!"

When Cora got back, the children were asleep. John and Ruby were rolled tightly in the quilts, and Pearl was lying on the bed with her coat over her. Her gingham dress was lying on the floor, marked with brown streaks of footprints. She had been crying, and the tears had not fully dried on her cheeks; her eyes were inflamed, and her face was swollen across the bridge of her nose.

Cora went to the side of the bed and threw the coat from her and looked down at her. Pearl had doubled herself into a knot, with her arms locked around her knees, and her head was thrust forward over her chest. Cora looked at her for a while, and then she carefully replaced the coat over her.

After unwrapping the bread and pressed meat, she stuffed the paper into the stove and struck a match to it. She drew her chair closer, and bent forward so she could stretch her arms around the sides of the stove and feel the heat as much as possible before the wrapping paper burned out.

When the stove became cold again, Cora laid the bread and pressed meat on a chair beside her and rolled up in her quilt to wait for day to come. When the children woke up, they would find the food there for them.

"Don't Cry, Mother" by Philip Evergood.

Cows and Horses Are Hungry

BY MERIDEL LE SUEUR

I

WHEN you drive through the Middle West droughty country you try not to look at the thrusting out ribs of the horses and cows, but you get so you can't see anything else but ribs, like hundreds of thousands of little beached hulks. It looks like the bones are rising right up out of the skin. Pretty soon, quite gradually, you begin to know that the farmer, under his rags, shows his ribs, too, and the farmer's wife is as lean as his cows, and his children look tiny and hungry.

Drive through Elbow Lake, Otter Tail County, Elk River and Kandiyohi County, Big Stone County, Yellow Medicine County and Mille Lacs, and you'll see the same thing. These are only the counties that are officially designated as in the droughty area by the Federal government. This is only in Minnesota. In the Dakotas they say cattle are leaning up against the fences. There is a shortage of water as well as of pasturage.

If you are officially in the droughty areas you will come in on the government purchasing of starving cattle. On May 31, the day after the last hot wind and the temperature at 112° in some areas, the papers announced the working plan of the machinery set up by the Federal government to aid farmers in the drought stricken areas of the Northwest. The animals will be bought and those that are not too far gone will be fattened and given to the F. E. R. A. for the relief departments. If you're on the breadlines you'll be getting some starved meat for your own starved bones. They could feed you some choice farmer's ribs, too. But you can't buy up farmers and their wives and shoot them. Not directly.

Meridel Le Sueur was born in Minneapolis and wrote extensively about the effect of the depression on the Middle West. She attended the American Writers' Congress in April of 1935 and delivered an address on "Proletarian Literature and the Middle West," in which she said that nowhere in America were "the ravages of *laissez faire* colonization so apparent as in the Middle West." "Cows and Horses are Hungry" first appeared in *American Mercury* in September 1934.

The government has been pushing straw into these communities all winter to keep the cattle from starving for lack of grain until the pasturage came in. Well, now there is no pasture. The grass is brown and burnt as if it might be mid-August instead of May and June. The farmer is milked at one end and given relief at another. Well, the farmer says, they wanted a scarcity, and by God, now they have it. They shot off the pigs and cows, they tried to keep what was left alive because they couldn't feed them, now they're trying to keep them from dying off and rotting on the ground and making too big a stench.

The farmer can't sell his cattle to the stockyards. They're too far gone, too thin. The cattle thus turned over to the government will be left temporarily on the farms, fed by the administration and then moved to the packing houses or redistributed to other farmers or turned directly over to relief channels.

The administration of this plan seems similar to the other plans, with a regional director for seven Northwest States, Minnesota, North and South Dakota, Montana, Wisconsin, Iowa and Nebraska; with State directors from the farm-schools working through county agents. The county director will have an advisory committee made up of the members of the corn-hog allotment committee that functioned in the county. This organization will appoint township committees that will visit the farms, check the stock, classify, appraise the value and fix the purchase price, secure necessary farmer and creditor signatures to sales contracts, and arrange for final check to see that the animals have been disposed of as agreed. They will also approve vouchers for payment. The same old rubbish. Committees and committees and committees. But the farmer will keep on starving. He has been rooked by nature and now he will be rooked by the Federal government.

II

THE farmer has been depressed a long time. For the last three years he has been going over into the abyss of pauperism by the thousands. This spring after a terrible winter there was no rain. The village where I live has not exchanged money for two years. They have bartered and exchanged their produce. Last year some had nothing to exchange. We cut down trees in the front yard for fuel and tried to live off the miserable crop of potatoes of last year.

Since April there has been hope of rain and even up until the day after Decoration day, until that bitter afternoon when the hot winds came and made any hope after that impossible. During April the farmers said that the winter wheat would be all right if it would rain even next week. The peas went in. They raise a lot of peas for the canneries both in Wisconsin and Minnesota. The peas came up a little ways and then fell down as if they had been mowed down. We waited to put in the corn day after day.

Then came a terrifying wind from the Dakotas, blew tens of thousands of dollars worth of onion seed away and half of North Dakota blew into Ohio with the spring sowing. That wind was a terror and blew dust and seed so high you couldn't drive through it in mid-day.

A kind of terror grew in the folk. It was too much, added up with the low prices they got, the drought, heat and high wind. A peculiar thing happened. Very much like what happened in the flu terror after the war. No one went outdoors. They all shut themselves up as if some terrific crisis, some horrible massacre, were about to occur. The last day of the wind, the radio announced every half hour that there was no menace in the dust, it would hurt no one actually. The wind died down, but it didn't rain. Well, they said, it *will* rain. It has to rain sometime. The winter wheat and rye began to whiten. A thin stand. You could sit in your house and look about and see the fields whiten and the wheat seemed to go back into the ground. You could see it stand still and then creep back into the ground.

But the farmers kept on ploughing in case it would rain. First you had to plough with two horses and then with four. You couldn't rip the earth open and when you did, a fume of dust went up like smoke, and a wind from hell whipped the seed out. Some planted their corn, though, in corn-planting time, some waited for rain. They waited until the day after Decoration day.

Every day the pastures became worse. The grass became as dry as straw in May and the cattle lost their flesh quickly. They weren't too well padded because of scarce food all winter. You had to look for a green spot every morning. Children were kept out of school to herd the cattle around near streams and creeks. Some farmers cut down trees so the cattle could eat the leaves even if they were poor picking. The leaves on the trees are poor, falling off already in some places due to the searing, driving wind and the lack of moisture at their roots. The man up the road has turned his cows into his winter wheat which is thin as a young man's first beard anyway.

On Decoration day the wind started again, blowing hot as a blast from hell and the young corn withered as if under machine gun fire, the trees in two hours looked as if they had been beaten. The day after Decoration day it was so hot you couldn't sit around looking at the panting cattle and counting their ribs and listening to that low cry that is an awful asking. We got in the car and drove slowly through the sizzling countryside.

Not a soul was in sight. It was like a funeral. The houses were closed up tight, the blinds drawn, the windows and doors closed. There seemed to be a menace in the air made visible. It was frightening. You could hear the fields crack and dry, and the only movement in the down-driving heat was the dead writhing of the dry blighted leaves on the twigs. The young corn about four spears up was falling down like a fountain being slowly turned off.

There was something terrifying about this visible sign of disaster. It went into your nostrils so you couldn't breathe: the smell of hunger. It made you count your own ribs with terror. You don't starve in America. Everything looks good. There is something around the corner. Everyone has a chance. That's all over now. The whole country cracks and rumbles and cries out in its terrible leanness, stripped with exploitation and terror—and as sign and symbol, bones—bones showing naked and spiritless, showing decay and crisis and a terrific warning, bare and lean in Mid-America.

We kept driving very slowly, about as slowly as you go to a funeral, with no one behind us, meeting no one on the road. The corpse was the very earth. We kept looking at the body of the earth, at the bare and mortgaged and unpainted houses like hollow pupas when the life has gone. They looked stripped as if after a raid. As if a terrible army had just gone through. It used to be hard to look at the fat rich-seeming farms and realize that they were mortgaged to the hilt and losing ground every year, but not now. Now it stands a visible sign. You can see the marks of the ravagers. The mark of that fearful exploitation stands on the landscape visible, known, to be reckoned with.

The cows were the only thin flesh visible. They stood in the poor shade of the stripped and dying trees, breathing heavily, their great ribs showing like the ribs of decaying boats beached and deserted. But you knew that from behind all those drawn blinds hundreds of eyes were watching that afternoon, that no man, woman or child could sit down and read a book or lie down to any dreams. Through all these windows eyes were watching—watching the wheat go, the rye go, the corn, peas, potatoes go. Everywhere in those barricaded houses were eyes drawn back to the burning windows looking out at next winter's food slowly burning in the fields. You look out and see the very food of your next winter's sustenance visibly, physically dying beneath your eyes, projecting into you your future hungers.

The whole countryside that afternoon became terrifying, not only with its present famine but with the foreshadowing of its coming hunger. No vegetables now, and worst of all, no milk. The countryside became monstrous with this double doom. Every house is alike in suffering as in a flood, every cow, every field mounting into hundreds, into thousands, from State to State. You try not to look at the ribs, but pretty soon you are looking only at ribs.

Then an awful thing happened. The sun went down behind the ridge, dropped low, and men and women began to pour out of the houses, the children lean and fleet as rats, the tired lean farm women looking to see what had happened. The men ran into their fields, ran back for water and they began to water their lands with buckets and cups, running, pouring the puny drops of water on the baked earth as if every minute might count now. The children ran behind the cows urging them to eat the harsh dry grass. It looked like an evacuated countryside, with the people running out after the enemy had passed. Not a word was spoken. In intense silence they hurried down the rows with buckets and cups, watering the wilted corn plants, a gargantuan and terrible and hopeless labor. Some came out with horses and ploughs and began stirring up the deadly dust. If the field was a slope, barrels were filled, and a primitive irrigation started. Even the children ran with cups of water, all dogged silent, mad, without a word. A certain madness in it all, like things that are done after unimaginable violence.

We stop and talk to a farmer. His eyes are bloodshot. I can hardly see from the heat and the terrible emotion. . . . How do you think my cows look? he asks. I think they are a little fatter today. I try not to look at his cows at all. Pretty thin, though, he says, pretty thin. I can see the fine jersey pelt beginning to sag and the bones rise out like sticks out of the sea at low tide.

We both know that a farmer across the river shot twenty-two of his cattle yesterday, and then shot himself. I look at him and I can see his clavicle and I know that his ribs are rising out of his skin, too. It is visible now, starvation and famine. So they are going to buy the starving cattle and shoot them and feed the rest to the bread lines. A man isn't worth anything—but a cow . . .

We drive on. When I shut my eyes the flesh burns the balls, and all I can see is ribs—the bones showing through.

The banks protest the Federal government's price for starving cattle. From six to twenty dollars, with your pedigreed bull thrown in. No difference. Hunger levels all flesh. When the skeleton shows through, all meat is worthless. The banks don't like this. Most of the cattle are mortgaged and they won't get much. The banks are protesting. All this sounds different in the language of the banks . . .

They say in their bulletin . . . We report further deterioration of crops since the May 1 report. In addition, weather conditions in a large part of the Ninth District, which embraces the States of Minnesota, North and South Dakota, Montana and part of Wisconsin, are bad. . . . And abandonment of 16% in Montana and 60% in South Dakota of winter wheat acreage. . . . Reports from grain, trade and railroads serving the grain-raising areas show condition poor of both winter wheat and rye.

In addition, weather conditions in the Ninth District have been more than usually favorable for the hatching of grasshopper eggs and tend to increase the seriousness of this menace. . . .

In human terms, of life and not credit and interest, this means— winter wheat and rye gone, pasturage gone, cattle gone; wholesale prices low, retail prices soaring; the government piles in feed, straw, and now buys up the lean cattle, but they milk the farmer faster than they resuscitate him.

Starvation stands up in the blazing sun naked at last; and bare and lean ribs for all the coming winter.

Still from "The Plow that Broke the Plains," documentary film produced by Pare Lorenz for the Resettlement Administration.

Dubious Battle in California

BY JOHN STEINBECK

IN sixty years a complete revolution has taken place in California agriculture. Once its principal products were hay and cattle. Today fruits and vegetables are its most profitable crops. With the change in the nature of farming there has come a parallel change in the nature and amount of the labor necessary to carry it on. Truck gardens, while they give a heavy yield per acre, require much more labor and equipment than the raising of hay and livestock. At the same time these crops are seasonal, which means that they are largely handled by migratory workers. Along with the intensification of farming made necessary by truck gardening has come another important development. The number of large-scale farms, involving the investment of thousands of dollars, has increased; so has the number of very small farms of from five to ten acres. But the middle farm, of from 100 to 300 acres is in process of elimination.

There are in California, therefore, two distinct classes of farmers widely separated in standard of living, desires, needs, and sympathies: the very small farmer who more often than not takes the side of the workers in disputes, and the speculative farmer, like A. J. Chandler, publisher of the Los Angeles *Times,* or like Herbert Hoover and William Randolph Hearst, absentee owners who possess huge sections of land. Allied with these large individual growers have been the big incorporated farms, owned by their stockholders and farmed by instructed managers, and a large number of bank farms, acquired by foreclosure and operated by superintendents whose labor policy is dictated by the bank. For example, the Bank of America is very nearly the largest farm owner and operator in the state of California.

In 1936, the year in which he published *In Dubious Battle,* John Steinbeck contributed a series of articles to the San Francisco *News* based on his observations of squatters' camps in California. Two years later, the articles were revised and published as a pamphlet entitled *Their Blood Is Strong.* The same year in which he wrote the articles for the *News,* Steinbeck contributed a piece about the Okies to *The Nation* (September 12, 1936), which he called "Dubious Battle in California." Both *Their Blood Is Strong* and "Dubious Battle in California" were put to considerable use by Steinbeck when he wrote *The Grapes of Wrath* (1939), which became one of the most celebrated novels of the time.

These two classes have little or no common ground; while the small farmer is likely to belong to the grange, the speculative farmer belongs to some such organization as the Associated Farmers of California, which is closely tied to the state Chamber of Commerce. This group has as its major activity resistance to any attempt of farm labor to organize. Its avowed purpose has been the distribution of news reports and leaflets tending to show that every attempt to organize agricultural workers was the work of red agitators and that every organization was Communist inspired.

The completion of the transcontinental railroads left in the country many thousands of Chinese and some Hindus who had been imported for the work. At about the same time the increase of fruit crops, with their heavy seasonal need for pickers, created a demand for this mass of cheap labor. These people, however, did not long remain on the land. They migrated to the cities, rented small plots of land there, and, worst of all, organized in the so-called "tongs," which were able to direct their efforts as a group. Soon the whites were inflamed to race hatred, riots broke out against the Chinese, and repressive activities were undertaken all over the state, until these people, who had been a tractable and cheap source of labor, were driven from the fields.

To take the place of the Chinese, the Japanese were encouraged to come into California; and they, even more than the Chinese, showed an ability not only to obtain land for their subsistence but to organize. The "Yellow Peril" agitation was the result. Then, soon after the turn of the century Mexicans were imported in great numbers. For a while they were industrious workers, until the process of importing twice as many as were needed in order to depress wages made their earnings drop below any conceivable living standard. In such conditions they did what the others had done; they began to organize. The large growers immediately opened fire on them. The newspapers were full of the radicalism of the Mexican unions. Riots became common in the Imperial Valley and in the grape country in and adjacent to Kern County. Another wave of importations was arranged, from the Philippine Islands, and the cycle was repeated—wage depression due to abundant labor, organization, and the inevitable race hatred and riots.

This brings us almost to the present. The drought in the Middle West has very recently made available an enormous amount of cheap labor. Workers have been coming to California in nondescript cars from Oklahoma, Nebraska, Texas, and other states, parts of which have been rendered uninhabitable by drought. Poverty-stricken after the destruction of their farms, their last reserves used up in making the trip, they have arrived so beaten and destitute that they have been willing at first to work under any conditions and for any wages offered. This migration started on a considerable scale about two years ago and is increasing all the time.

For a time it looked as though the present cycle would be identical with the earlier ones, but there are several factors in this influx which differentiate it from the others. In the first place, the migrants are undeniably American and not deportable. In the second place, they were not lured to California by a promise of good wages, but are refugees as surely as though they had fled from destruction by an invader. In the third place, they are not drawn from a peon class, but have either owned small farms or been farm hands in the early American sense, in which the "hand" is a member of the employing family. They have one fixed idea, and that is to acquire land and settle on it. Probably the most important difference is that they are not easily intimidated. They are courageous, intelligent, and resourceful. Having gone through the horrors of the drought and with immense effort having escaped from it, they cannot be herded, attacked, starved, or frightened as all the others were.

Let us see what the emigrants from the dust bowl find when they arrive in California. The ranks of permanent and settled labor are filled. In most cases all resources have been spent in making the trip from the dust bowl. Unlike the Chinese and the Filipinos, the men rarely come alone. They bring wives and children, now and then a few chickens and their pitiful household goods, though in most cases these have been sold to buy gasoline for the trip. It is quite usual for a man, his wife, and from three to eight children to arrive in California with no possessions but the rattletrap car they travel in and the ragged clothes on their bodies. They often lack bedding and cooking utensils.

During the spring, summer, and part of the fall the man may find some kind of agricultural work. The top pay for a successful year will not be over $400, and if he has any trouble or is not agile, strong, and quick it may well be only $150. It will be seen that rent is out of the question. Clothes cannot be bought. Every available cent must go for food and a reserve to move the car from harvest to harvest. The migrant will stop in one of two federal camps, in a state camp, in houses put up by the large or small farmers, or in the notorious squatters' camps. In the state and federal camps he will find sanitary arrangements and a place to pitch his tent. The camps maintained by the large farmers are of two classes—houses which are rented to the workers at what are called nominal prices, $4 to $8 a month, and camp grounds which are little if any better than the squatters' camps. Since rent is such a problem, let us see how the houses are fitted. Ordinarily there is one room, no running water; one toilet and one bathroom are provided for two or three hundred persons. Indeed, one large farmer was accused in a Growers' Association meeting of being "kind of communistic" because he advocated separate toilets for men and women. Some of the large ranches maintain what are called model workers' houses. One such ranch, run by a very prominent man, has neat single-room houses built of whitewashed adobe. They are said to have cost $500 apiece. They are rented for $5 a month. This ranch pays twenty cents an hour as opposed to the thirty cents paid at other ranches and indorsed by the grange in the community. Since this rugged individual is saving 33⅓ per cent of his labor cost and still charging $5 a month rent for his houses, it will be readily seen that he is getting a very fair return on his money besides being generally praised as a philanthropist. The reputation of this ranch, however, is that the migrants stay only long enough to get money to buy gasoline with, and then move on.

The small farmers are not able to maintain camps of any comfort or with any sanitary facilities except one or two holes dug for toilets. The final resource is the squatters' camp, usually located on the bank of some watercourse. The people pack into them. They use the watercourse for drinking, bathing, washing their clothes, and to receive their refuse, with the result that epidemics start easily and are difficult to check. Stanislaus County, for example, has a nice culture of hookworm in the mud by its squatter's camp. The people in these camps, because of long-continued privation, are in no shape to fight illness. It is often said that no one starves in the United States, yet in Santa Clara County last year five babies were certified by the local coroner to have died of "malnutrition," the modern word for starvation, and the less shocking word, although in its connotation it is perhaps more horrible since it indicates that the suffering has been long drawn out.

In these squatters' camps the migrant will find squalor beyond anything he has yet had to experience and intimidation almost unchecked. At one camp it is the custom of deputy sheriffs, who are also employees of a great ranch nearby, to drive by the camp for hours at a time, staring into the tents as though trying to memorize faces. The communities in which these camps exist want migratory workers to come for the month required to pick the harvest, and to move on when it is over. If they do not move on, they are urged to with guns.

These are some of the conditions California offers the refugees from the dust bowl. But the refugees are even less content with the starvation wages and the rural slums than were the Chinese, the Filipinos, and the Mexicans. Having their families with them, they are not so mobile as the earlier immigrants were. If starvation sets in, the whole family starves, instead of just one man. Therefore they have been quick to see that they must organize for their own safety.

Attempts to organize have been met with a savagery from the large growers beyond anything yet attempted. In Kern County a short time ago a group met to organize under the A. F. of L. They made out their form and petition for a charter and put it in the mail for Washington. That night a representative of Associated Farmers wired Washington for information concerning a charter granted to these workers. The Washington office naturally replied that it had no knowledge of such a charter. In the Bakersfield papers the next day appeared a story that the A. F. of L. denied the affiliation; consequently the proposed union must be of Communist origin.

But the use of the term communism as a bugbear has nearly lost its sting. An official of a speculative-farmer group, when asked what he meant by a Communist, replied: "Why, he's the guy that wants twenty-five cents an hour when we're paying twenty." This realistic and cynical definition has finally been understood by the workers, so that the term is no longer the frightening thing it was. And when a county judge said, "California agriculture demands that we create and maintain a peonage," the future of unorganized agricultural labor was made clear to every man in the field.

The usual repressive measures have been used against these migrants: shooting by deputy sheriffs in "self-defense," jailing without charge, refusal of trial by jury, torture and beating by night riders. But even in the short time that these American migrants have been out here there has been a change. It is understood that they are being attacked not because they want higher wages, not because they are Communists, but simply because they want to organize. And to the men, since this defines the thing not to be allowed, it also defines the thing that is completely necessary to the safety of the workers.

This season has seen the beginning of a new form of intimidation not used before. It is the whispering campaign which proved so successful among business rivals. As in business, it is particularly deadly here because its source cannot be traced and because it is easily spread. One of the items of this campaign is the rumor that in the event of labor troubles the deputy sheriffs inducted to break up picket lines will be armed not with tear gas but with poison gas. The second is aimed at the women and marks a new low in tactics. It is to the effect that in the event of labor troubles the water supply used by strikers will be infected with typhoid germs. The fact that these bits of information are current over a good part of the state indicates that they have been widely planted.

The effect has been far from that desired. There is now in California anger instead of fear. The stupidity of the large grower has changed terror into defensive fury. The granges, working close to the soil and to the men, and knowing the temper of the men of this new race, have tried to put through wages that will allow a living, however small. But the large growers, who have been shown to be the only group making a considerable profit from agriculture, are devoting their money to tear gas and rifle ammunition. The men will organize and the large growers will meet organization with force. It is easy to prophesy this. In Kern County the grange has voted $1 a hundred pounds for cotton pickers for the first picking. The Associated Farmers have not yielded from seventy-five cents. There is tension in the valley, and fear for the future.

It is fervently to be hoped that the great group of migrant workers so necessary to the harvesting of California's crops may be given the right to live decently, that they may not be so badgered, tormented, and hurt that in the end they become avengers of the hundreds of thousands who have been tortured and starved before them.

"Departure of the Joads" by Thomas Hart Benton.

Talking Dust Bowl*

WORDS AND MUSIC BY WOODY GUTHRIE

I hit Pampa in the Panhandle of Texas, and stuck there a while. Then the dust storms begun blowing blacker and meaner, and the rain was getting less, and the dust more and more. I made up a little song that went:

Back in 1927, I had a little farm, and I called that heaven.
Prices up, and the rain come down;
I hauled my crops all into town, got the money . . .
Bought clothes and groceries . . . fed the kids
and raised a big family

But the rain quit and the wind got high
Black old dust storm filled the sky;
I traded my farm for a Ford machine,
Poured it full of this gas-i-line
 And started—rockin' and a-rollin'
 Deserts and mountains—to California

Way up yonder on a mountain road
Hot motor and a heavy load,
Goin' purty fast, wasn't even stoppin'
Bouncin' up and down like popcorn a-poppin',
 Had a breakdown—kind of a nervous breakdown,
 Mechanic feller there charged me five bucks
 Said it was en-gine trouble.

Way up yonder on a mountain curve,
Way up yonder in the Piney Wood,
I give that rollin' Ford a shove,
Gonna coast just as far's I could,
 Commenced a-rollin' . . . pickin' up speed,
 Come a hair-pin turn . . . and I didn't make it.

Perhaps the greatest of all folk balladers, Woody Guthrie was born in western Oklahoma and brought up in the Texas Panhandle. When the dust storms came, he began his life of ceaseless wanderings: "Walking down the big road, no money, no job, no home, no nothing, nights I slept in jails, and the cells were piled high with young boys, strong men and old men. They talked and they sung and they told the story of their lives . . . So somehow I picked up an old rusty guitar and started to picking and playing the songs I heard and making up new ones about what folks said."

Man alive, I'm a-tellin' you,
The fiddles and guitars really flew,
That Ford took off like a flyin' squirrel,
Flew half-way around the world.
        Scattered wives and children
        All over the side of that mountain.

Got to California so dad gum broke,
So dad gum hungry I thought I'd choke;
I bummed up a spud or two,
Wife fixed up some tater stew.
        We poured the kids full of it . . .
        Looked like a tribe of ther-mometers
                a-runnin' around.

Lord, man, I swear to you,
That was shorely mighty thin stew.
So damn thin, I really mean,
You could read a magazine
        Right through it . . . look at pictures too.
        Purty whiskey bottles . . . naked women.
Always have thought, always figgered,
If that damn stew'd a-been a little bit thinner,
        Some of these here politicians
        Could of seen through it.

On the road to Los Angeles. Dorothea Lange for the Farm Security Administration.

I Ain't Got No Home*

Words and Music by Woody Guthrie

I ain't got no home
I'm just a-ramblin' 'round
I'm just a wanderin' workin' man
I go from town to town
    Police make it hard wherever I may go
    And I ain't got no home in this world anymore

My brothers and sisters
Are stranded on this road
It's a hot and dusty road
That a million feet have trod
    Rich man took my home and he drove me from my door
    And I ain't got no home in this world anymore

I was farmin' on the shares
And always I was poor
My crops I lay
Into the Banker's Store
    My wife took down and died upon my cabin floor
    And I ain't got no home in this world anymore

Now as I look around
It's mighty plain to see
This wide and wicked world
Is a funny place to be
    The gambling man is rich and the working man is poor
    And I ain't got no home in this world anymore

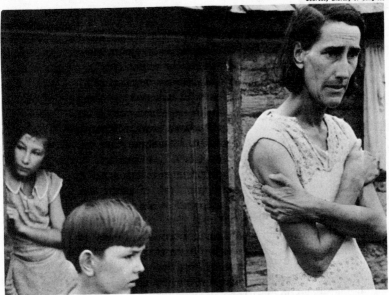

*Above, Family in Boone County, Arkansas. Ben Shahn for the Farm Security Administration.
Below, Okies in California. Dorothea Lange for the Farm Security Administration.*

From Let Us Now Praise Famous Men

BY JAMES AGEE

AT THE FORKS

On a road between the flying shadows of loose woods toward the middle of an afternoon, far enough thrust forward between towns that we had lost intuition of our balance between them, we came to a fork where the sunlight opened a little more widely, but not on cultivated land, and stopped a minute to decide.

Marion would lie some miles over beyond the road on our left; some other county seat, Centerville most likely, out beyond the road on our right; but on which road the woods might give way to any extension of farm country there was no deducing: for we were somewhere toward the middle of one of the wider of the gaps on the road map, and had seen nothing but woods, and infrequent woods farms, for a good while now.

Just a little behind us on our left and close on the road was a house, the first we had passed in several miles, and we decided to ask directions of the people on the porch, whom, in the car mirror, I could see still watching us. We backed slowly, stopping the car a little short of the house, and I got slowly out and walked back toward them, watching them quietly and carefully, and preparing my demeanors and my words for the two hundredth time.

There were three on the porch, watching me, and they must not have spoken twice in an hour while they watched beyond the rarely traveled road the changes of daylight along the recessions of the

In 1936 James Agee and Walker Evans were commissioned by *Fortune* to prepare an account of a typical white tenant farm family; Agee was to supply the text, Evans the photographs. The two men found that one family could not adequately represent all of tenantry and chose instead to study three—the Ricketts, the Woods, and the Gudgers—with whom they lived for little less than four weeks. *Fortune* decided not to print the article, and it was released to Agee and Evans. The material was expanded into book form and was finally published in 1941 as *Let Us Now Praise Famous Men*. "The immediate instruments are two," Agee wrote, "the motionless camera and the printed word. The governing instrument—which is also one of the centers of the subject—is individual, anti-authoritative human consciousness." We have reprinted all of the chapter entitled, "At the Forks," as well as excerpts from "The Front Bedroom."

woods, and while, in the short field that sank behind their house, their two crops died silently in the sun: a young man, a young woman, and an older man; and the two younger, their chins drawn inward and their heads tall against the grained wall of the house, watched me steadily and sternly as if from beneath the brows of helmets, in the candor of young warriors or of children.

They were a kind not safely to be described in an account claiming to be unimaginative or trustworthy, for they had too much and too out-landish beauty not to be legendary. Since, however, they existed quite irrelevant to myth, it will be necessary to tell a little of them.

The young man's eyes had the opal lightings of dark oil and, though he was watching me in a way that relaxed me to cold weakness of ignobility, they fed too strongly inward to draw to a focus: whereas those of the young woman had each the splendor of a monstrance, and were brass. Her body also was brass or bitter gold, strong to stridency beneath the unbleached clayed cotton dress, and her arms and bare legs were sharp with metal down. The blenched hair drew her face tight to her skull as a tied mask; her features were baltic. The young man's face was deeply shaded with soft short beard, and luminous with death. He had the scornfully ornate nostrils and lips of an aegean exquisite. The fine wood body was ill strung, and sick even as he sat there to look at, and the bone hands roped with vein; they rose, then sank, and lay palms upward in his groins. There was in their eyes so quiet and ultimate a quality of hatred, and contempt, and anger, toward every creature in existence beyond themselves, and toward the damages they sustained, as shone scarcely short of a state of beatitude; nor did this at any time modify itself.

These two sat as if formally, or as if sculptured, one in wood and one in metal, or as if enthroned, about three feet apart in straight chairs tilted to the wall, and constantly watched me, all the while communicating thoroughly with each other by no outward sign of word or glance or turning, but by emanation.

The other man might have been fifty by appearance, yet, through a particular kind of delicateness upon his hands, and hair, and skin— they were almost infantine—I was sure he was still young, hardly out of his twenties, though again the face was seamed and short as a fetus. This man, small-built and heavy jointed, and wandering in him motions like a little child, had the thorny beard of a cartoon bolshevik, but suggested rather a hopelessly deranged and weeping prophet, a D. H. Lawrence whom male nurses have just managed to subdue into a straitjacket. A broken felt hat struck through with grass hair was banged on flat above his furious and leaky eyes, and from beneath its rascally brim as if from ambush he pored at me walleyed while, clenching himself back against the wall, he sank along it trembling and slowly to a squat, and watched up at me.

None of them relieved me for an instant of their eyes; at the intersection of those three tones of force I was transfixed as between spearheads as I talked. As I asked my questions, and told my purposes, and what I was looking for, it seemed to me they relaxed a little toward me, and at length a good deal more, almost as if into trust and liking; yet even at its best this remained so suspended, so conditional, that in any save the most hopeful and rationalized sense it was non-existent. The qualities of their eyes did not in the least alter, nor anything visible or audible about them, and their speaking was as if I was almost certainly a spy sent to betray them through trust, whom they would show they had neither trust nor fear of.

They were clients of Rehabilitation. They had been given a young sick steer to do their plowing with; the land was woods-clearing, but had been used as long as the house (whose wood was ragged and light as pith); no seed or fertilizer had been given them until the end of May. Nothing they had planted was up better than a few inches, and that was now withering faster than it grew. They now owed the Government on the seed and fertilizer, the land, the tools, the house, and probably before long on the steer as well, who was now so weak he could hardly stand. They had from the start given notice of the weakness and youth of the steer, of the nearly total sterility of the soil, and of the later and later withholding of the seed and fertilizer; and this had had a great deal to do with why the seed was given them so late, and they had been let know it in so many words.

The older man came up suddenly behind me, jamming my elbow with his concave chest and saying fiercely *Awnk, awnk,* while he glared at me with enraged and terrified eyes. Caught so abruptly off balance, my reflexes went silly and I turned toward him questioning 'politely' with my face, as if he wanted to say something, and could, which I had not quite heard. He did want urgently to say something, but all that came out was this blasting of *Awnk, awnk,* and a thick roil of saliva that hung like semen in his beard. I nodded, smiling at him, and he grinned gratefully with an expression of extreme wickedness and tugged hard at my sleeve, nodding violently in time to his voice and rooting out over and over this loud vociferation of a frog. The woman spoke to him sharply though not unkindly (the young man's eyes remained serene), as if he were a dog masturbating on a caller, and he withdrew against a post of the porch and sank along it to the

floor with his knees up sharp and wide apart and the fingers of his left
hand jammed as deep as they would go down his gnashing mouth,
while he stayed his bright eyes on me. She got up abruptly without
speaking and went indoors and came back out with a piece of stony
cornbread and gave it to him, and took her place again in her chair. He
took the bread in both hands and struck his face into it like the blow
of a hatchet, grappling with his jaws and slowly cradling his head like
a piece of heavy machinery, while grinding, passionate noises ran in
his throat, and we continued to talk, the young woman doing most of
the talking, corroborative and protective of the young man, yet always
respectful toward him.

The young man had the asthma so badly the fits of it nearly killed
him. He could never tell when he was going to be any good for work,
and he was no good for it even at the best, it was his wife did the
work; and him—the third—they did not even nod nor shift their eyes
toward him; he was just a mouth. These things were said in the voice
not of complaint but of statement, quietly stiff with hatred for the world
and for living: nor was there any touch of pride, shame, resentment, or
any discord among them.

Some niggers a couple of miles down a back road let them have
some corn and some peas. Without those niggers there was no saying
what they'd be doing by now. Only the niggers hadn't had a bit too
much for themselves in the first place and were running very short now;
it had been what was left over from the year before, and not much
new corn, nor much peas, was coming through the drought. It was—

The older man came honking up at my elbow, holding out a rolled
farm magazine. In my effort to give him whatever form of attention
could most gratify him I was stupid again; the idea there was something he wanted me to read; and looked at him half-questioning this,
and not yet taking what he offered me. The woman, in a voice that
somehow, though contemptuous (it implied, You are more stupid than
he is), yielded me for the first time her friendship and that of her husband, so that happiness burst open inside me like a flooding of sweet
water, said, he wants to give it to you. I took it and thanked him very
much, looking and smiling into his earnest eyes, and he stayed at my
side like a child, watching me affectionately while I talked to them.

They had told me there was farm country down the road on the
right a piece: the whole hoarded silence and quiet of a lonesome and
archaic American valley it was to become, full of heavy sunflowers
and mediocre cotton, where the women wore sunbonnets without shy-
ness before us and all whom we spoke to were gracious and melancholy, and where we did not find what we sought. Now after a little

while I thanked them here on the porch and told them good-bye. I had not the heart at all to say, Better luck to you, but then if I remember rightly I did say it, and, saying it or not, and unable to communicate to them all what my feelings were, I walked back the little distance to the car with my shoulders and the back of my neck more scalded-feeling than if the sun were on them. As we started, I looked back and held up my hand. The older man was on the dirt on his hands and knees coughing like a gorilla and looking at the dirt between his hands. Neither of the other two raised a hand. The young man lowered his head slowly and seriously, and raised it. The young woman smiled, sternly beneath her virulent eyes, for the first time. As we swung into the right fork of the road, I looked back again. The young man, looking across once more into the woods, had reached his hand beneath the bib of his overalls and was clawing at his lower belly. The woman, her eyes watching us past her shoulder, was walking to the door. Just as I glanced back, and whether through seeing that I saw her I cannot be sure, she turned her head to the front, and disappeared into the house.

THE FRONT BEDROOM

The Altar

The three other walls are straight and angled beams and the inward surfaces of unplaned pine weatherboards. This partition wall is made of horizontals of narrow and cleanly planed wood, laid tightly edge to edge; the wood is pine of another quality, slenderly grained in narrow yellow and rich iron-red golds, very smooth and as if polished, softly glowing and shining, almost mirroring bulks: and is the one wall of the room at all conducive to ornament, and is the one ornamented wall. At its center the mantel and square fireplace frame, painted, one coat, an old and thin blue-white: in front of the fireplace, not much more than covering the full width of its frame, the small table: and through, beneath it, the gray, swept yet ashy bricks of the fireplace and short hearth, and the silent shoes: and on the table, and on the mantel, and spread above and wide of it on the walls, the things of which I will now tell.

On the table: it is blue auto paint: a white cloth, hanging a little over the edges. On the cloth, at center, a small fluted green glass bowl in which sits a white china swan, profiled upon the north.

On the mantel against the glowing wall, each about six inches from the ends of the shelf, two small twin vases, very simply blown, of pebble-grained iridescent glass. Exactly at center between them, a fluted

saucer, with a coarse lace edge, of pressed milky glass, which Louise's
mother gave her to call her own and for which she cares more dearly
than for anything else she possesses. Pinned all along the edge of this
mantel, a broad fringe of white tissue pattern-paper which Mrs. Gudger
folded many times on itself and scissored into pierced geometrics of lace,
and of which she speaks as her last effort to make this house pretty.

On the wall, pasted or pinned or tacked or printed, set well discrete
from one another, in not quite perfected symmetric relations:

A small octagonal frame surfaced in ivory and black ribbons of thin
wicker or of straw, the glass broken out: set in this frame, not filling it,
a fading box-camera snapshot: low, gray, dead-looking land stretched
back in a deep horizon; twenty yards back, one corner of a tenant
house, central at the foreground, two women: Annie Mae's sister
Emma as a girl of twelve, in slippers and stockings and a Sunday dress,
standing a little shyly with puzzling eyes, self-conscious of her appearance and of her softly clouded sex; and their mother, wide and high, in
a Sunday dress still wet from housework, her large hands hung loose
and biased in against her thighs, her bearing strong, weary, and noble,
her face fainted away almost beyond distinguishing, as if in her death
and by some secret touching the image itself of the fine head her
husband had cared for so well had softly withered, which even while
they stood there had begun its blossoming inheritance in the young
daughter at her side.

A calendar, advertising ——'s shoes, depicting a pretty brunette
with ornate red lips, in a wide-brimmed red hat, cuddling red flowers.
The title is Cherie, and written twice, in pencil, in a schoolchild's
hand: Louise, Louise.

A calendar, advertising easy-payment furniture: a tinted photograph
of an immaculate, new-overalled boy of twelve, wearing a wide new
straw hat, the brim torn by the artist, fishing. The title is Fishin'.

Slung awry by its chain from a thin nail, an open oval locket, glassed.
In one face of this locket, a colored picture of Jesus, his right hand
blessing, his red heart exposed in a burst spiky gold halo. In the other
face, a picture by the same artist of the Blessed Virgin, in blue, her
heart similarly exposed and haloed, and pierced with seven small swords.[1]

Torn from a child's cheap storybook, costume pictures in bright
furry colors illustrating, exactly as they would and should be illustrated,
these titles:

> The Harper was Happier than a King as He Sat
>   by his Own Fireside.
> She Took the Little Prince in Her Arms
>   and Kissed Him. ('She' is a goosegirl.)

Torn from a tin can, a strip of bright scarlet paper with a large white fish on it and the words:

SALOMAR
EXTRA QUALITY MACKEREL

At the right of the mantel, in whitewash, all its whorlings sharp, the print of a child's hand.

The Tabernacle

In the table drawer, in this order:

A delicate insect odor of pine, closed sweated cloth, and mildew.

One swooning-long festal baby's dress of the most frail muslin, embroidered with three bands of small white cotton-thread flowers. Two narrow courses of cheap yet small-threaded lace are let in near the edge of the skirt. This garment is hand-sewn in painfully small and labored stitchings. It is folded, but not pressed, and is not quite clean.

One plain baby's dress of white cotton; a torn rag: home-sewn, less studiously; folded.

Another, as plain, save for pink featherstitching at the cuffs. Torn, not folded.

Another, thinlined gray-blue faded checks on a white ground. The silhouettes of two faded yellow rabbits, cut out at home, are stitched on the front, the features are x'd in in pink thread.

A nearly flat blue cloth cat doll, home-made, a blue tail, nearly torn off, the features in black thread.

A broad and stiff-brimmed soft-crowned hat, the brim broken in several places, the fabrics stained and moldered. The crown is gold, of thin plush or the cheapest velvet. The ribbon is wide plain woodsilk weltering lights of orange and of pearl. It is striped white at the edges and the stripes are edged in gold thread. The brim is bordered an inch wide with gold brocade. The underbrim is creamcolored mercerized cotton, marked in one place by an indelible pencil. Through a tear the pasteboard brim is visible: it was cut out of a shoe-box. The stitching throughout is patient, devoted, and diminutive. The hat is one broken, half-moist, moldered chunk.

A blue foursided tall box of Dr. Peters Rose Talcum Powder, empty save for some small hard object which rattles. The odor of the powder, a little like that of perfume-machines in theater toilets.

One smallchecked pink and white baby's dress.

One baby's dress, a rag. Blue featherstitching in mercerized thread.

One child's brown cotton glove, for the right hand. The index finger ends in a hole. . . .

The two parts of a broken button.

A small black hook, lying in its eye.

Another small black hook.

In the corners of the pale inward wood, fine gray dust and a sharp-grained unidentifiable brown dust.

In a split in the bottom of the drawer, a small bright needle, pointed north, as the swan above it is.

Photo by Walker Evans from Let Us Now Praise Famous Men.

Courtesy Library of Congress

Bonus Army on steps of Capitol building, July 1932.

A Lack of Confidence

Any lack of confidence in the economic
future or the basic strength of business
in the United States is foolish.
—HERBERT HOOVER *(November 1929)*

W HICH side are you on?/ Which side are you on?", wrote Mrs. Sam Reece, after armed deputies finished ransacking her cabin in search of her husband, who had helped to organize a miner's strike in Kentucky. The question was to take the form of a leit-motif during the thirties. Something had to be done; sides had to be taken. There was little exaggeration in Aunt Molly Jackson's lament: "This mining town I live in is a sad and lonely place,/ Where pity and starvation is pictured on every face." Relief was essential, and eventually it came. But it came slowly, and, at first, grudgingly.

In his final campaign speech for the presidency in 1928, Herbert Hoover expressed the dedication not only of himself but of the entire Republican party to the philosophy of "rugged individualism"; it was a dedication to which he was to remain firm for the rest of his life. Even the depression could not shake Hoover's belief that a centralized government which undertook unprecedented responsibilities in peace-time would destroy both the progress and freedom which were an essential part of the American system. It was only through the in-sistence upon individual responsibility, Hoover exclaimed at the height of the depression, that "there accrue the great sums of individual ac-complishment which carry the Nation forward. . . ." Afraid of the creation of a superstate, which would deprive man of his liberties, Hoover believed that the problem of unemployment had to be left to private charities and to state and local authorities. It was only with the greatest reluctance that he accepted the necessity of expanding govern-ment interference to cope with the problems of the depression.

Despite the Reconstruction Finance Corporation, the Federal Home Loan Bank, the Federal Land Banks, the President's Emergency Com-mittee for Employment, the Unemployment Relief Act, and the Fed-eral Farm Board, Hoover could not get the country moving. In Harlan and Gastonia, Dearborn and Sioux City, hunger increased; and so did talk, by some, of a revolution. Nothing was more symbolic of the dis-content which was overtaking the country than the march on Washing-ton by the Bonus Army. Some fifteen thousand unemployed war veterans converged on Washington in the spring of 1932 to lobby for a bill which would give them immediate payment of the face value of the "adjusted compensation" certificates, which called for a bonus payable in 1945. The bill was defeated in the Senate on June 18, three days after the House had passed it. Although obviously disappointed, the veterans remained orderly; and, when Congress appropriated funds for the marchers' return home, about 5,000 left Washington. Shortly after, however, Hoover ordered Douglas MacArthur to evacuate the rest.

With tear gas and bayonets, the soldiers routed the veterans. MacArthur, whose moral sensibility apparently faded long before he became an old soldier, told the reporters that the men had become "a bad-looking mob animated by the spirit of revolution"; any delayed military action might have led to "insurgency and insurrection." Perhaps so, but certainly a better solution was suggested by Fiorello La Guardia, who wired the President: "Soup is cheaper than tear bombs and bread and butter than bullets in maintaining law and order in these times of depression, unemployment, and hunger."

Because Hoover willingly gave Federal aid to corporations while denying it to those who were starving, his "rugged individualism" was soon being parodied as "ragged individualism." His defeat in 1932 was as certain as had been his election in 1928. Not only did Franklin Roosevelt pledge himself to a "new deal" for the American people, but he immediately identified his cause with that of the underprivileged when he spoke of his concern for "the forgotten man at the bottom of the economic pyramid."

Although despised and feared by many as a potential dictator, Roosevelt was able to do in one hundred days what Hoover could not do in three years; he gave the American people a renewed confidence in the strength of the country, as well as a renewed faith in their own worth and dignity. When Roosevelt delivered his first inaugural address, and boldly stated that "the only thing we have to fear is fear itself," it suddenly became clear that America was no longer on the defensive; the problems of the depression were about to be attacked with vigor and confidence. And so they were. The National Industrial Recovery Act and the Agricultural Adjustment Act were intended to stabilize prices and raise wages; large sums of money were appropriated for direct relief to stricken areas and for public-works programs. In 1935 Congress passed the Wagner Act, which guaranteed the right to collective bargaining and set up a National Labor Relations Board to see that this right was not violated. The Farm Security Administration, the Civilian Conservation Corps, the Workers Progress Administration, and the Tennessee Valley Authority were all part of Roosevelt's program to restore America to prosperity. But the task was too enormous. Although the New Deal was able to instill a new spirit into American life, it could not restore prosperity.

Strikes and riots continued throughout Roosevelt's first administration. *The Sharecropper's Voice* complained that "Too often the progressive word has been the clothing for a conservative act. Too often he [Roosevelt] has talked like a cropper and acted like a planter." Farmers rioted in Le Mars and Denison, Iowa; longshoremen went on strike in

San Francisco; truckers struck in Minneapolis; and, in Flint, Michigan the employees at General Motors went on a massive sit-down strike that lasted for forty-four days and directly involved more than 40,-000 workers. Occasionally, the strikes were successful; more often, especially in the early years of the New Deal, they resulted in bloodshed and defeat. (In Georgia, Governor Eugene Talmadge set up a concentration camp for pickets who got out of hand, while in Minneapolis, Eric Severeid, then of the *Minneapolis Star,* watched as the police shot at sixty-seven unarmed pickets who were trying to stop a scab truck and wrote: "Suddenly, I understood deep in my bones and blood what Fascism was.") By 1934, labor had sustained some disastrous defeats and the unions were severely crippled.

As the campaign for the 1936 presidential election got under way, the hatred which many people had for Roosevelt suddenly surfaced. H. L. Mencken told his readers that F.D.R. had become "simply a politician scratching along." And Mark Sullivan warned that 1936 might see "the last presidential election America will have. . . . It is tragic that America fails to see that the New Deal is to America what the early phase of Nazism was to Germany." But to the laborer, Roosevelt was "the biggest-hearted man we ever had in the White House." As one worker put it: "Mr. Roosevelt is the only man we ever had in the White House who would understand that my boss is a son-of-a-bitch." It was the labor vote that assured Roosevelt's election in 1936, and it was Roosevelt's support of labor—which gave rise to a strong union movement—that marked the high point of the New Deal.

When the American Federation of Labor failed to respond to the impetus given unionism by the passing of the Wagner Act, several militant union leaders (including John L. Lewis and David Dubinsky) set up a Committee for Industrial Organization. With Lewis as its leader, the CIO quickly became an important force in American labor, winning important battles in steel and automotives (in March of 1937, United States Steel, long a stronghold of the open shop, agreed to collective bargaining). At the same time, the AFL regained much of its original force and by 1940 total union membership in the United States numbered about 9,000,000. The price the unions had to pay for their new strength, it is true, was high. The battles between pickets and the police were long and violent; the 1937 Memorial Day Massacre in Chicago alone resulted in the death of ten pickets and the injury of seventy-five more. But the unions rolled on, and by the end of the decade they had assumed a position of ever-increasing importance in American life. No longer did the worker cry to indifferent ears: "All I want is the right to live, mister"; the union had given him an effective voice.

Pennsylvania miner. Jack Delano for the Farm Security Administration.

Harlan: Working under the Gun

BY JOHN DOS PASSOS

EVERYBODY knows that the coal industry is sick and that the men working at our most dangerous occupation (every sixth man is injured in the course of a year) are badly off, but few Americans outside of the miners themselves understand how badly off, or how completely the "American standard of living" attained in some sections during boom years, with strong unions working under the Jacksonville agreement, has collapsed. The coal operators, who have been unable to organize their industry commercially or financially along modern lines, have taken effective common action in only one direction: in an attack against the unions, the wage scales and the living conditions of the men who dig the coal out for them. Harlan County in eastern Kentucky, which has been brought out into the spotlight this summer by the violence with which the local Coal Operators' Association has carried on this attack, is, as far as I can find out, a pretty good medium exhibit of the entire industry: living conditions are better than in Alabama and perhaps a little worse than in the Pittsburgh district. The fact that the exploited class in Harlan County is of old American pre-Revolutionary stock, that the miners still speak the language of Patrick Henry and Daniel Boone and Andrew Jackson and conserve the pioneer traditions of the Revolutionary War and of the conquest of the West, will perhaps win them more sympathy from the average American than he would waste on the wops and bohunks he is accustomed to see get the dirty end of the stick in labor troubles.

In 1931, reports of violence in Harlan County, Kentucky, attracted the attention of the newly organized National Committee for the Defense of Political Prisoners. The committee, which consisted of Theodore Dreiser, chairman, and such other literary figures as Lincoln Steffens, Sherwood Anderson, Waldo Frank, Josephine Herbst, and John Dos Passos, went to Harlan to investigate the situation and published their findings in 1932 in a pamphlet entitled, *Harlan Miners Speak: Report on Terrorism in the Kentucky Coal Fields.* The article by John Dos Passos here reprinted, which was published independently of the committee's report, appeared originally in *The New Republic* on December 2, 1931 (one year after the publication of *The 42nd Parallel,* the first novel in the famous *U.S.A.* trilogy).

I: WAR ZONE

I am sad and weary, I've got the
    hongry ragged blues,
Not a penny in my pocket
    to buy one thing I need to use
I was up this mornin
    with the worst blues ever had in my life
Not a bit to cook for breakfast
    or for a coalminer's wife.

The mines in Harlan County are in the forks and creeks of the upper part of the Cumberland River. A comparatively new coal field,
first developed on a large scale during the boom in production that
went along with the European War, its output is said to be a very high
grade of bituminous. The miners were organized 90 percent by the
United Mine Workers of America around 1917. In the 1920 boom a
union miner was sometimes able, hiring several "chalkeyes" (inexperi-
enced helpers) at $8 a day, to clear two or three hundred dollars a
month. Railways pushed into the leafy valleys of the Cumberland
range, fairly prosperous towns grew up. The population of Harlan
County increased three or fourfold. Local business men who had managed to get hold of coal lands prospered on leases and royalties.
Mountaineers who had lived poor and free on their hillside farms
came down into the valleys to work in the mines and live in "patches"
of temporary houses, put up by the companies. The race for riches
went to the heads of the operators. The fact of having a little cash
every two weeks went to the heads of the miners. The union turned
into a racket and lapsed. Financiers skimmed the cream off the coal
companies and left them overcapitalized and bankrupt. In the fat years
no one thought of taking any measures of civic organization to help
tide them over the lean years that were to follow—a typical American
situation. Headlong deflation left the coal operators broke and the miners starving.

Last winter was pretty bad. When spring came along, the miners
around Evarts began to think something ought to be done to revive
the old locals of the U. M. W. of A. Wages had been steadily slipping.
Conditions of safety were getting worse. A few old Wobblies and radicals began to talk class war; some of the youngsters began to wonder
about socialism. A meeting was held in Pineville to talk about union
organization. Two hundred men lost their jobs and were blacklisted.
The coal operators, scared by the flood of anti-Red propaganda fed
them through detective agencies and professional labor-baiting organizations, began to hire extra guards. Their position depended on their

underselling the coal regions where traces of unionism still remained. Trusting to the terrible unemployment to break any strike that might be pulled, they took the offensive. In April they started evicting active union men from their houses. In the eastern counties of Kentucky every man considers himself entitled to carry a gun and to protect himself with it against insult and aggression. It was not long before a skirmish took place between miners and guards sworn in as deputies. This was followed, on May 5, by an out-and-out battle on the road outside of Evarts.

The townspeople of Evarts explain it this way: The town was full of evicted miners who seem to have had the pretty complete sympathy of the townspeople (the small merchants and storekeepers are against the mine operators because they force the miners to trade at the company commissaries). Feeling was running high. The mine guards made a practice of riding slowly through the town with their cars in second, machine guns and sawed-off shotguns sticking out of the windows, "tantalizing us," as one man put it. The morning of the fight, a rumor went around that the sheriff was going to bring in some carloads of scabs. Miners congregated on the road across the bridge from Evarts. The Coal Operators' Association claims that the miners were lying in ambush, an assertion which the miners deny. A carload of deputies came in from Harlan town. Shooting began, and lasted for thirty minutes. In the course of it three deputies were killed and several wounded; one miner was also killed and others wounded. Deputies then took Evarts by storm and arrested everybody they could lay their hands on. For some time the town had been under the cross-fire of their machine guns. The next morning Judge D. C. Jones—his wife is a member of the Hall family, which has mining interests in the vicinity —called a grand jury which the miners assert was illegally picked, made them a fiery speech denouncing I. W. W.'s and Reds. This grand jury returned thirty triple-murder indictments and thirty indictments for banding and confederating. Among those indicted were the town clerk and chief of police of Evarts. From then on through the summer the elected town officers of Evarts were superseded by the high sheriff's men, whose salaries are paid by the coal operators. No indictments were returned against mine guards or deputy sheriffs who had taken part in the battle, or against a mine guard who later killed Chasteen, a restaurant owner in Evarts who was on the miners' side.

About that time, so far as I can make out, the communist-affiliated National Miners' Union, which was conducting a strike against the Pittsburgh Terminal Company, sent organizers into eastern Kentucky, and N. M. U. locals began to be formed out of the wreckage of the old U. M. W. of A. In Evarts itself the I. W. W. seems to have had more influence than the Communists. The thing is that the miners felt that they were fighting for their lives and were ready to join any organization that would give them back solidarity and support them in their struggle against intolerable conditions. I talked to men who had joined all three unions.

Meanwhile the Coal Operators' Association was out to crush radicalism in Harlan County. The automobile of the I. L. D. relief worker was mysteriously dynamited. The soup kitchen in Evarts, which was feeding four hundred men, women and children a day, was blown up. In an attack on another soup kitchen at the swimming hole near Wallins Creek, two union men were killed and several wounded. Union organizers were beaten and run out of the county. Bruce Crawford of Crawford's Weekly, who greatly annoyed Sheriff Blair by publishing the miners' side of the story, was mysteriously shot from ambush. Boris Israel, Federated Press correspondent, was seized on the steps of the courthouse at Harlan, taken for a ride in perfect Chicago style, thrown out of the car on a lonely road and shot. Houses were raided, and many union sympathizers (among them Arnold Johnson, a theological student, who was an investigator for the American Civil Liberties Union) were arrested and jailed on the charge of criminal syndicalism. The Knoxville News Sentinel, a Scripps-Howard paper which printed stories about the frightful plight of the miners, was taken out of the newsstands in Harlan and its reporters were so intimidated the editor never dared send the same man up to Harlan twice.

All this time in the adjacent Bell County, where living conditions among the miners are worse if possible than in Harlan, the high sheriff has told the coal operators that if they make any trouble, he will cancel the deputy commissions of the mine guards, with the result that there has been no bloodshed, although there have been successful strikes in several small mines along Straight Creek.

II: ENTER THE WRITERS' COMMITTEE

When my husband works in the coalmines,
    he loads a car on every trip,
Then he goes to the office that evenin
    an gits denied of scrip—
Jus because it took all he had made that day
    to pay his mine expenses—
Jus because it took all he had made that day
    to pay his mine expenses.
A man that'll jus work for coal light an carbide
    he ain't got a speck of sense.

Breakfast in the station at Cincinnati. After that the train crosses the Ohio River and starts winding through the shallow valleys of the rolling section of central Kentucky. At lunch time to get to the dining car we have to walk through a federal prison car on its way to Atlanta. Change at Corbin onto a local train for Pineville. The Louisville papers say Governor Sampson is sending a detachment of militia into Harlan County. As we get near Pineville the valleys deepen. Steep hills burnished with autumn cut out the sky on either side. There's the feeling of a train getting near the war zone in the old days

At the station is a group of miners and their wives come to welcome the writers' committee: they stand around a little shyly, dressed in clean ragged clothes. A little coaldust left in men's eyebrows and lashes adds to the pallor of scrubbed faces, makes you think at once what a miserable job it must be keeping clean if you work in coal. At the Hotel Continental Mr. Dreiser is met by newspaper men, by the mayor and town clerk of Pineville, who offer their services "without taking sides." Everybody is very polite. A reporter says that Judge D. C. Jones is in the building. A tall man in his thirties, built like a halfback, strides into the lobby. There's something stiff and set about the eyes and the upper part of his face; a tough customer. When he comes up to you you realize he must stand six-feet-six in his stocking feet. He and Mr. Dreiser meet and talk rather guardedly. Judge Jones says he's willing to answer any questions put to him about the situation in Harlan County. Mr. Dreiser and Judge Jones are photographed together on the steps of the hotel. Mrs. Grace of Wallins Creek, the wife of Jim Grace, a union organizer who was beaten up and run out of the county, comes up and asks Judge Jones why the sheriff's deputies raided her house and ransacked her things and her boarders' rooms. The interview comes abruptly to an end.

When the members of the committee settle down at a long table in a room off the lobby to decide on a plan of procedure, stories start pouring in.

Mr. Dreiser, after questioning Mrs. Grace about her husband's former employment—a former miner now working in a store, he was prominent in organizing the N. M. U.—asks her how he was arrested:

A. I was not with him, but he was arrested in Letcher County. Neon. Him and Tom Myerscough were together.

Q. What were they doing?

A. They were trying to get the union organized. They were organizing against starvation. They were establishing a union for better conditions.

Q. What happened to him?

A. After they came to the house looking for him, he went away and stayed at a friend's house and then he and Tom went to Neon, Letcher County. There he was arrested and took to jail in Neon. Then he was turned over to the Jenkins' bunch of gunmen.

Q. Well, what happened then?

A. Him and Myerscough were turned over to the Harlan County bunch and they takes them over to the Big Black Mountains of Virginia. They bust him in the face and broke his cheek bone. They kicked him in the back. He ran into the woods and they fired at him.

Q. How many shots did they fire?

A. About fifty I guess.

Q. Did they hit him?

A. Well he was grazed at the elbow.

Q. What did he do?

A. He went on to Middlesboro and stayed at a friend's house. But I didn't know. When I first got word that Mr. Grace and Tom was held in jail, I didn't know whether he was in Harlan, Jenkins, or Neon. I goes out and went to get somebody to find out. We thought they were killed. I started to get hold of the I. L. D. and I just happened in where Mr. Grace was and I asked the lady whether her husband was there and I found out that Jim was there. His face and eyes was ⸱llen black and blue. He was crazy as a loon.

Then she testified to raids on her house and her boarders' rooms being searched for I. W. W. and Com-MU-nist literature. Then an organizer for the union testified about having his house broken into and his guns seized (the possession of firearms is legal in Kentucky), a vice president of the Kentucky State Federation of Labor turned over some documents to the effect that when the state militia came in after the Evarts battle last spring the operators had promised the U. M. W. of A. that they wouldn't take that opportunity of importing scabs, and in spite of that had imported scabs. A young man brought a mysterious message warning the writers' committee not to attend the meeting called by the National Miners' Union at Wallins Creek on Sunday, as there'd surely be trouble there. Bruce Crawford told the story of his quarrel with Sheriff John Henry Blair: how Blair had gone to see him in Norton and complained of the attitude of his paper, had taken a subscription and left, and how the next time Crawford went to Harlan several shots had been fired at him as he crossed the swinging footbridge over the river, one of them nicking him in the ankle. The most moving testimony was that of Jeff Baldwin, whose brother Julius had been killed by deputies at the swimming-hole soup kitchen. His story was that two or more deputies had driven up the dirt road that leads up the hill from the main road to the shack where the soup kitchen was located, had stopped the sedan so that the headlights shone full in the door dazzling the group of miners standing around it, that one deputy, Lee Fleener by name, had first yelled "Put up your hands" and then immediately opened fire. Baldwin's brother and another man had been killed and he himself wounded in the shoulder as he ducked for shelter inside the shack. In spite of the fact that the coroner's jury had named Lee Fleener and other persons unknown as the murderers, no action had been taken by the county prosecutor.

Next day the committee went up to Harlan, a fine ride up the magnificent valley of the Cumberland River. Harlan is a lively little town; stores and bank buildings attest to the slightly flimsy prosperity of the boom period; the handsome courthouse takes away a little from the gimcrack air of a Southern industrial town.

Meanwhile, in a crowded room in the Llewellyn Hotel, miners and their wives were telling their stories:

Q. For how many years have you been a miner?
A. From twenty to twenty-five years.
Q. Have you done most of your mining here in Harlan County?
A. Since 1917. . . .
Q. When you were in good standing with this union [the United Mine Workers] how much did you make a day?
A. When we had a union here I could make from four dollars to five dollars to six dollars a day.
Q. How much did you make a month?
A. Anywhere maybe along from eighty dollars to one hundred.
Q. How much did you work for after the union broke up?
A. They kept cutting wages down till you hardly couldn't make anything at all. . . .
Q. This thirty dollars that you would get, was it in scrip or in cash?
A. No, sir, you hardly ever drew any money on that. You traded your scrip in at the store, the company store, and part of the time they had you in debt.
Q. Did you buy clothing at the company store or food?
A. Food. I couldn't get enough to buy clothes.
Q. How did you get clothing?
A. I generally sent out to beg and did the best I could.

This miner testified that since he'd been fired he had lived "on the mercy of the people." Being asked what criminal syndicalism, the charge on which he had been arrested and bonded over to keep the peace, meant to him, he said: "The best I can give it is going against your country, but that is something I never did do. I never thought about such a thing. . . . My family always fought for the country and I've always been for it."

Then Mr. Dreiser questioned a woman who refused to give her name, saying she was afraid her husband would lose his job if the boss found out she'd testified. They were living in a company house, where they'd been living for three weeks. In that time the husband had received only scrip.

Q. How do you manage to live?

A. We have just managed to exist. I will tell you that I've had just one dollar in the last three days to live on, my husband and myself and two children.

Q. I wonder how you distribute that money around.

A. We live on beans and bread. We don't get no dinner. . . . There don't none of you know how hard a man works that works in the mines and I'll tell you what I had to put in his bucket this morning for him to eat and work hard all day. There was a little cooked punkin and what you folks call white meat, just fat white bacon, and that's what he took to the mines to eat and work on and he had water gravy for breakfast and black coffee.

Q. And what's water gravy?

A. Water and grease and a little flour in it.

Q. What do you give the children?

A. They had the same breakfast and they don't get no dinner. . . . They're not in a situation to go to school because they have no shoes on their feet and no underwear on them and the few clothes they have, they are through them.

In the afternoon Mr. Dreiser visited Sheriff Blair in his office and asked him some questions. The sheriff said that the National Mine Workers was a Communist organization and that the U. M. W. of A. had not been, that he considered The Daily Worker and all other Communist, I. W. W. or Red publications illegal, and explained that most of the deputies he had sworn in were mine guards paid by the coal operators. He didn't know how many deputies he had sworn in. The only money they got from his office were fees for arrests and summonses. He brought the interview to a lively close by serving Bruce Crawford with a $50,000 civil suit for slander.

Next morning County Prosecutor Will Brock was interviewed. He said he approved of unionism, if it was a legal unionism like that of the U. M. W. of A., but that he considered all this I. W. W.-Communist agitation illegal and seditious. As an example of a fellow that he'd thought at first was decent and that had then turned out to be a Communist, he mentioned Arnold Johnson, investigator for the American Civil Liberties Union. The interview was made fairly tense by the interruptions of an attorney named Jones, who shares his office with him, who said he was just waiting to tell the whole damned bunch what he thought of them; on being asked about a deputy named Heywood who was reputed to be a Chicago gunman, he said grimly through his teeth: "All right, if you want to see him so bad, you'll see him." We learned afterward that his brother had been killed in the Evarts fight, and that he himself had taken part in raids on miners' houses.

III: THE MEETING IN STRAIGHT CREEK

All the women in this coalcamp
are sittin with bowed down heads
All the women in this coalcamp
are sittin with bowed down heads
Ragged an barefooted an their
children acryin for bread
No food no clothes for our children
I'm sure this ain't no lie
No food no clothes for our children
I'm sure this ain't no lie
If we can't get no more for our labor
we will starve to death and die.

Straight Creek is the section of Bell County that has been organized fairly solid under the National Miners' Union. Owing, the miners say, to the fair-minded attitude of the sheriff, who has not allowed the mine guards to molest them, there has been no bloodshed, and a three weeks' strike ended the week before we got there with several small independent operators signing agreements with the union at thirty-eight cents a ton and allowing a union checkweighman. They say thirty-eight cents is not a living wage but that it's something to begin on. The committee had been invited to attend a meeting of the N. M. U. local at the Glendon Baptist Church and walked around the miners' houses first. The militia officers who accompanied us were impressed with the utter lack of sanitation and the miserable condition of the houses, tumble-down shacks set up on stilts with the keen mountain wind blowing through the cracks in the floor.

The midwife at Straight Creek, Aunt Molly Jackson, who later spoke at the meeting and sang these blues of her own composing that I've been quoting at the heads of the sections, was questioned by Mr. Dreiser:

Q. Can you tell us something about the conditions of the people in this hollow?

A. The people in this country are destitute of anything that is really nourishing to the body. That is the truth. Even the babies have lost their lives and we have buried from four to seven a week during the warm weather . . . on account of cholera, flux, famine, stomach trouble brought on by undernourishment. Their food is very bad, such as beans and harsh foods fried in this lard that is so hard to digest

. . . Families have had to depend on the Red Cross. The Red Cross put out some beans and corn.

Q. Do they give it to everyone that asks?

A. No, they stop it when they know a man belongs to the union.

Q. What did they say about it?

A. The Red Cross is against a man who is trying to better conditions. They are for the operators and they want the mines to be going, so they won't give anything to a man unless he does what the operators want him to. . . . I talked to the Red Cross lady over in Pineville. I said there's a lot of little children in destitution. Their feet are on the ground. They have come so far. They are going to get pneumonia and flu this winter that will kill them children off.

Q. Did she offer to give you any relief?

A. No, because they was members of the National Miners' Union. They said, "We are not responsible for those men out on strike. They should go back to work and work for any price that they will take them on for."

The meeting in the Baptist Church was conducted by a young fellow who'd been a preacher. Men and women spoke. Two representatives of the I. L. D. made speeches. One of the miners said in his speech that the reason they called them Reds was because the miners were so thin an' poor that if you stood one of 'em up against the sun you'd see red through him. All through the meeting a stout angry woman, who we were told was the bookkeeper at the Carey mine and the Red Cross distributor, stood in the aisle with her arms akimbo glaring at the speakers as if she was going to start trouble of some kind. All she did was occasionally to taunt the chairman with the fact that he owed her ten dollars. The high point of the meeting was Aunt Molly Jackson's singing of her blues:

> Please don't go under those mountains
>   with the slate ahangin over your head,
> Please don't go under those mountains
>   with the slate ahangin over your head
> An work for jus coal light and carbide
>   an your children acryin for bread;
> I pray you take my council
>   please take a friend's advice:
> Don't load no more, don't put out no more
>   till you get a livin price.

IV: LAST VESTIGE OF DEMOCRACY

> This minin town I live in
>   is a sad an a lonely place,
> This minin town I live in
>   is a sad an a lonely place,

For pity and starvation
>is pictured on every face,
Everybody hongry and ragged,
>no slippers on their feet,
Everybody hongry and ragged,
>no slippers on their feet,
All goin round from place to place
>bummin for a little food to eat.
Listen my friends and comrades
>please take a friend's advice,
Don't put out no more of your labor
>till you get a livin price.

Evarts is probably one of the few towns in the United States that still has democratic government. In spite of the fact that it's hemmed in on every side by coal-company property, that the chief of police and town clerk were arrested and charged with murder after the battle in May and that the town policing was done all summer by company guards, at the November election they put in a pro-miner town council by something like 200 to 80 votes. Most of the men at present on trial for their lives come from Evarts, and as far as I could find out from talking around, they have the complete sympathy of the local population. It is in Evarts that the union movement started, and there the miners were first accused of being Reds when it was discovered by the Coal Operators' Association that one of the U. M. W. of A. locals had taken out an I. W. W. charter. The miners on trial for murder are being defended by the General Defense Committee, the old Wobbly defense, that is unwilling to coöperate with the Communist-affiliated I. L. D. defending the criminal syndicalism and banding and confederating cases that have grown out of attempts to suppress the National Miners' Union. So far as I could make out, the county authorities consider members of either organization equally without human rights. Possibly the I. W. W. occupies a slightly better position, owing to its connection with U. M. W. of A. officials who have contacts with state (Democratic) politics, and to its soft pedaling of class-war talk. But the real point is that the situation of the miners is so desperate that they'll join anything that promises them even temporary help. I asked one man if he'd go to work again under the present scale, supposing he could get past the blacklist. He said, "You starve if you work an' you starve if you don't work. A man 'ud rather starve out in the woods than starve workin' under the gun."

The meeting at Wallins Creek took place in the high-school building and passed off without disorder, though you got the impression that the people who attended it were pretty nervous. The local small merchants seemed strong for the N. M. U. and somebody had put up a banner across the main street that read, "Welcome I. L. D., National Miners' Union, Writers' Committee." The next morning the committee packed up its testimony and left for New York, to be followed by the "toothpick indictment" of Mr. Dreiser and a general indictment of all concerned, including the speakers at the miners' meeting, for criminal syndicalism.

Which Side Are You On?*

BY FLORENCE REECE

Come all you good workers,
Good news to you I'll tell
Of how the good old union
Has come in here to dwell.

Which side are you on?
Which side are you on?

Don't scab for the bosses,
Don't listen to their lies.
Us poor folks haven't got a chance
Unless we organize.

They say in Harlan County
There are no neutrals there;
You'll either be a union man,
Or a thug for J. H. Blair.

Oh workers can you stand it?
Oh tell me how you can.
Will you be a lousy scab
Or will you be a man?

My daddy was a miner
And I'm a miner's son,
And I'll stick with the union
'Til every battle's won.

SUN. MON. JULY 7-8

STRIKE IN THE MINES
COAL POLICE!
MEN, WOMEN AND CHILDREN
DIE OF HUNGER!
— SEE —
THE GREATEST SHOW EVER
MADE ABOUT MINERS!

Above, detail of poster for the movie "Black Fury." Below, Kentucky coal miners.
Both by Ben Shahn for the Farm Security Administration.

A Union Meeting

BY SHERWOOD ANDERSON

I WENT to a union meeting in a mill town. Most of those in attendance were out of work. Every one wanted to talk, and many did. There was reference to the stool pigeon. "We know you're here, stool pigeon. I'm going to say something now. You go and tell Tom Grey." (Tom Grey was the manager of the mill in this town.) It gave you a queer feeling.

I had on a tweed suit and rather loud checked socks, and had been introduced to the meeting by a newspaper man known to be more than friendly to unions. He had told them that I was a city newspaper man. "Anyway, they should know that a stool pigeon wouldn't dress like this," I thought.

The strike is more exciting than just a meeting—it brings out the real leaders. The real leaders are seldom speech-makers. In an amazing number of cases just now, they are rather small, sincere, determined women. Going about among union men and women in America gives you a curious respect for women. They have nerve.

The unions, when they have any, in these Southern industrial towns, meet in curiously depressing halls. The walls are always such an ugly, drab color.

This particular hall had formerly been used by a Ku Klux Klan organization and I asked the newspaper man, "How many of these people were in on that?"

"A good many," he said. He thought the Ku Klux Klan had been rather an outlet for the workers in the days when America was outwardly so prosperous. "The boom market never got down to these," he said, making a sweeping movement with his arm.

Some of these Southern mill-owned towns are rather attractive; good frame houses with green lawns and trees. But not this one. The mill itself, a great brick structure, looked clean and bright. It was, I was told, financially successful, and if you ever have been in such a mill you know the big light rooms, the fast-flying machinery. There was the now so-old contrast—the lives of the workers, the lives of the machines. I like machines. They won't stand being neglected, being made to live dirty, neglected lives. They quit on you.

Late in 1933 Sherwood Anderson became interested in doing a series of articles on America's struggle with the depression and approached Robert Moley, the editor of *Today* magazine, with the idea. Moley agreed, and Anderson began a two month trip, "a kind of roving venture," he said, "looking and listening." Most of the articles which resulted from the trip—including "A Union Meeting"—were collected in 1935 under the title, *Puzzled America*.

This one was a big mill; employing a thousand workers, and was owned in the North. All of the employees were of the north Georgia hill-country type. The manager of this mill is also a Northern man. I am covering him up. His name isn't Tom Grey. I'm not telling where his mill is.

During the union meeting, as I listened, there was a curious atmosphere of the back-country, small-town church meeting—references to God—"God wants me to be frank and honest in what I am going to say to you." That sort of thing. I suspected that when Tom Grey talked to his workers, he didn't refer so often to God, but maybe he did.

A delegation had been to see Mr. Grey and the leader of the delegation was to report results. Two other men and a woman had gone with him as members of the delegation.

"We agreed I would do most of the talking. Ain't that right, Sister Smedley? Ain't it right, Brother Small?" the speaker asked. Brother Small and Sister Smedley agreed.

Sister Smedley was attractive. She might have been fifty-five, a thin little old worn woman, with curiously alive eyes. The speaker, the one who had been spokesman for the delegation, was Brother Hadley. Sister Smedley watched him intensely. It was evident that she had taken notes of the conversation with the mill manager. She held a cheap pencil tablet in her hand and fingered it nervously.

"I'll begin at the gate," the speaker said.

"You wait," I whispered to my companion; "in a minute he will begin telling us how he wasn't afraid."

It was a little pitiful to hear. He said that since he had got religion, four years ago, he hadn't lied to any man. "I ain't going to lie to you," he said.

"We were at the mill gate. It was sprinkling a little. There was Sister Smedley, Brother Small, Brother Houseman, and me. It had begun to rain. Now I want to get this straight. It wasn't really raining. It was sprinkling. Am I right, Sister Smedley? Am I right, Brother Small?" Sister Smedley looked quickly at her notebook. "That's right. It was sprinkling," she said. A man sitting near me whispered that Sister Smedley had been in the mill since she was twelve, although she now was an "out." The man said she was a good weaver—"one of the best."

My neighbor was a long, thin man with a long, thin nose, red at the end. He was a loom-fixer.

There had been a strike, the whole mill out, and it had lasted for several weeks. The mill had brought in non-union men, some three hundred of them and when the strike was settled, the manager refused to fire them. The mill took back about seven hundred of the strikers, but there were three hundred left outside, without work.

The union men at the meeting said that the three hundred left outside were their best, their most active union members. The mill management had agreed—"We'll take them back as fast as we can. Whenever any one quits, or gets fired, we'll take back one of the old workers."

There was a persistent cry—"They ain't doing it. They ain't. We want our own people back in there." There was a kind of hesitating, timid desire for loyalty to each other. I was told that most of those at the union meeting that night were outside. Brother Hadley and Brother Small were outside, just as Sister Smedley was.

A collection had been taken for one of the workers. He had been sick and his wife had been sick.

A man got up and reported on his case, not naming him.

"They were pretty near starving down there, so I went to a grocer, Ed Case, it was, and he let me have credit for it, for four dollars and ninety cents.

"So I think Ed Case ought to be paid. I won't tell who it is if he don't want me to tell."

A young workman jumped up. He had been sitting with his face in his hands, looking at the floor. "It's me," he said. He looked as though he were going to cry. Long-nose told me about him. "He was one of our best speakers during the strike. He was a lot of help, all right.

"You wouldn't think to look at him that he would be a good speaker, but, boy, he is. He's hard to get started, but when he gets started, gets himself worked up, he can go it, I tell you.

"He ought to have been a preacher," Long-nose said. "You can bet Tom Grey ain't going to take him back into the mill."

The report of the delegates who went to see Tom Grey went drearily on. You knew that they had made no progress. There was the tedious story of their getting in, past the mill gate, what the gateman said, what a young man in an office said—"He was one of them young squirts with a pencil in back of his ear."—There was a story of a young woman, evidently Tom Grey's stenographer—"She was scared, wasn't she, Brother Small? Ain't that the truth, Sister Smedley, wasn't she scared?"

It was painfully evident that Brother Hadley had wanted to find some one in the mill office who was scared.

Sister Smedley jumped up. She wiped her thin lips with a thin old hand. This time she spoke in a sharp, frightened voice. "I don't know whether she was scared or not, but I was," she said, and every one laughed.

There was a sense of quick relief in the hall. Sister Smedley sat down and again fingered her notebook. She looked at it. You thought perhaps she had written the words in the notebook, "I was scared." Brother Hadley, who stood upon the little raised platform, swallowed hard and stopped talking to roll a cigarette. His fingers trembled and the tobacco fell in a little shower to the floor.

I turned to my neighbor. "Why was she scared?" I asked. I thought I knew, but wanted to see what he would say. He said he didn't exactly know.

"They've got it on you," he said. "We don't have nothing but our job and they can take it away."

He began a whispered story about Tom Grey, the mill manager. There was the curious thing you find so often among American workers, a kind of understanding of the men over them, a kind of sympathy with a man in Tom Grey's position.

"Maybe I don't blame Tom Grey for being like what he is," Longnose said to me. Tom Grey, I gathered, had had family troubles. He had a son and two daughters and they had all left him. The wife took the three children and went back up North where they formerly had lived. She never came back.

There had been this delegation, from the workers, going to see Tom Grey. They had been stopped at the mill gate, had been made to stand in a drizzling rain for an hour. Then they were in the office of the plant—They stood in the little hallway. Tom Grey popped out of his office and then popped back in—he didn't speak to them, didn't even look at them.

Sister Smedley jumped up. "I was so mad, I wanted to scream," she cried. Sister Smedley sat down and rubbed her lips.

The tale of the delegation went on. Now they were in Tom Grey's big office. There was a stenographer in there. Tom Grey told her to take down everything they said. "Who are you? What's your name?" he asked each member of the delegation in turn.

Brother Hadley said he had tried to tell him. It was about the workers outside the mill. He said he wasn't a bit afraid. "I talked right out, as plain as I am talking here."

He said Tom Grey had tried to be slick with him. He couldn't chase the old workers who had been in the strike all over town when he needed some help. "I send my foreman to the mill gate. If a worker isn't there and doesn't get hired it isn't my fault."

The mill manager had asked a question, "Do you people represent the outs or the ins? How many members have you got in your dinged old union?" You gathered that he didn't care about the delegation, wasn't much bothered. Obviously, Brother Hadley had talked to Tom Grey as he now was talking to us, hesitatingly, in a half-frightened manner. He had been appointed to do something and hadn't done it.

Now the young man out of work, who had been helped by other union members to the extent of four dollars and ninety cents, stood up suddenly.

"You look in the books," he said. "You'll see that my dues are paid up. I got sick, going and standing at the mill gate in the rain, and Tom Grey, he sent right past me and got men who had never been in the mill before."

The speaker was interrupted by another worker. When the collection had been taken for the man with the sick wife, the second worker had put nothing in the hat.

"I didn't have nothing to put in, Joe," he said, addressing the destitute young worker. "I ain't got no money, but I got canned stuff at home and I got some meal." He asked Joe to come and see him.

On the platform, Brother Hadley had reached the end of his rope. He sat in a chair and tried again to roll a cigarette. When the paper broke again he jumped up and talked rapidly. "I'm one of the outs myself," he said. "We're nearly all out. I was in the other strike we had here six years ago. They got my record. It may be, you ought to have another delegation, another leader, some one else to do your talking. I ain't very good at talking."

He stepped down off the little platform. There was silence in the room. I looked at Sister Smedley, who was still fingering nervously her notebook. I saw something happen. She began to cry silently. Brother Hadley went and stood in the centre of the room, all of us staring at him. There was a queer nervousness.

"I guess we'd better be getting along," the newspaper man said. He also was upset.

"Ain't you visitors going to say nothing to us?" a voice asked.

We stood embarrassed. Brother Hadley was standing in the centre of the room. "I wasn't afraid of him," he said fiercely.

"Why didn't you tell him to go to hell?" a voice cried. "All we want is our jobs."

Several people, men and women, got to their feet. "I think we ought to hear from Sister Smedley," a woman's voice said. Sister Smedley jumped up. She opened and closed her mouth. "I can't make no report," she said.

The newspaper man and I slipped quietly through the door and out into the darkness of a mill town street. It was raining outside.

Above,
workers during
Chrysler plant strike, 1937.

At right,
pickets' signs
outside a copper mine
in Tennessee, 1939.
Marion Post Wolcott
for the Farm Security
Administration.

From **Pins and Needles**

LYRICS BY HAROLD ROME

O P E N I N G

NARRATOR

Ladies and Gentlemen, the first impression is very important we know. We've just decided that the best impression is made by telling the truth. Almost every Broadway revue starts out by saying . . .

ENSEMBLE

We're going to give you something different, something new.
Up to date
Fresh and great.
For our show will be
quite a novelty.
We're going to give you something different, something new. HAH!

NARRATOR

And then, just as you expected it to,
You get the same old stuff, but we—

ENSEMBLE

we say it too.

NARRATOR

Ah—

ENSEMBLE

This time it's true—for that's exactly what we have for you.

BOY

And no baloney!

NARRATOR

We really have something new.

VARIOUS MEMBERS OF THE ENSEMBLE

If you expect plumes and spangles
And stages at all angles
And rhinestone laces on show girls
And kick-in-a-row girls
With voluptuous, nude,

Pins and Needles was presented by the International Ladies' Garment Workers' Union Players at the Labor Stage Theatre in New York on November 27, 1937. The revue was written by Arthur Arent, Marc Blitzstein, Emanuel Eisenberg, Charles Friedman, and David Gregory; lyrics and music were by Harold Rome. In *The Best Plays of 1937-1938*, Burns Mantle wrote of *Pins and Needles:* "It was performed by amateurs and semi-professionals taken from the trade, was bright with humorous sketches, lightly satirical in furthering labor's cause, adequately if not brilliantly played and surprisingly good entertainment. Within a fortnight 'Pins and Needles' had become a hit with both workers and employers, as well as many rich loafers."

undraped . . . faces!!!
And the chromium finish and
streamlined flare with
tickets around
ten bucks a pair—

ENSEMBLE
Forget it!

NARRATOR
Park Avenue knows where it can go
If it wants to see that kind of show
We wouldn't do it even if we could—

GIRL
And of course we can't.

NARRATOR
For we've got a different slant.
We want this to be the kind of show
We'd like to see, if we were you
and you were we.
We're alive and wide awake—and
we've got something to say.

BOY
We know what's going on in the
world today—

NARRATOR
Say, who's making this speech anyway? But to get back to what's new
—we want to tell you without fan-
fare or fuss, the cast of this show
is

ENSEMBLE
US!

NARRATOR
And who is us?

BOY
That's what's new.

VARIOUS MEMBERS OF THE ENSEMBLE
We're not George M. Cohans or
Noel Cowards
Or Beatrice Lillies
Or Willie Howards

We've never played in stock or
studied at the Playhouse
And the only line we've ever said
in a Broadway house is:

GIRL
Which way to the gallery?

VARIOUS MEMBERS OF THE ENSEMBLE
The dancing we've done has been
for fun at the Savoy or Webster
Hall.

And our singing too. . . .

It's the bathtub kind and rough
But it's always been good enough
For meetings, parades and for
Picket lines.

As you see we're not tragedians or
comedians, or show girls or kick-
in-a-row girls, or troupers or even
supers.

NARRATOR
We're plain, simple, common,
ordinary, everyday men and women
who work hard for a living—

ENSEMBLE
WE'RE FROM THE SHOPS!!

VARIOUS MEMBERS OF THE ENSEMBLE
Dressmakers, cloakmakers—
—cutters

Underwear workers, knitgoods
workers—

—basters

Neckwear workers, embroiderers—

—stampers, checkers, examiners,
graders, pressers, trimmers,
binders, pinkers—all of us—
FROM THE SHOPS!!

"BACK TO WORK"

Hey, here comes Joe now running
    down the street (Hey Joe)
He must have news the way he
    moves his feet (Hey Joe)
He's coming from the meeting with
    the boss (Hey Joe)
I hope they didn't throw him
for a loss
    He must have news about the
    strike
I wonder what it's like
    Hey Joe, Hey Joe, Hey Joe,
    don't be so slow
    Tell us Joe, Spill it Joe Joe,
    whaddya know—

Chorus
Ain't had such good news
Since Lord knows when
For the strike is over boys
Back to work again

The fighting's thru now
There's no more fuss
For the strike is over boys
Back to work for us—
(AD LIB—What about terms?)
We gave a little (Ohhh—)

And we took a little (Ahhh—)
It was quite a fight
But things came out all right

Call in the pickets
Let them all know
That the striking all is done
Tell them that the day is won
Back to work we go

(Hey Ike, Hey Mike)
Let's tell the good news
To all the men
Boys the strike is over now
Back to work again

(Hey Schmool, O'Toole)
Bring in the whole gang
From the third floor
Tell them that the strike is won
Back to work once more

We gave a little (Ohhh—)
And we took a little (Ahhh—)
It was quite a fight
But things came out all right

(Hey Salvatore Hey Isidore)
Here come the pickets
They're in a glow
For the strike is done and won
Now it's time to have some fun
Back to work we go.

Patter
It's back to work we go
It's back to work we go
The strike is done, the day is won
It's back to work we go.
    Tadiddy—Tadiddy—Tadiddy
    Hooray for delegate Joe
    Tadiddy—Tadiddy—Tadiddy

It's back to work we go.

Say baby's gonna get a pair of shoes
    —Yes sir!
Now maybe you'll pay up your
    back dues—you bet!
Just wait till I tell Mary we can eat
    —oh boy!
Tomorrow night for dinner we'll
    have meat, oh boy!
Now we can keep the tenement
You'll pay up last years rent
    Good news, good news
    —it's what we're waiting for
    Hip hooray—what a day!
    We work once more.

No signs to carry
No to and fro
For the strike is over now
Back to work we go

We'll get our pay checks
Friday at ten
For the strike is over now
Back to work again

We had to do it
Didn't want to do it
But sometimes you fight
For what is right is right

Now it's all fixed up
We'll have a blow
For the striking all is done
We made terms the fight is won
Back to work we go.

"SOCIAL SIGNIFICANCE"

GIRLS

(Coming out from their side and singing to boys)

Verse:
We're tired of moon songs
Of star and of June songs
They simply make us nap.
And ditties romantic
Drive us nearly frantic
We think they're all full of pap.
Nations are quaking
History making
Why sing of stars above?
While we are waiting
Time is creating
New things to be singing of.

Chorus I
Sing us a song
With Social Significance
All other tunes are taboo
We want a ditty with heat in it
Appealing with feeling
and meat in it
Sing us a song
With Social Significance
Or you can sing 'till you're blue
Let meaning shine from every line
Or we won't love you.

Sing us of wars
And sing us of breadlines
Sing us of front page news.
Sing us of strikes
And last minute headlines
Dress your observation with
Syncopation.

Sing us a song
With Social Significance
There's nothing else that will do
It must be packed
With social fact
Or we won't love you.

Chorus II

BOYS

We'll sing a song
With Social Significance
All other tunes are taboo
We'll get a song that's satirical
Putting the "mere" into miracle.
We'll sing a song
With Social Significance
We'll get a song that will do,
Entirely frought with social thought
Tell us will that do?

We'll sing of wars
And conferences martial
Tell you of mills and mines
Sing you of courts
That aren't impartial
Dress our economics
In the best harmonics.

We'll sing a song
With Social Significance
There's nothing else that will do
It will be tense
With common sense

GIRLS

Then we will love you.

Chorus III

Sing us a song
With Social Significance
All other tunes are taboo
We want a song to make history
Robbing the great of their mystery
Sing us a song
With Social Significance
Or you can sing 'till you're blue
It must get hot with what is what
Then we will love you.

Sing us of kings

And of revolutions

Sing us

Of Social trends

Sing us of old

And new constitutions

What's to be done with 'em

We want it in rhythm

Sing us a song
With Social Significance
There's nothing else that will do
It must ring true
With social view

Or we won't

BOYS

Oh please!

GIRLS

No we won't

BOYS

Oh please!

GIRLS

No we won't

BOYS

Oh Hell!!

BOTH

Love you.

From **The Land of Plenty**

BY ROBERT CANTWELL

THERE was a crowd in front of the plant. Coming across the tide-flat, he saw the men moving into a tight mass before the factory office. A slight wind was blowing inland with the rising tide and the line of smoke over the firehouse moved lazily, a dark flag over the tapering brick pole of the stack. Always thereafter he would remember what happened as beginning then, when they stepped off the road and on to the tideflat, going over the plank laid across the drainage ditch and seeing the men gathering in a black knot before the office. He would remember the curious look on his father's face and his even walk, as though he forced himself to walk slowly and to show no surprise, but years would pass before he would understand what it must have meant to his father, before he understood that this was the last time he could expect to walk over a path that had grown so familiar and so even. For how many—twenty?—years, Hagen had come to the factory every day, coming down by the same streets and turning off at the same place to the path through the brush, seeing the crew of the night or the day shift converging from all parts of town at the same time he arrived. Now he knew it was over. Even if they took him back the old way was over, and it would only be a question of time before they found a new way to get rid of him.

But that was later. Now the scene drove itself into his memory with excitement, and he was irritated with his father's deliberate walk. His father swung his lunch pail easily, but Johnny packed his under his

---

Robert Cantwell's *The Land of Plenty* was written in 1934 and deals with a spontaneous strike in a wood veneer factory located in the state of Washington. Of the novel, which is the best of the many books dealing specifically with a class battle, Jack Conroy wrote: "I know Robert Cantwell's factory. I can smell it and see it, and every character in *The Land of Plenty* will be recognized as an old friend by anyone who has learned about workers by being one, who felt the itch that sweat and sawdust bring, who has hated a high-balling foreman or thrown a brick at a scab."

arm like a football, getting ready to run to find out what was happening. Before they reached the crowd a man broke away from it and ran out to them. "Your card's pulled!" he cried to Hagen. "They pulled about twenty of them!"

"Twenty?"

"Dwyer, Sorenson, old Mike . . ."

"I'll be damned," his father said.

They went up to the crowd. About a hundred men had gathered in the parking space. The rest of the night shift stood about in smaller groups near the fireroom or around the few cars. The car-loaders on the loading platform had gathered at the green doors of the box cars. In the office the girls stood at the windows, looking down with remote inquisitive stares, like people watching a wreck in which no one was hurt. Winters came up to his father.

"He did it," he said. "Every God-damn one of us."

His father said, "They must have finished the export order."

"He's got nerve," Winters said. "Fifteen men at once."

"Did they finish the export?"

"I don't know . . . How could they?" Winters looked at the men. "Who knows if they finished the export order today?" No one answered. "Go ask the shipping clerk," he said to Johnny. "Don't tell him why you want to know."

"Hurry up," his father said. "Find out before the whistle."

He went into the stockroom. Someone pointed out the shipping clerk to him, a rushed, worried-looking man who leaned over an improvised desk at the entrance to the loading platform. When Johnny asked if the export order was finished he looked down in annoyance.

"Who wants to know?"

He flushed. "I wondered if we would have to work on it tonight."

"You work on what they give you," the shipping clerk said. "They'll give you enough so you won't have to worry about what order you're working on."

He turned back to his desk and Johnny stopped indecisively. Then he walked off through the stockroom until he came to some of the men pushing on truckloads of doors down the alley. He called to them. "Who would know if they finished that export order today?"

"The shipping clerk."

"He's busy. Who else?"

"Go ask the tally man. A little guy with glasses down by the graders. But they couldn't finish it."

The tally man looked at him suspiciously, "What do you want to know for?"

He said nervously, "Molly sent me to ask you. He said Carl . . ."

The tally man pulled a ruled sheet out of his book and handed it to him. "They didn't get started," he said. "Tell Molly if he'd do something on the night shift besides walk around with his finger up maybe we'd finish that God-damn order."

He ran back out to the office. The crowd had grown. The cars were coming up to the parking strip and the watchman came up to the crowd, saying, "All right, fellows. Let's break it up. Let the cars park," but no one moved. Someone said to the watchman, "Lay off, lay off," and he grinned uncomfortably and stopped pushing. The newcomers were crowding in, trying to find out what was happening, but Johnny ducked past them and got to the center of the crowd where his father and Winters and Sorenson were talking earnestly and looking toward the office.

"Go see MacMahon!" somebody yelled. "Don't monkey with Carl!"

"He ain't here!"

He handed the tally sheet to Winters. "I got it," he said. For a moment Winters looked in surprise at the ruled paper. He pushed the men back so he could lift it up to read it.

"Hell," he said. "They didn't do anything. They didn't do as much as we did last night."

Sorenson said, "Why monkey with that? They can buy enough to fill out the order. That won't stop 'em."

"No, but they don't want any delay on it . . . Look. It ain't half out."

The crowd split. Frankie Dwyer pushed up to them, waving his dismissal notice in his hand. His eyes were always narrowed because of the heat where he worked, but now they were almost closed and his lips were drawn back from his uneven teeth. He asked in a strangled voice, "Where's that little pot-bellied bastard?" pushing Johnny back into the crowd as he shoved his face up to Winters. "You seen him? Is he here?"

"What are you going to do?"

"I'm going to shove this," Dwyer said. He waved the dismissal notice. "This is to notify you," he said. "I'll notify the son of a bitch. I'll notify him." He moved on to the entrance of the office. The crowd broke and some of the men stopped at the steps. Dwyer went on inside. At the railing that separated the entrance from the desks of the girls he stopped and one of the girls came up to him timidly, her eyes wide with fright, faltering as she asked him what he wanted. Behind her the other girls sat paralyzed at their desks. He snapped at her, *"Where's Carl?"*

She replied automatically. "Mr. Belcher is busy just now. . . . If you care to wait . . . he'll be free."

Dwyer looked at the row of closed doors across the office. Behind him the men crowded up into the entrance. "Where is he?" he repeated. "Is he in there?" But she looked at the crowd behind him, at his large hands clamped on the railing, and suddenly turned on him with contempt.

"If you want to see Mr. Belcher you'll have to wait until he's free. . . . Is that clear? You can't see him now."

"Where is he?"

Winters and Sorenson pulled Dwyer back. "Hell, you'll have the law on us," Sorenson said.

The girl looked past them at the men crowding into the office. "Have you men any business here?"

They stared at her.

"Do you want to see someone? You can't stay in here unless you have business here. You can't loiter in here."

"I got business here," Dwyer said.

"Then sit down and wait. . . . You can't disturb the office like this." Then she called out, the disgust hot in her voice. "All of you men who haven't any business here, get out! Get out!"

The five-minute whistle blew its brief warning blast. The men stepped back out on the parking space. "I'll wait," Dwyer said. He sat down on one of the benches. The girl turned her back to him and returned to her desk. She picked up a notebook and stared at it sightlessly for a few moments, breathing deeply, her features rigid and controlled. Now some of the other girls began typing again, the hesitant clatter bringing the office back to normal. Johnny moved out with the others, getting a last glimpse of Dwyer staring at the floor, the dismissal notice trembling in his hand. Outside the night crew had stopped at the factory entrance. The day foreman and some of his helpers, the shipping clerk, the tally man, the order clerks, came out on the loading platform to look down at the crowd, and in a few moments some of the men from the day shift began to move through it asking, "What's up? What's the trouble? What are you waiting for?" but no one paid any attention to them, and no one went inside to stand by his machine. Then from inside the factory there was an odd, dwindling sound as the machines began stopping before the whistle had blown. The saws stopped first, and when their high whine had quieted the deeper throb of the transfer chains and the rolls sounded louder, like the bass in an orchestra growing strong as the trumpets ceased. They waited, they listened; unable to believe what they heard until they saw the first of the day crew coming out of the factory five minutes before quitting time. Now the rolls began stopping as the men went through the factory and pressed the switches or called to the men still at work, and finally the main conveyor rumbled in the quiet factory before someone thought to press the switch that stopped it. The men on the night shift began yelling as they came out the main entrance of the plant, and then in a moment they were dropping down on all sides, off the loading platform and out through the side doors, the shouts rising as the two shifts came together. Johnny was caught up in the crowd that began moving steadily around the office, shouting to the girls who crowded at the windows inside. On the second floor a group of men stared down thoughtfully. He could see them turn to speak to one another. Beside him a little girl danced along in excitement, waving her lunch bucket to the girls who stood at the office windows. She was only fifteen or sixteen years old and she was too excited to march with the others—she danced, moving along sideways and letting her feet snap together and swinging her arms. One of the old women pressed up to him. "What is it?" she asked. "What's the matter?" but before he could explain, the voices rose again and they moved forward more rapidly; she shouted with the others and raised her hand when the rest did to call to the girls in the office. Then he was swept off his feet. He began to shout, *"Come on out! Come on out!"* and all around him they took it up, calling in time as they marched around the office, *"Come on out!"* The sound rose irregularly. After they had shouted, the words would come back to them like an echo from some other part of the crowd. *"Come on out!"* How did it sound inside? The girls looked out sightlessly; the deaf men on the second floor turned and spoke to one another as the cries broke in waves against the glass. When he broke free they were still shouting. *"Come on out!"* He looked at the moving crowd packing the space between the factory and the office. So many of us, he thought, feeling sorry for the bewildered girls on the other side and for the few forlorn figures in the factory. *"Come on out!"* they cried. *"Come on out!"*

That was the beginning. Nothing else ever gave him the same strange feeling of excitement and strength, and all during the next week he treasured the memory, calling on it like some powerful charm to help him in the moments of despair. At home he used it most, making himself remember when the wrangling in the house got too bitter and when the disorder and the lack of any quiet wore on his nerves, but he used it every day on the picket line when the waiting got tiresome or when someone got caught and was hauled off by the cops; he called on it when Sorenson and Dwyer had a fight and when, after the third day, a part of the factory began to run with scabs who came from nowhere. In a week it had lost its strength for him, for in the bitterness of defeat and in all the misery he lived through nothing, for a while, could give him any hope. But then that feeling died too, and years later he could call up the memory of the afternoon when the machines began stopping, when the day shift raced out to join them, when the girl danced along beside him as they went around and around the office.

At home he thought of it after the first meeting, when he came in still burdened with all that had happened and found them waiting distrustfully, badgering him with questions he did not know how to answer. As he came in the door his sister said, "I suppose you're one of them!" and he was dumbfounded that they already knew more about it than he did. His father was still with Winters and Dwyer and the rest of them. When he tried to explain what had happened Mildred interrupted him in a voice that seemed to have grown more shrill and nervous: "Well, why did they have to beat up the poor man! No wonder he wanted to fire them!" Then in a few moments he learned how the newspapers were run. There it was, the whole story, with everything just a little bit wrong.

STRIKERS STORM OFFICE: THREATEN GIRLS

A mob which threatened for a time to get out of hand today stormed the office of the Past Bay Manufacturing Company's plant in the industrial development district, called for the foreman of the factory and threatened the girls employed in the office until quelled by the quick action of one of the employees, it was asserted by officials of the company late this afternoon. The action, which came as a climax to labor trouble which had been brewing in the factory for some time, came after the discharge of fifteen men who, company officials claim, were involved in an assault on Carl Belcher, an industrial consultant now serving as night foreman in the factory, late Thursday night, when the lights were temporarily extinguished.

He read it again and again, and after the argument was over he gave up trying to explain, he found the paper and studied the article until he knew it by heart, trying to figure out how anybody could get anything so twisted. It was all there: the strike and the marching around the office; even Frankie Dwyer's going into the office and Sorenson's saying, "You'll have the law on us," but it was all mixed up and no one could understand it. Instead of stopping work the day shift broke into disorder and forcibly shut off the motors, and instead of marching around the office calling *"Come on out!"* they all, he now learned, milled steadily around the building, calling threats and were with difficulty induced to disband.

"It looks funny," Mildred said, "You don't even know what was going on. You didn't even know they beat up a man. Does pop know?"

"They didn't!" he cried. "I tell you I know what they did, don't I? I was there, wasn't I? I was down there and saw it, wasn't I?"

"Well, there it is. You can read, can't you?"

Troubled, he replied. "They made a mistake."

Gerald said impatiently, "He wouldn't know. It's always a little bunch of trouble-makers do all the damage." He was gloomy. "I'm afraid they've got your Old Man in hot water," he said, "they've put something over on him."

They kept it up all week, and even after his father was shot Gerald said, "They put something over on him. He got mixed up with that bunch and they used him." After a few days Johnny had to force himself to go to the house, only returning to it to sleep and occasionally to eat and to prevent his mother from worrying about him. She never doubted that what had happened was as he told it and as his father told it, but she was lost because she tried to keep peace in the family and to keep the girls from feeling that the little they and their children ate was begrudged them. Then Bill and Gerald got into arguments and Bill went down to the picket line while Gerald nagged at Mildred and spoke mysteriously of letters and telegrams he was getting secretly from the South.

Johnny hugged the memory of that first sweet hour when they danced out of the factory; it was a lamp that would keep him warm. Lying in bed at night he polished it until it shone. He remembered tiny details, the look on someone's face; the friendliness of people he had never seen before. Some day it would happen again. Some day all the people would come out of the factories, singing in the streets. . . . He slept now on a cot in the front room with his younger brother sleeping beside him. Across the room was Gerald and Mildred's bed, and at night Gerald would go on with his talking, remembering all the little triumphs of his dealings in the past, the money he had made and the wealthy people with whom he did business. He would talk whether they listened or not, speculating on things he would like to be doing, and after they fell asleep he would stare wide-eyed into the darkness, sometimes murmuring some half-formed plan that came to his mind. From time to time he would rise up on his elbow and grope beside the bed for his cigarettes. The match would flare; the tip of his cigarette glow dully.

Each day Gerald dressed carefully, walked to town each morning after reading the paper, and talked to men he met in an insurance office and in the lobby of a hotel. Before he left the house he would warn them that he was expecting a telegram, and that if it came to send it back to the office, where he could stop for it. . . . Sometimes late at night Johnny would be awakened by their whispering; several times he heard Mildred crying, trying to muffle her sobbing so she would not awaken him.

The days passed in a rush. He learned to look through the paper for the new stories they made up. He read them, checking them with his own knowledge of what had happened, with a bitter amusement, only occasionally driven to fury by some cunning lie and spitting on the print or tearing the paper into bits. But now he had learned how to read them and he searched in the back pages for good news, and when he read of labor trouble at some other factory or of some mob threatening somewhere he could see between the lines and understand what had actually happened. Every morning, when his mother gave him his breakfast, she said, "I'll try to fix something better for you tomorrow," with a painful, apologetic smile. Then he went down to the picket line to take his place and march back and forth before the factory.

The line stretched for a hundred yards along the track. There was a steady blur of talk, almost as loud as the diminished sound from the factory. The men moved restlessly from one group to another, checking their own feelings, their ideas, with the others, driven by anxiety to move back and forth to find out the changes in the way people felt. Midway down the line the women were clustered in a small colorful group, some of the girls in their bright cheap dresses and some in the costumes they wore to work. When the mill was running and the young girls on the night shift came to work, they walked proudly through the streets, conscious of how their overalls fitted them and of how completely their costumes set them apart from the crowd. Some of them had learned how to decorate the men's shirts they wore with colorful neckties or a sash around the waist, and as they moved through the downtown crowds on the way to work these girls felt no shame or uneasiness at how they looked; they knew that if the well-dressed girls of their own age looked at them scornfully, and if the old women frowned at the way their clothing fitted them, no one else did.

The line was steady. The police trained it. On the second morning an invisible boundary was drawn at the edge of the company's property. No one could see it, but it was there, and sometimes fifty police were on hand to see that no one crossed it. It got to be something wonderful and mysterious, this invisible boundary of private property that the police would defend with their lives. They were told that anyone who stepped across this line was liable to arrest, and the picketing became something like a children's game, like dare-base, but perverted into something risky and mean. Some of the boys from the stockroom got into the forbidden territory and were taken off to the station while the crowd yelled and the boys waved back good-naturedly. As long as they were in sight the police handled them gently, but when the boys were released from jail after two days some of them were terribly beaten; one's wrist was broken and one had lost his teeth where a club smashed against his mouth. They waited. The boy who had been beaten came back to the line but left after Vin Garl searched him and took away a revolver he carried.

Each morning after Johnny had looked at the paper and eaten a small breakfast he joined the line without ever thinking that there might be something else he could do. The way it looked when he came on the tideflat made a difference to him. He left the house with the disorder there lingering like an unpleasant taste in his mind. A big crowd swept it away. If the crowd had thinned he suffered. Sometimes he went with Waino and Bill in his brother-in-law's car to call out the people who had decided to stay at home. He was bewildered that some of them preferred to sit in their houses or walk downtown —bewildered and indignant, and after they had been turned down he worried about it and used the refusal as a way of measuring people and deciding whether or not they were worth anything. Back on the tideflat he joined the pickets as they walked before the factory, watching the cops who lounged in the doorway or sat for hours in their cars; memorizing their faces and wondering what they were thinking and how they explained their actions to themselves. How out of place and awkward they looked! Their blue uniforms, padded and grotesque, their sullen and uncomprehending features, now reflecting contempt and the fear they felt at the strikers' number, and now reflecting only boredom and irritation at the interruption in their usual ways of life—there was not one of them who would have fitted into the life of the factory or performed the tasks that it demanded. Always keeping at the very edge of the invisible line, the pickets walked back and forth, beating down the dirt of the tideflat, never letting the police rest for fear their line would be crossed or someone would rush them. Sometimes at the remote ends of the line the pickets and the police would begin talking, someone asking a cop if he wasn't sick of his work; or some of the girls would waylay an outpost and ask him if he didn't get tired scowling and making faces. Sometimes the police would call back, sometimes conversations would start, sometimes they would even tell the men what the company intended to do and how many scabs were working. But then their officers would move down the line, saying, "Break it up," or "Keep moving, there," frightening the pickets less than the few friendly men in their own ranks.

"The Spectre" by William Gropper.

From To Make My Bread

BY GRACE LUMPKIN

FOR two days the mill did not try to bring in anyone to take the places of the strikers. Months before they had selected the best workers and laid off the others. Now they wished, if possible, to keep these since it would hold back production to take on new hands, or those who were not skillful with the machines.

So they waited for the workers to come back of their own accord, and when they did not, but picketed the mill, succeeding in getting almost everyone out, they did some positive things toward bringing the strike to an end.

First they sent for the leaders separately. Mr. Burnett, in the office, made certain promises to each one. To John he said: "You are a fine worker and we want you back. If you will come we will give you two months rent free, and forget that you have ever been out."

And John asked, "Can we keep the union?"

Mr. Burnett answered no. So John returned to his people. Each one who was called in was asked the same question, and asked the same one in return that John had asked, "Can we keep the union?" and was answered, "No."

The third morning a truck arrived at the relief store. It was piled high with boxes and bags of food, and toward the front there were clothes. All had been sent by workers and others who were interested in the struggle that was going on. In the front seat of the truck were two young women who had come down to help with the food. They

---

The unsuccessful strike of textile workers in 1929 at Gastonia, North Carolina, during which several strikers were arrested and convicted of homicide, was the basis for at least six novels in the thirties: Mary Heaton Vorse's *Strike!;* Sherwood Anderson's *Beyond Desire;* Fielding Burke's *Call Home the Heart;* Myra Page's *Gathering Storm;* William Rollins' *The Shadow Before;* and Grace Lumpkin's *To Make My Bread.* From Miss Lumpkin's novel, which is perhaps the best of the group, we have reprinted Chapter 53. * * * In 1953, Miss Lumpkin testified to a congressional committee that the Communist propaganda in her early work was written under pressure. She has been described by Whittaker Chambers as "a devout woman whose days are filled with good works."

brought a message from those who had sent the truck of supplies. The message said to the strikers: "What we send is not charity. Because your fight is ours, in sharing what we have with you we are only helping our own."

The news about the truck spread all over the village. Before it left people came to look at it as at a curiosity. Some even wanted to touch it, though it was empty of food and clothing, for all bundles had been taken into the store.

The two relief workers who had come with the truck, along with Bonnie, Ora and Zinie, worked all morning getting the supplies put away on the shelves. When the friends from the North had gone to Mrs. Sevier's boarding house where they would have a room, the three others sat down on bags of corn meal to rest. Bonnie had a blank book before her. She had been given the work of keeping accounts and was very proud. They were to begin giving out food the next day, and she was to put down everything taken in and everything given out.

A handbill lay on the counter near her. Copies of it had been left at the doors of all the houses in the village that morning. It said:

"YOUR UNION DOES NOT BELIEVE IN WHITE SUPREMACY.
THINK ABOUT THAT, WHITE PEOPLE."

They had read it over and over.

"It's just going t' get us in trouble," Zinie said fearfully. "I told John back yonder that he ought not to countenance that."

"The colored people work alongside of us," Bonnie spoke up. "And I can't see why they shouldn't fight alongside us, and we by them."

"It did worry me at first," Ora admitted, "when we spoke of it at the secret meetings. But I've come to see that if people let colored folks tend their babies and cook their food, they really don't think their color makes them dirty. A black hand can be as clean as my white one. And they've got souls the same as us."

"And they are just the same." Bonnie looked at Zinie. "The color don't seem to make any difference when you see that."

"Would you marry one of them?" Zinie asked spitefully.

"I'm not a-talking about marrying," Bonnie said. "I'm a-talking about working together and fighting together. The marrying can take care of itself. We are all working people and I can see without looking very far that what Tom Moore says is true. That if we don't work with them, then the owners can use them against us. Where would we be if they went over to Stumptown and got them in our places? It's plain common sense that we've got to work together."

"Are you going over to Stumptown like they want ye to?" Zinie asked.

"Yes, I'm a-going," Bonnie said stubbornly, and added, "I offered to go."

"I think it's a shameful thing for ye to be going and speaking with niggers."

"And it's a shameful thing for ye not t' know they're human beings the same as us," Ora said to her.

Jennie Martin came in looking for Zinie. She was trembling.

"I just came by the mill," she said. "They've got the militia there, guarding the whole mill."

"It's what the Governor threatened to do," Bonnie said.

"I didn't think he would," Jennie lamented. "I didn't think he would."

"Well, he's only protecting his own, for he's the same Hellman that owns stock in this mill. I know for when he was elected governor Granpap was so proud that he was the one that got him out of jail that time."

"It looks like Granpap's not the only one in the McClure family that will be a convict," Zinie said, and got up to go.

They looked at her, and did not speak. Because she was to have a baby in a few months, they were trying to be patient with her. She wanted rest and peace, that they knew from their own experience, but when did they ever get it while working at machinery? This was what they could understand and Zinie could not, for John had kept her out of the mills, working extra time so that she might not be forced to go in. And Jennie, small Jennie Martin and the younger children had worked. Zinie was a little spoiled.

That evening the picket line went down to the mills and faced the militia. And it was only then that Ora learned that Young Frank was among the soldiers dressed up in uniforms, with their guns to fight against the strikers. She called out to him from across the road.

"Young Frank," she said, "are you going t' fight against your own?

"Look," she said and walked toward him from out the ranks of the strikers. "Look, here I am. Why don't you kill me?"

Young Frank stood sullenly in the line of soldiers and looked straight in front. Ora spoke to them all. "Boys," she said. "Why don't you go home and stop fighting against women and children? Air we not your people? Don't you have mothers that have worked themselves to the bone for ye, and fathers that have slaved? And don't you slave in mills and other places for low wages? Go home, and don't fight your own people any more."

Others spoke to the boys. And during the rest of the week when the mill was bringing in truck loads of workers from other states and the strikers persuaded them not to go in, the soldiers did not advance once toward the strikers. If any came too near the gate they held out their bayonets, but did not advance a step.

Ora tried to see Young Frank but they would not allow her to go in, and he never came to the house. John saw him later under curious circumstances. But before that night something was done that made everyone feel the power of the mill.

Handbills were distributed through the village which spoke in no uncertain terms:

> "TO THOSE OF OUR EMPLOYEES WHO HAVE PARTICIPATED IN THE LATE HAPPY HOLIDAYS—GREETINGS:
>
> THOSE OF YOU WE CONSIDER RELIABLE MAY RETURN TO WORK BY WEDNESDAY NOON OR INDICATE YOUR DESIRE TO DO SO.
>
> TO THOSE WHO DO NOT WISH TO REMAIN IN OUR EMPLOY: YOU MUST UNDERSTAND THAT YOU CANNOT CONTINUE TO OCCUPY OUR HOMES, NOR REMAIN ON THE PREMISES OF THE COMPANY."
>
> THE WENTWORTH MILLS.

John spoke to the strikers. "If they force us out of our homes," he said, "we will put up tents. And there will be food. Do not go back."

He said much more. Yet on Wednesday at noon the picket line was noticeably smaller, and before the quarter of one whistle blew many of the strikers, with faces averted, went through the gates protected by the drawn bayonets of the militia. Some turned at the gate and came back to join the line, but most of them walked through and entered the door of the mill. They could not bear the thought of being put out on the streets with their young. Some of them had sick people at home, and there were others who were timid and frightened.

Their return to work was a great blow to the rest, for it had been a heartening thought that the mill could not go on without them: that the great building was closed and dark. For if it was kept so, sometime in the near future the owners would say to them, "Come back, and we will do as you wish." They were not asking for much. What they asked for was entirely reasonable. But they could see that the mill had power to hurt them and force them to their knees.

And the next day they felt the power more. For on that day men went to the houses of those who had not gone back into the mill, emptied them of furniture, and locked the doors of their own homes against them. They came to Ora's about eleven in the morning, and though it was raining they took everything she had and piled it out in the mud.

"You, Dewey Fayon," Ora said. "You'd better not do this. Hit's against the law. I'll get the law to you."

"Just try it," Dewey Fayon said. "I'm the Law," and he spat some tobacco juice on one of the matressses.

When Bonnie came from Stumptown the furniture was still there in the rain, and Ora with her own, Sally's and Bonnie's young was standing on the porch of the house.

Next door they heard Sara Smith crying. Her husband was with her. He had been in the strike and would not go back, but he had been sorely tempted to do so, for his wife had a two days' old child. He had brought a mattress from the street back on the porch and laid his wife and baby there. Ora had helped to make her comfortable, then returned to the young ones on her porch.

Bonnie said, "John and Tom Moore and the rest are getting tents put up in the hollow north of Company land."

"Ain't it terrible?" Ora said.

"Yes. But we've got to work and not cry," Bonnie was almost downed to see that Ora had lost her grit for once. "I saw Sally Thomas' two young ones with small pox put right out on the street, in the wet and rain."

Fifty families were put out of their homes that day, and there were many sick among them. The furniture stayed on the streets in the mud. Fortunately the rain stopped about evening.

Some of those who had been evicted had oil stoves, and in the early evening the smell of kerosene mixed with the odor of food that was being cooked on these stoves for the families evicted. Many were still wet from the rain, and after supper fires were built in the streets, where people gathered to dry out, and to talk about what was to be done. All night they kept up the fires. The men who were striking made up watches, and walked the streets, watching the fires and those who were trying to sleep on the hastily made up beds. The fires flickered up and shone on the closed houses and the scraggly dark piles of furniture in front of them.

Toward midnight John and some of the other men went to the union hall, for that needed a guard. Yet they felt almost helpless without firearms. What could they do if the mill decided to make any sort of raid on the hall? Later in the night they found out what could be done when the mill decided to use all its forces to bring them to their knees.

Tom Moore was in Sandersville with John Stevens, for in that place as in several other mills people were wishing to strike. John took the first watch in the hall, and the others lay on the floor and on the counters to get some sleep. He sat on the one chair in front of the table where they took in the names of the strikers. He was not sleepy and could have taken the watch for the whole length of the night, but knew that later he must try to get some rest. That there was danger he knew, for the mill was now roused like a beast that has been disturbed in its pleasant slumbers, and comes lumbering forth to kill or maim what has disturbed it. Everything that could be done to break them would be done.

He had learned this, among other things: That so long as he was docile and humble the owners would be kind to him. But if he once began to think for himself and ask for a better life they wanted to crush him. There was a telephone in the union hall and many times a day it would ring and voices spoke to them threatening death if they did not give up the strike. And they received many letters, he and Bonnie and Tom Moore. They addressed Bonnie as "nigger lover" because she worked in Stumptown among the colored people. But Bonnie went right on, for she was strong in knowing that Mary Allen and the others there needed the message as much as her people did. She could not be so selfish as to keep it only for herself and hers. She was not made in that fashion.

Suddenly John became aware that people were walking in the street outside. He realized that for some time he had been hearing the noises some distance away, but they had come into his thoughts as noises come in a dream. He touched Jesse on the shoulder and woke him.

"I think there may be trouble," he said.

They listened. There were voices outside.

"Had I better call the militia to protect us?" Jesse asked. "They're not far away."

"Wait," John said. He woke the others. They sat sleepy-eyed, huddled together on the floor, and singly on the counters. John stood in the middle of the long room, facing the door. There was a heavy crash on the door, and then another. The butt of a gun came through the splintered boards, and then the head of an ax crashed through. The others were wide awake now. All were standing, waiting for what was coming through the door.

"If I had my gun!" Jesse cried out as if he was in pain.

"Get away from that door," John called out.

There was no answer, but a hand reached through the splintered part and unlocked the door. It was filled with men. They had on masks which hid the lower part of their faces. The first ones entered, and others followed them. There must have been a hundred altogether, crowding into the room and filling the street outside. They had guns and axes in their hands.

"Get out," the leader said to the strikers. "Get out of here. If you don't want to be carried out."

John looked at the faces of his friends. "Comrades," he said, using a word that he had not thought of using, "I reckon since they're armed and we not, hit's best for us t' go."

The men turned slowly without speaking. Together they walked through the back entrance, down the alley between stores, and came out on the other side of the street. There in the dark they watched the mob at its work.

Everything was smashed. The whole wooden structure was made into a heap of wood. As each wall went down a hate like fire came up in John. It was not a hate against the men who were tearing down the building, but against those he knew had sent them, against the Power that was behind the lawlessness. He and the others in the strike had not broken one law since it had begun. And the Power could break every law.

Standing in the dark with the others he saw the masked men go to the relief store. They knocked in the glass windows. The splintering of the glass fell on him as if it was the splintering of his hopes for the union. They knocked in the door and came out carrying the precious bags and boxes of food. These they scattered on the sidewalk and in the mud of the road and stamped on them. Then they went back for more. When everything was finished one of the leaders stood outside the door and fired his revolver three times into the air. As he raised his face the mask fell off and John saw that it was the night superintendent of the mills, Jim Strothers.

The mob moved off to the east, and before they were out of sight the militia came running from the other direction.

John and the others crossed the street to see the wreck that had been made. The militia halted before them with bayonets outstretched. Their commander came up and spoke to John. He did not look at the mob that was still near enough for him to reach.

"What is this?" he asked sternly. John pointed to the smashed union hall.

"You might see," he said. "That mob you see going up the street did it. A mob from the mill. Jim Strothers, the night Super, was one of them."

"You can tell that when you come up in court," the commander told him. He called up some of his men and they surrounded the strikers.

"Where are we going?" John asked.

"To jail," the commander said.

"What for?"

"For disturbing the peace."

They marched along the road, surrounded by the militia. John saw

Young Frank two rows ahead. Without seeming to hurry he moved forward faster than the others and pulled the militiaman who was holding his arm forward until he was just behind Young Frank.

Young Frank was holding the arm of Henry Sanders.

"How long, Young Frank," John said to him in a low voice as they walked along, "how long you going t' fight us?"

"Here," Young Frank said to the militiaman who had John's arm. "You take this man and give me yours." The young militiaman sleepily reached ahead and took Henry's arm. Young Frank came to John's side.

"Look here," he whispered, "we don't like this kind of work. We want to go home, and told them so. We hope to get away by the end of the week. It's dirty work. I may be mean . . . but I don't like dirty work."

When John was bailed out of jail two days later, he found the militia gone. But something had come in its place. Over a hundred of the worst men in the town and county had been sworn in as deputy sheriffs. They were stationed day and night on every street leading to the mills.

Deputy sheriffs marching through coal districts of Pittsburgh during labor disturbance in 1933.

The Earth Does Move

BY JOSEPHINE HERBST

HE woke with a jerk. His head had rolled off the cotton waste to the icy cement floor of the plant. Steve Carson pushed the waste back under his head, stretched cautiously on the mat of waste under his body and strained to see in the long dim room. It must be nearly six o'clock in the morning, the hour when he would, on other days, be gulping down his breakfast, hurrying into his coat and crunching over the stiff snow to check in before the line started up on the first shift. A light from outside flickered on the ceiling and the long line of windows facing the street glittered in a dimmed glare. The soldier boys were keeping up their fires.

In a few minutes he would get up and walk over to the window to look at them. Last night before quieting down, a long line of men had stared out the windows at the huddle of young kids in uniforms stacking rifles, looking like a picture in the paper of how to play soldier. The guns had barrels, they were real. At the corner of the street, the kids had been busy playing fort. They had mounted two machine guns into place, had roped off the street and a nice tall kid could be seen strutting up and down, busy pacing off the hours of his duty.

It didn't look real. It was real. By the long window now looking at the fires in the street were Fred and Charley, keeping guard. He

---

Josephine Herbst was one of the most active writers of the thirties. In addition to reporting on the strikes in Iowa in 1932 and Michigan in 1937, she also reported on the effects of the Hitler régime for the *New York Post* and *The Nation;* and she was in Madrid in 1937 during its bombardment. Of her work, Miss Herbst has said: "To write historical stuff not in the romantic method or as history but as living, breathing language and life is my job." "The Earth Does Move" is from *Rope of Gold* (1939), the third novel in Miss Herbst's trilogy of middle class decay and "upthrust of a new group society," which also includes *Pity Is Not Enough* (1933) and *The Executioner Waits* (1934). The action of *Rope of Gold* covers the period from 1930 to the sit-down strikes of 1937, which proved to be one of the most powerful weapons of the CIO, enabling the union to win major victories against General Motors and the United States Steel Corporation.

could see their heavy legs a little apart, the shape of their skulls, the inert position of their arms. They weren't talking, only looking. It was pretty quiet. The steam had been shut off, the electricity was off. It had been cold and dark as the tomb. This was the sitdown strike.

This was what it was like. Not like you thought, but like this. The excitement of it was churning inside him like watching a big newsreel of the world, like looking at a history of your own life. He lay still. Ike McGee was breathing hard through his mouth, Willy Benson was snoring like a locomotive. Last night the guys hoisted up on slabs looked as if they were laid out in a morgue. The rest had piled on the floor on top of cotton waste. The steam bath where you washed the acid off metal was still piping hot. They laid planks on top of the steam and the boys lay on the planks roasting the cold from their bones. Today they would make a fight for some heat. They might threaten to make a fire inside. Last night they had just dropped down where they could. Everybody wanted a turn on the steam bath. "Hey, me next," and it had sounded like a lot of kids up in a mountain camp playing tricks on each other like you see it in the rotogravure. "This is our cheerleader," they wrote on a tag and tied it around Joe Polaski's ankle when he was laid out on his slab. It was a job to quiet down. The din of the big trucks moving around, getting into place along the windows by the river, hummed in your head. For hours the big crane had swung trucks, three high and three deep for a barricade. The heavy noise of the trucks moving had pounded like great big feet.

The boys were lying all over the place now, looking flattened and empty but by the window he could see by Fred's and Charley's legs what a man looks like. A man gets smaller as he gets older in this game. Steve was twenty-five but before a man is forty he is out. Out you go. No time to spit. Here's your time card for taking a drink. For talking. Get going. If the union is so smart, let it take care of you.

The union. A warm glow rushed over his body under his stiff clothes as if he were looking out at the street again late yesterday afternoon just after the plant shut down. That was some smart trick. For two days the whisper had gone around that they would pull Plant No. 9 at four in the afternoon. All the dicks and thugs had run to be on hand. Even the boys in that plant thought they were pulling the real thing. But *this* was the plant that was important. Right here. There hadn't been a minute to lose. They were beginning to move out the machines; the old trick that always beat the union. So they had to work fast. It was smooth sailing. When the boys began sitting down, the company dicks were at Plant nine. But outside, what a commotion.

The second they got wind and the foremen were kicked out, the police began coming down. Then the women popped out of the ground from nowhere, locking arms, backing themselves up against the gate.

Steve was going over and over it in his mind, the high moment when the union sound-truck began talking to the boys inside right over the heads of the police and the company yes-men milling around in the crowd like specks of pepper. What a wonderful invention a sound-car was. It had talked right out loud, and he heard again Jerry Stauffer's voice, almost as even and clear as if he were talking to them earlier in the year in the basements of fellows' homes, telling them not to be scared, that they had their constitutional rights and must fight for them. He was talking yesterday just like a general back of the lines, giving orders like in a war, *"Watch the doors, guard the windows, look out for the overhead passage, barricade along the river, we are with you,"* and then the boys had crawled along the scaffolding connecting the two upper stories. Some company sniper might be hiding there waiting to shoot. They had crawled, single file, like Indians hunting for a phantom army. But the phantoms had gone.

The men were pushing out the foremen through the back doors. "Hey, get going, you guys." The foremen turned ashy. Not the boys, the foremen. Not some fellow told to turn in his tools and beat it, he wasn't any good anymore after using himself up so fast for twenty years. Run along with your old creaky bones, peddle them somewhere else. Try to get on a charity list in your old age. If you live that long. Old bones and old rags for sale. Oh, Christ, it was bitter.

He'd seen his own cousin Charley Egstrom get it in the neck. And what about himself? They hadn't welcomed him with a band when he went back to Chicago, had they? They didn't hang any roses around his neck and say, "Welcome home." Not on your life. Nothing doing for you, kid, beat it. We got no use for guys like you. Go on, let your union take care of you. This plant is for fine loyal workers willing to keep their mouths shut and work like we tell them, we're protecting such guys. You mean to say a guy can't work in this country? Without the o. k. of some snotty union. Peddle your stuff somewhere else. And he had got himself to Michigan. Every day he'd got it taken out of his own hide, pitching into the speedup like the house was on fire and you ran around tossing everything out the door and windows trying to save it before the flames got it. Tearing the carpet off the floor, the bed, the baby's crib. The baby. His own kid seemed to be putting his spoon in one eye and laughing at him, making faces. This is for you, kid, too. Maybe this was the way men felt when they went to war, holding all their life in one hand, like water, fearful that someone might jog the elbow and spill it so it would be gone forever. Well, they had the goods on the foremen now.

They couldn't go on saying how they never tried to get the men to join *their* organization, as long as joining was such a sin. The little cards had fallen right out of their coat pockets, the files they hadn't time to close gaped with their secrets. They had little files with all the secrets written down in black and white. They had cards to sign up the boys in the yellow organization that was claiming to represent the "good workers" who were just dying to work for their company and never ask for anything. Oh, sure, the foremen wouldn't dirty their lily fingers with a union; they'd only sneak around trying to scare guys and sew them up with promises.

As if they didn't all want to work. Hell, if a man gets wrung through the speedup wringer it's all he's good for. He's no mortal good to himself or to his wife anymore. All he wants is to hit the hay when he gets home and he's a bundle of muscles shaped like legs and arms, and the second the whistle blows, the line starts up, he begins moving like he was wound up in back and doomed to jerk up and down until the toy can run no more.

Whoever thought to see such a sight? He snickered remembering the foremen running like rabbits. Thought this was their last stand. It was all UP. No time for their lunch pails. A run for your life. The boys had cleaned up the lunch pails last night but none of the fellows would so much as touch the company canteen. They could have left money for the cigarettes and the candy, but no, sir, don't touch it. Don't buy off the company, fellows. Don't take a stick of gum or one cigarette. You'll never hear the end if you do. Such a squawk will go up as will deafen you. They're touching our property. They're destroying our valuables. Wait for the union, boys, they'll take care of us.

Then the men were clearing the decks for godknowswhat action. The big crane was humping around with a truck dangling in its jaws. A jab here, a jab there, delicate as a finger and the tiny truck settled down, truck on top of truck. Try to break through that, you bastards. Shoot if you can.

Shoot. They might. The guns were real. The word die emerged cold and strange and new to his mind. Serious business was on the table. They mean business. We, the workers, mean business. Take your choice, ladies and gentlemen. The line forms to the left and to the right. On your right, a nice bit of concrete, steel, stone. On the left, only men. Here you have two assortments, take your pick. No, lady, we can't give you a mixed assortment. We can't mix the goods today. Don't crowd, sir. Easy. Plenty of time. In his mind he could see the men lined up for their tool clearance, their pants baggy in the rump, their shoulders sloping, their faces sweated up and streaked. Big guys and little guys, tough and stringy, all tired to the bone. Dog-tired, heads hanging, homeward bound. In old tin cars, straphanging on streetcars, or in secondhand cars or cars that would take a couple of years to pay off, riding around so the wife won't take it so hard. Would they shoot?

He could hear the click of a gun but that had been his own gun back home in South Dakota getting ready to pop off a fat pheasant streaking through the edge of wheat or a rabbit bounding over toward the buttes. Did a bullet going through a man tear the same kind of hole? He thought of the hole, round and bloody, the skin ripped out, the hole that looked so small and so fatal in a rabbit or a bird.

Men shot men in war. Make no mistake, we are now at war. The bright blue burning of the acetylene torches as the men welded plates over the door with openings for hoses to go through, blazed again in front of his eyes. He went over the events of the last twenty-four hours, turned backward to his whole life, full of wonder that the tools of a man's mind are brightest when he meets danger. He hears words all his life, sees sun, tables, cars, streets, and then he looks down the barrel of a gun. His whole life swoops up into his face as if he had taken off in an airplane at dawn. He can pick out the things he knows with amazement. So that's what a horse looks like. And his own life sticks out sharp and clear, as if, now he might lose it, he was privileged at last to look at it, handle it like a jackknife he'd never rightly had the use of.

"I'm a lucky man," he thought, seeing his whole life spin out, fitting itself together, wondering how a man in danger begins to look at himself almost for the first time and now he may soon go out like a light, he wants to understand how it has happened and how he came to be. He thought of himself in the cyclone cellar and his mother's cold hand growing colder, then his father's voice with its indignation against the wrongs in the world. He had escaped death from the cyclone but now if he should die, he at least knew why. He searched in his pocket for a bit of paper to write a word to Lorraine. Oh, my dear wife, my darling, and it seemed to him he had never loved her so much as now, lying on this cold stone floor with all the men around him who were thinking his same thoughts.

This is my job, he thought, and he seemed to see his job like a box that could be carried in his hand. Nothing elegant like a doctor's medicine kit or a lawyer's briefcase or a dentist's elaborate shiny tools. Just a job, like a brick, at the foundation of a skyscraper. Not a fancy job, just the run of luck that most men had. A job at the bottom where a man had to feel a man if there was to be any sense to the world. A job belonged to a man, more than a wife or child or mother. He had to have it to live and the world, much as it might pretend he was nothing to it, had to have him.

The men were stirring. One fellow was sucking the end of a pencil, hunched up over a letter to his wife. These are the facts of my life, Steve thought, fitting the last piece together. Over by the window the boys still stood on guard. Steve got up and his feet felt like clods of iron; his legs creaked as he stretched but he grinned at Fred. "They'll be bringing us some grub soon," Fred said, and sure enough, the union would find a way. The men were thinking of the union, shyly, proudly, with all the loyalty they had. Steve's throat hurt as he thought. He could remember a dozen things, the foremen mocking at Jerry Stauffer, "You got too much piss and vinegar in your blood. Why don't you let the peaceful guys who are satisfied with their life alone?" He was seeing the fellows from Saginaw with their heads cut open by the company thugs. Hey, get back to your line, quit trying to be something. Even if they won this round, no one need think it over. It would just be beginning and the bosses knew all the tricks, could make favorites, say honeysweet things. "Why, Mr. Barker, we were planning such a nice future for you. We were just going to suggest you take our foreman's course and work up. We simply don't understand how you come to be dissatisfied and join the union. Can't we talk it over?"

The fire outside had made a big black scar in the white snow and the young guards, looking more than ever like kids at play, were passing around cups of something hot. "Wish our fellows would hurry," said Fred. "That makes me hungry." The snow was white and crunchy the way it looked in the picture at home called "Snow Scene," only the world didn't look like that anymore with a peaceful house resting on a hill and smoke like warm fur pouring from the chimney. He could see the lips of the young National Guards kidding each other on the other side of the high iron gate and only yesterday the last man over the gate had clung to the top to fling back a word to the friends of the union milling in the street. "Brothers and sisters, we're only fighting for our human rights, better to die like men than live like dogs on the speedup." Then the crowd had backed off a little as from a fort about to explode. The brother had clung there for a second and it was terribly quiet. Steve could feel his whole life pound through his body. Then the crowd began to breathe again and the brother swung over the top of the gate. He eased down on the other side and walked up the steps to the fellows inside.

Above, Bonus army and police clash in 1932. Below, Riot at Fisher Auto Body, 1939.

The Strike

BY TILLIE LERNER

Do not ask me to write of the strike and the terror. I am on a battle-field, and the increasing stench and smoke sting the eyes so it is impossible to turn them back into the past. You leave me only this night to drop the bloody garment of Todays, to cleave through the gigantic events that have crashed one upon the other, to the first beginning. If I could go away for a while, if there were time and quiet, perhaps I could do it. All that has happened might resolve into order and sequence, fall into neat patterns of words. I could stumble back into the past and slowly, painfully rear the structure in all its towering magnificence, so that the beauty and heroism, the terror and significance of those days, would enter your heart and sear it forever with the vision.

But I hunch over the typewriter and behind the smoke, the days whirl, confused as dreams. Incidents leap out like a thunder and are gone. There flares the remembrance of that night in early May, in Stockton, when I walked down the road with the paper in my hands and the streaming headlines, LONGSHOREMEN OUT. RIOT EXPECTED; LONGSHORE STRIKE DECLARED. And standing there in the yellow stubble I remembered Jerry telling me quietly, ". . . for 12 years now. But we're through sweating blood, loading cargo five times the weight we should carry, we're through standing morning after morning like slaves in a slave market begging for a bidder. We'll

---

In the 1920's, employers in San Francisco formed an Industrial Association and tried to force all national unions off the waterfront. For many years they were successful, but in 1934, a local of the International Longshoremen's Association sought union recognition. When the employers refused, the longshoremen went on strike. Violence came quickly. On Thursday, July 5, an attempt to break the strike resulted in the death of two strikers and many injuries on both sides. On July 12, motivated in large part by the events of "Bloody Thursday," the Teamsters struck the entire city of San Francisco. Four days later the first general strike in America since 1919 formally began. Among those arrested for picketing was a young Nebraskan writer, Tillie Lerner, who was a member of the Young Communist League. This is her account of the San Francisco strike, which appeared in the September-October 1934 issue of *Partisan Review*.

be out, you'll see; it may be a few weeks, a few months, but WE'LL BE OUT, and then hell can't stop us."

H-E-L-L C-A-N-T S-T-O-P U-S. Days, pregnant days, spelling out the words. The port dead but for the rat stirring of a few scabs at night, the port paralyzed, gummed on one side by the thickening scum of prostrate ships, islanded on the other by the river of pickets streaming ceaselessly up and down, a river that sometimes raged into a flood, surging over the wavering shoreline of police, battering into the piers and sucking under the scabs in its angry tides. HELL CAN'T STOP US. That was the meaning of the lines of women and children marching up Market with their banners—"This is our fight, and we're with the men to the finish." That was the meaning of the seamen and the oilers and the wipers and the mastermates and the pilots and the scalers torrenting into the river, widening into the sea.

The kids coming in from the waterfront. The flame in their eyes, the feeling of invincibility singing in their blood. The stories they had to tell of scabs educated, of bloody skirmishes. My heart was ballooning with happiness anyhow, to be back, working in the movement again, but the things happening down at the waterfront, the heroic everydays, stored such richness in me I can never lose it. The feeling of sympathy widening over the city, of quickening—class lines sharpening. I armored myself with that on National Youth Day hearing the smash and thud of clubs around me, seeing boys fall to their knees in streams of blood, pioneer kids trampled under by horses. . . .

There was a night that was the climax of those first days—when the workers of San Francisco packed into the Auditorium to fling a warning to the shipowners. There are things one holds like glow in the breast, like a fire; they make the unseen warmth that keeps one through the cold of defeat, the hunger of despair. That night was one —symbol and portent of what will be. We League kids came to the meeting in a group, and walking up the stairs we felt ourselves a flame, a force. At the door bulls were standing, with menacing faces, but behind them fear was blanching—the people massing in, they had never dreamed it possible—people coming in and filling the aisles, packing the back. Spurts of song flaming up from downstairs, answered by us, echoed across the gallery, solidarity weaving us all into one being. 20,000 jammed in and the dim blue ring of cops back in the hall was wavering, was stretching itself thin and unseeable. It was OUR auditorium, we had taken it over. And for blocks around they hear OUR voice. The thunder of our applause, the mighty roar of it for Bridges, for Caves, for Schumacher. "Thats no lie." "Tell them Harry" "To the Finish" "We're with you" "Attaboy" "We're solid." The speeches, "They can never load their ships with tear gas and guns," "For years we were nothing but nameless beasts of burden to them, but now. . . ." "Even if it means . . . GENERAL STRIKE," the voices rising, lifted on a sea of affection, vibrating in 20,000 hearts.

There was the moment—the first bruise in the hearts of our masters—when Mayor Rossi entered, padding himself from the fists of boos smashing around him with 60 heavyfoots, and bulls, and honoraries. The boos had filled into breasts feeling and seeing the tattoo of his clubs on the embarcadero, and Rossi hearing tried to lose himself into his topcoat, failing, tried to puff himself invincible with the majesty of his office. "Remember, I am your chief executive, the respect . . . the honor . . . due that office . . . don't listen to me then but listen to your mayor . . . listen," and the boos rolled over him again and again so that the reptile voice smothered, stopped. He never forgot the moment he called for law and order, charging the meeting with not caring to settle by peaceful means, wanting only violence, and voices ripped from every corner. "Who started the violence?" "Who calls the bulls to the waterfront?" "Who ordered the clubbing?"—and in a torrent of anger shouted, "Shut up, we have to put up with your clubs but not with your words, get out of here, GET OUT OF HERE." That memory clamped into his heart, into the hearts of those who command him, that bruise became the cancer of fear that flowered into the monstrous Bloody Thursday, that opened into the pus of Terror—but the cancer grows, grows; there is no cure. . . .

It was after that night he formed his "Citizens Committee," after that night the still smiling lips of the Industrial Association bared into a growl of open hatred, exposing the naked teeth of guns and tear gas. The tempo of those days maddened to a crescendo. The city became a camp, a battlefield, the screams of ambulances sent the day reeling, class lines fell sharply—everywhere, on streetcars, on corners, in stores, people talked, cursing, stirred with something strange in their breasts, incomprehensible, shaken with fury at the police, the papers, the shipowners . . . going down to the waterfront, not curious spectators, but to stand there, watching, silent, trying to read the lesson the moving bodies underneath were writing, trying to grope to the meaning of it all, police "protecting lives" smashing clubs and gas bombs into masses of men like themselves, papers screaming lies. Those were the days when with every attack on the picket lines the phone rang at the I.L.A.—"NOW—will you arbitrate?"—when the mutter GENERAL STRIKE swelled to a thunder, when everywhere the cry arose—"WE'VE GOT TO END IT NOW." Coming down to headquarters from the waterfront, the faces of comrades had the strained look of men in battle, that strangely intense look of living, of feeling too much in too brief a space of time. . . .

Yes, those were the days crescendoing—and the typewriter breaks, stops for an instant—to Bloody Thursday. Weeks afterward my fists clench at the remembrance and the hate congests so I feel I will burst. Bloody Thursday—our day we write on the pages of history with letters of blood and hate. Our day we fling like a banner to march with the other bloody days when guns spat death at us that a few dollars might be saved to fat bellies, when lead battered into us, and only our naked hands, the fists of our bodies moving together could resist. Drown their strength in blood, they commanded, but instead they armored us in inflexible steel—hate that will never forget. . . .

"It was as close to war . . . as actual war could be," the papers blared triumphantly, but Bridges told them, "not war . . . MASSACRE, armed forces massacring unarmed." Words I read through tears of anger so that they writhed and came alive like snakes, you rear in me again, "and once again the policemen, finding their gas bombs and gas shells ineffective poured lead from their revolvers into the jammed streets. Men (MEN) fell right and left." " . . . And everywhere was the sight of men, beaten to their knees to lie in a pool of blood." "Swiftly, from intersection to intersection the battle moved, stubbornly the rioters refused to fall back so that the police were forced. . . ." "and the police shot forty rounds of tear gas bombs into the mob before it would move. . . ."

Law . . . and order . . . will . . . prevail. Do you hear? It's war, WAR—and up and down the street "A man clutched at his leg and fell to the sidewalk" "The loud shot like that of the tear gas bombs zoomed again, but no blue smoke this time, and when the men cleared, two bodies lay on the sidewalk, their blood trickling about them"—overhead an airplane lowered, dipped, and nausea gas swooned down in a cloud of torture, and where they ran from street to street, resisting stubbornly, massing again, falling back only to carry the wounded, the thought tore frenziedly through the mind, war, war, it's WAR—and the lists in the papers, the dead, the wounded by bullets, the wounded by other means—W-A-R.

LAW—you hear, Howard Sperry, exserviceman, striking stevedore, shot in the back and abdomen, said to be in dying condition, DEAD, LAW AND ORDER—you hear and remember this Ben Martella, shot in arm, face and chest, Joseph Beovich, stevedore, laceration of skull from clubbing and broken shoulder, Edwin Hodges, Jerry Hart, Leslie Steinhart, Steve Hamrock, Albert Simmons, marine engineer, striking seamen, scaler, innocent bystander, shot in leg, shot in shoulder, chest lacerated by tear gas shell, gassed in eyes, compound skull fracture by clubbing, you hear—LAW AND ORDER MUST PREVAIL—it's all right Nick, clutching your leg and seeing through the fog of pain it is a police car has picked you up, snarling, let me out, I don't want any bastard bulls around, and flinging yourself out into the street, still lying there in the hospital today—

LAW AND ORDER—people, watching with horror, trying to comprehend the lesson the moving bodies were writing. The man stopping me on the corner, seeing my angry tears as I read the paper, "Listen," he said, and he talked because he had to talk, because in an hour all the beliefs of his life had been riddled and torn away— "Listen, I was down there, on the waterfront, do you know what they're doing—they were shooting SHOOTING—" and that word came out anguished and separate, "shooting right into men, human beings, they were shooting into them as if they were animals, as if they were targets, just lifting their guns and shooting. I saw this, can you believe it, CAN YOU BELIEVE IT? . . . as if they were targets as if . . . CAN YOU BELIEVE IT?" and he went to the next man and started it all over again. . . .

I was not down . . . by the battlefield. My eyes are anguished from the pictures I pieced together from words of comrades, of strikers, from the pictures filling the newspapers. I sat up in headquarters, racked by the howls of ambulances hurtling by, feeling it incredible the fingers like separate little animals hopping nimbly from key to key, the ordered steady click of the typewriter, feeling any moment the walls would crash and all the madness surge in. Ambulances, ripping out of nowhere, fading; police sirens, outside the sky a ghastly gray, corpse gray, an enormous dead eyelid shutting down on the world. And someone comes in, words lurch out of his mouth, the skeleton is told, and goes again. . . . And I sit there, making a metallic little pattern of sound in the air, because that is all I can do, because that is what I am supposed to do.

They called the guard out . . . "admitting their inability to control the situation," and Barrows boasted, "my men will not use clubs or gas, they will talk with bayonets" . . . Middlestaedt . . . "Shoot to kill. Any man firing into the air will be courtmartialed." With two baby tanks, and machine guns, and howitzers, they went down to the waterfront to take it over, to "protect the interests of the people."

I walked down Market that night. The savage wind lashed at my hair. All life seemed blown out of the street; the few people hurrying by looked hunted, tense, expectant of anything. Cars moved past as if fleeing. And a light, indescribably green and ominous was cast over everything, in great shifting shadows. And down the street the trucks rumbled. Drab colored, with boys sitting on them like corpses sitting and not moving, holding guns stiffly, staring with wide frightened eyes, carried down to the Ferry building, down to the Embarcadero to sell out their brothers and fathers for $2.00 a day. Somebody said behind me, and I do not even know if the voice was my own, or unspoken, or imagined, "Go on down there, you sonovabitches, it doesn't matter. It doesn't stop us. We won't forget what happened today. . . . Go on, nothing can stop us . . . now."

Somehow I am down on Stuart and Mission, somehow I am staring at flowers scattered in a border over a space of sidewalk, at stains that look like rust, at an unsteady chalking—"Police Murder. Two Shot in the Back," and looking up I see faces, seen before, but utterly changed, transformed by some inner emotion to faces of steel. "Nick Bordoise . . . and Sperry, on the way to punch his strike card, shot in the back by those bastard bulls. . . ."

OUR BROTHERS

Howard S. Sperry, a longshoreman, a war vet, a real MAN. On strike since May 9th, 1934 for the right to earn a decent living under decent conditions. . . .
Nickolas Bordoise, a member of Cooks & Waiters Union for ten years. Also a member of the International Labor Defense. Not a striker, but a worker looking to the welfare of his fellow workers on strike. . . .

Some of what the leaflet said. But what can be said of Howard Sperry, exserviceman, struggling through the horrors of war for his country, remembering the dead men and the nearly dead men lashing about blindly on the battlefield, who came home to die in a new war, a war he had not known existed. What can be said of Nick Bordoise. Communist Party member, who without thanks or request came daily to the Embarcadero to sell his fellow workers hot soup to warm their bellies. There was a voice that gave the story of his life, there in the yellowness of the parched grass, with the gravestones icy and strange in the sun; quietly, as if it had risen up from the submerged hearts of the world, as if it had been forever and would be forever, the voice surged over our bowed heads. And the story was the story of any worker's life, of the thousand small deprivations and frustrations suffered, of the courage forged out of the cold and darkness of poverty, of the determination welded out of the helpless anger scalding the heart, the plodding hours of labor and weariness, of the life, given simply, as it had lived, that the things which he had suffered should not be, must not be. . . .

There were only a few hundred of us who heard that voice, but the thousands who watched the trucks in the funeral procession piled high with 50¢ and $1.00 wreaths guessed, and understood. I saw the people, I saw the look on their faces. And it is the look that will be there the days of the revolution. I saw the fists clenched till knuckles were white, and people standing, staring, saying nothing, letting it clamp into their hearts, hurt them so the scar would be there forever—a swelling that would never let them lull.

"Life," the capitalist papers marvelled again, "Life stopped and stared." Yes, you stared, our cheap executive, Rossi—hiding behind the curtains, the cancer of fear in your breast gnawing, gnawing; you stared, members of the Industrial Association, incredulous, where did the people come from, where was San Francisco hiding them, in what factories, what docks, what are they doing there, marching, or standing and watching, not saying anything, just watching. . . . What did it mean, and you dicks, fleeing, hiding behind store windows. . . .

There was a pregnant woman standing on a corner, outlined against the sky, and she might have been a marble, rigid, eternal, expressing some vast and nameless sorrow. But her face was a flame, and I heard her say after a while dispassionately, as if it had been said so many times no accent was needed, "We'll not forget that. We'll pay it back . . . someday." And on every square of sidewalk a man was saying, "We'll have it. We'll have a General Strike. And there won't be processions to bury their dead." "Murder—to save themselves paying a few pennies more wages, remember that Johnny . . . We'll get even. It won't be long. General Strike."

Listen, it is late, I am feverish and tired. Forgive me that the words are feverish and blurred. You see, If I had time, If I could go away. But I write this on a battlefield.

The rest, the General Strike, the terror, arrests and jail, the songs in the night, must be written some other time, must be written later. . . . But there is so much happening now. . . .

Cops Are Funny People—If at All

BY ROBERT FORSYTHE

THE police are a constant source of wonder to us. Their élan, their spirit, their soft-spoken politeness in making arrests, their flat feet, their kindness to prisoners in the station house—all these qualities are only equaled by their efficiency and integrity. Their remarkable record during the General Strike in San Francisco is only another bannered page in their history. The efficiency of operation there was almost beyond belief. It could have been only sheer intuition and the innate clairvoyance of fine officers which allowed the police to be on the scene exactly two minutes after the Vigilantes had smashed the headquarters of various radical organizations. If it had been one headquarters and one raid, it would have been remarkable but when the same amazing thing happened at least half a dozen times, it could only be put down to heavenly guidance. The fact that they arrested the radicals who were being raided rather than the Vigilantes doing the raiding can only have been an oversight, for it is a well-established fact that the police are sworn to preserve law and order and protect private property. A striker caught kicking a can of peaches off a wharf will undoubtedly and justly be shot in the lower abdomen as a lesson in democracy, so it is merely a question of time until the police realize their error and make the proper amends.

As an Easterner I must insist, however, that our officers here are equally proficient and alert, yielding to none in their courage in the face of pregnant women seeking food from relief agencies. The New York police have never flinched in bringing their clubs to rest on such subversive influences. It was, therefore, a source of some embarrassment to have the San Francisco police triumph coincide with the

---

The general strike in San Francisco—of which Tillie Lerner wrote—gave Robert Forsythe (the pseudonym of Kyle Crichton) an opportunity to inveigh against police brutality. Although liberals have long been concerned with the abuse of power by the police, it became an almost obsessive matter to the writers and cartoonists of the *New Masses* and the *Daily Worker*. In 1935, Forsythe, who was generally regarded as the dean of proletarian humorists, published *Redder than the Rose*, which consisted of many of his *New Masses* articles, together with illustrations by such left-wing artists as William Gropper, John Mackey, and Gardner Rea. It is from this collection that "Cops Are Funny People—If At All" is reprinted.

"kidnaping" of the Connor child in Hartsdale, N.Y. The Hearst papers had a particularly difficult time with this case because a kidnaping, according to the sacred code of San Simeon, is a matter of transcendent importance and yet there had to be headlines left over for scare stories about the Reds. The police in this instance seem to have had trouble in their semaphore service with God because the child, after five days, was found in a thicket several hundred yards from the house. The countryside in the meantime had been practically demolished by flat feet for miles around, but the Connor child seems to have been backward in cooperation. The police had done their usual thorough job of arresting peddlers, knife-grinders and broken-down bootblacks, some of whom would undoubtedly have languished in durance vile for years to come if the child had not made the error of wandering too close to home. If the Connor baby grows up to be a capitalist, he will realize that he had nothing to fear from the *gendarmerie*. He will find that the police are always kind to capitalists, both large and small.

The psychology of a policeman has always baffled us. Being dependent upon the favor of the political bosses who are for their part dependent upon the favors of the industrial bosses, they are naturally prepared to defend the interests of these same people. But coming as they do out of the homes of working people, it is always an amazing spectacle to see them turning almost immediately against their own class interests. It is due no doubt to their infinitesimal stake in the larger graft of big business, which brings them in plenty of fives and tens and which assumes, at the holiday seasons, an air of the old good days of serfdom. The limousines of the Wall Street gentlemen and of the dowagers from Park Avenue pass sedately by the patrolmen on their beats, dropping little tokens of their appreciation and love. For this they may be assured of the humbling tipping of the officer's hat when they pass on their way to work or shopping next day and every day throughout the year. It is a charming feudal custom and makes up for the hard dealing the police must do with slot-machine proprietors, bootleggers, dope-peddlers and bail-bond sharks. From the latter elements they get the larger money, but not the same social contacts.

If we read the history of the Russian Revolution correctly, it was the winning of the army units which prepared the way for revolt; the police were never won over. Nothing seems to shake their faith in the ruling order, no matter what that order may be. Despite La Guardia's promise not to cut the wages of civil service workers, he reduced the pay for teachers, firemen and policemen almost as soon as he got into office. If this affected the morale of the police or made them more understanding of the troubles of others who were in similar straits, the results failed to show it. The terror used by General O'Ryan's men against the workers and unemployed has been more murderous than ever before. O'Ryan saw to this by his threat that any officer failing to act in a terroristic manner would be charged with insubordination, but even without that the temper of the New York police was well understood. The fact that they are predominantly Irish and thus under the domination of the Catholic Church with its hatred of all forms of radicalism and particularly of Communism is undoubtedly an important factor, but it does not explain the police of San Francisco or the police of Berlin and Paris.

Some months ago, Talcott Powell of the Indianapolis *Times*, a Scripps-Howard paper, was arrested in Gary, Indiana, where he had gone to inspect the terrain in the event of violence growing out of the proposed steel strike. When they brought him to the police station, an officer started to push Powell around. Powell immediately sat down in a chair. He explained this in his article by saying: "I know what that pushing around means. I've seen it before in police stations. If the prisoner should attempt to defend himself or even ward off the blows, they'll give him a real going over. This is what is known as 'resisting an officer.' "

This statement by Powell interested us particularly because we had seen something of the police of Powell's town of Indianapolis some short time before. We were doing an article on the Dillinger case and were sitting around with the reporters in the press room at police headquarters getting their notion of things in general. While sitting there a policeman came in.

"How do you find a name like St. Ives in the directory—under the S's or under the I's?" he asked.

The reporters told him and he found the address and went out again.

"What did he want to know that for?" he asked.

"St. Ives is one of the strikers out at the Real Silk Hosiery plant," said the reporters. "They're going to watch the house and see what goes on."

"Why would they watch it?"

"Why would they watch it!" they demanded in surprise. "Why d'ye think they'd watch it? They're going to get something on the guy. The Chief of Police is a stockholder in Real Silk. He's busting this strike."

To relieve your mind at once, we can tell you that the reporters were not excited about it. They had no hesitation in saying that the Indianapolis police were so low-down that Dillinger, Genghis Khan or even Hitler would be angels by comparison, but they had even less use for the strikers.

"A bunch of damned red necks," they said.

But anyone who has seen that police station from within or any big city station can be under no misapprehension about justice, equity or the mere elements of humanity. Those police know who does the buttering of the bread, they know when to be rough and when to fawn, they know when to swing the clubs and shoot the guns and when to tip the hat. When Governor Merriam makes a speech and Mayor Rossi makes a speech and General Hugh Johnson makes a speech—all open invitations to murder—the police are not long in understanding their place in life. In such momentous circumstances they can sacrifice a few days of collections on the beat to go out to do a good deed for their masters.

a. Redfield

"God, what a day! I've been clubbing strikers for eight hours!"

Communists and Cops

BY EDMUND WILSON

THE Communists have announced their intention of leading a "hunger march" on January 20. The city administration has agreed to receive a delegation at City Hall, but has not unreasonably refused a request to allow the Communists to make speeches from the steps.

In consequence, from ten o'clock on, a cordon of two hundred policemen are on guard around City Hall and the little park in front of it. You cannot get anywhere near the building without running the gauntlet of the cops and presenting unimpeachable credentials. It is like some scene on an old-fashioned German parade ground. The only human figures in the park are the immobile policemen, equestrian and on foot, with their blue coats and flat blue military caps, and the great snow-white booby Civic Virtue, with his thick trunk and sulky Irish face, trampling on confused female bodies.

At one o'clock promptly, the Communists arrive to the number of about 2,000 and the demonstration begins. The demonstrators deliver speeches and march around City Hall Park. A good many of them are Jews and some are Negroes—mostly small scrubby zealous people wearing red neckties, red hats or red dresses. A good many of the women have glasses. They have also succeeded in recruiting from the breadlines and employment agencies a considerable number of seedy men, to whom they have held out the hope that the authorities may be induced to provide unemployment insurance. They carry placards: "We Want No Charity," "No Evictions for the Unemployed," "We Demand Armories and Public Buildings for the Unemployed." They

---

By the early thirties Clifton Fadiman was able to write enthusiastically that Edmund Wilson, one of the foremost literary critics of our time, had emerged from his absorption "in the great values—Culture, Truth, Beauty—into the real world of collapsing America." It was at this time that Wilson began to investigate and really understand the Marxist position. Although he was shortly to disavow the Communist Party, the publication of The American Jitters: A Year of the Slump (1932) and Travels in Two Democracies (1936) show Wilson's social concern and absorption in Marxism. From 1926 to 1931, Wilson was associated with The New Republic, where "Communists and Cops" first appeared on February 11, 1931.

concentrate at the foot of the park opposite the Federal Building, and speakers get up on the iron dustbins. A crowd gathers—the newspaper photographers climb onto the roofs of the Coca-Cola and orange-drink stands and dominate the scene with their cameras.

The first speaker is a young Negro named Newton, the editor of the Communist Negro paper and secretary of the League of Struggle for Negro Rights, who was one of the Communists arrested last May in Atlanta for circulating radical leaflets. He was threatened with the death penalty under an ancient law which was originally intended as a weapon for dealing with rebellious slaves. Newton had never been in the South before: he is an educated Negro from Boston. Some years ago, while working in a hotel, he got a two-week vacation and arranged to go to a Y.M.C.A. camp; but when he arrived there, they wouldn't have him and gave him his money back. Later on, he met a Negro Communist, who told him that the Communists were working to abolish race discrimination, and he joined the Communist party. He is a good-looking fellow, with large sensitive dark eyes, skin closer to coffee than to mahogany and a thick but straight and rather unnegroid nose. He is joined almost immediately by other speakers, among them a Negro of a quite different type, blacker, with a round face and an old soft hat, whose voice sounds falsetto above the rest. Speaker after speaker leaps onto the dustbin till there is only a babel of yelling—then speechmaking is given up. The group on the dustbin begins rousing the crowd with methods like those of a college cheerleader—"We—want—*work-or wages!* We—want *work-or wages!*" The harsh fanatical rhythm goes on and on—the people in the crowd get caught up into it and begin to shout with the leaders.

The street has become packed and impassable, and now the crowd is jamming the road. The taxis and the mail trucks cannot get by, and the police decide to break things up. Coming behind the speakers' stand, they push the people along the sidewalk. "Oh-oh!" exclaims a gaping bystander. "He's hittin' 'em on the head." From the road a mounted policeman starts out to ride into the crowd. As he does so, he screws up one side of his mouth: he is a clean-cut young fellow with his mind on holding in his horse. He scarcely does more than turn its head in the direction of the overthronged sidewalk and make a pretense of riding into it. "That's right!—go after 'em!" a young man among the bystanders eggs him on.

The crowd becomes liquefied and begins to move. A nice-looking boy about ten in an old red-plaid Mackinaw—Comrade Charley, a Young Pioneer, who lives in Brighton Beach—shouts from above people's heads with a voice that sounds strangely fresh and live amid the systematic yelling of the grown-ups. He is carried aloft on the shoulders of an exceedingly tall Negro, another worker in the League of Struggle for Negro Rights, who has recently served a sentence of three months for breaking up an anti-lynching meeting of the Pullman porters' association. The Pullman porters' association are Socialists, but, according to the Negro Communists, keep on the right side of white respectability and have been guilty of suppressing the evidence in connection with the lynching of a porter in Georgia.

The demonstration pushes slowly around the park. "Aw that's a lotta crap!" yells one of the spectators. "Oh, yeah?" retorts a fierce little Communist. "What the hell do you know about it?" "We want bread!" another shouts. "Try and get it!" somebody answers. A shabby elderly Jew, who speaks English very thickly, is handing out leaflets on unemployment insurance and repeating conscientiously again and again: "Dis has got to become a law vedder de bosses like it or not!"

The police watch behind iron posts that protect City Hall from the traffic. Some are Negroes brought down from Harlem, who have almost the same Prussian stature, the same square faces and mail-slot mouths as their white fellow officers. The policemen seem to fall into two classes: the husky good-natured kind who accomplish their disciplinary duties with conviction but without ferocity, and the stupid staring-eyed type frankly hired as mobilizable brutes. Some of these are evidently Jews, especially provided like the Negroes to deal with agitators of their own race. In any case, the police offer a curious contrast to everybody else present: if the Communists mostly look stunted, the office workers out for lunch are hardly more prepossessing; and the policemen seem the only healthy full-sized people and the only people decently dressed in these choked-up streets of milling human beings, bewildered or determined or half-scared or angry at being delayed, but all alike looking undersized, undernourished, dingy-featured, drearily dressed.

Only when the Communists sing one of their songs—*Solidarity Forever* or *The International*—does any note arise from among them of enthusiasm or human warmth.

> *It's the final conflict!*
> *Let each stand in his place!*
> *The International Soviet*
> *Shall be the human race!*

The bald words, the banal tune, by reason of all they have been coming to mean, do lift up the heart for a moment as the Communists raise their arms and wave them in time to the refrain.

All around them under the gray winter sky rise the high ugly walls of downtown New York, keeping the marchers, the crowd and the traffic crammed into the tight little space still left between the impregnably guarded park and the dense concentration of buildings: the men's wear shops, Schrafft's soda fountains, Liggett's drug-stores and cafeterias of Nassau Street and Broadway; the World Building with its rusty green dome, the red brick with green trimmings of the Sun Building, standing narrow and perpendicular like the fragments of some incomplete structure; a corner with cheap chop-suey signs over cheap investment-loan signs, a brick office building from whose flat cold red every suggestion of genuine color seems to have faded out past hope of revival by the sun; the somewhat handsomer high gray cliff of the Woolworth Building, eroded and lined like a giant butte and diminishing in tiers toward the top; the lower Federal Building, with its squashed-down, square-sided dome and its spotting of portholes like moles above a bulk of gray machine-made public dignity.

In this cramped and inhospitable area, the Communists produce simply confusion—a confusion which gets worse and worse. From the other side of the park, a woman's dreadful scream is heard.

In the meantime, at City Hall, to which it has been escorted by cops, a delegation is presenting demands. Mayor Walker is said to be ill—according to the Communists, afraid to face them—and they are received by the affable Mr. Kerrigan.

F. G. Biedenkapp, who acts as the spokesman, demands unemployment insurance; free gas, electricity and coal, no evictions for the unemployed, and free clothing and food for their children; reduced rents; the throwing open of vacant apartments and public buildings, and the use of schools and public halls for meeting places; the distribution of unemployment relief through a board composed entirely of workers and Communists, which shall also take over all the employment-agency work now being done by the State Labor Department, the Y.M.C.A. and all other organizations; no discrimination among workers on account of race, color, nationality or sex; and the immediate release of comrades who have been jailed in connection with previous demonstrations.

To this Mr. Kerrigan replies that "the city is constituted according to law, and a number of your demands would be illegal if carried out," that "if the city officials tried to carry them out they would be immediately removed," that the city officials are contributing out of their salaries for unemployment relief, that the city employment fund is to be increased, that the city is going to try to bring pressure to bear at Albany to amend the law in such a way as to make it possible to stop evictions, that the city has set up a free employment agency which will have the effect of suppressing private agencies and eliminating "the deception and dishonesty practised by some of them," that the Board of Education is already doing what it can to feed the children of the unemployed.

"I don't want to say," he concludes, "that if you don't like it here, you can go back to Russia, because many of you were born here—but I will say that I will pay the full fare, one way, of any ten of you who want to go there. That is about all we can do under the present system." F. G. Biedenkapp, in reply to this, declares the committee "entirely dissatisfied" with Mr. Kerrigan's "explanations and excuses"— and the Communists, under escort, withdraw.

Once outside, they make haste to climb onto the statue of Benjamin Franklin in front of the Sun Building. They shout that their demands have been refused: "We saw the acting mayor and told him our demands and he said that it was against the law to grant them. The unemployed workers must change the laws!"

This is a signal for the demonstration to swarm. They hang their placards all over the statue. Franklin stands with a discolored green bronze crown, one hand stretched out to the world as if in patriarchal blessing and at his feet some large funereal wreaths, presented by the Sons of the American Revolution. Comrade Charley, full of pep in his red Mackinaw, climbs up on the great bourgeois's shoulders and displays a placard: "Free Food for Our Children!" A crowd gathers on the opposite curbs. The statue is situated on a little lozenge of pavement between Nassau Street and Park Row, in such a way that any disturbance around it will cause a maximum jam of the traffic to and from Brooklyn Bridge: the Communists have picked a strategic point for obstructing the downtown life of the city. Taxis bawl and streetcars clang—curious office workers overflow the sidewalks, asking one another what is going on. Somebody in the Sun Building, from a high-up floor, drops a paper-bag full of water over the massed swarm around the statue. The bag comes apart in the air, and people watch the falling whirl of water.

The police decide at last to put an end to the demonstration. They force their way into the crowd and start pulling down the placards and speakers. An unintelligible mêlée ensues. The Communists flee before the police, and the bystanders get mixed up with them. One has a glimpse of a last indomitable speaker with a wild livid crazy face still vituperating alone on the statue—he has vanished a second later. People suddenly yell: "Look out!" Mounted cops begin galloping along the sidewalks, and everybody runs before them, demonstrators and in-

nocent pedestrians alike. A Communist, grabbing apples from an unemployed apple-vendor, bombards the policemen with them and then
crowns one of the horses with the crate. Another seizes a horse by the
tail—a detective clutches him by the collar and beats him—two women
rush to his rescue and almost pull the policeman off his horse. The
traffic is impatient; the spectators dismayed; the unemployed have
scattered like leaves.

The Communists rally, shouting "Close up ranks!", and rush up
the entrance of the flat raised tunnel which leads to the Brooklyn
Bridge subway, completely taking possession of the wide flight of
steps and booing and hooting the police as if from baseball bleachers.
The police stretch a rope along the back of the park and excitedly
patrol the paths. At one stop, quite remote from the disturbance, there
is a shoe-shining stand with a row of men peacefully sitting in the
chairs and reading the tabloids as they have their shoes shined—but
at the sudden appearance of the charging police, they all spring out of
their seats simultaneously and leap over the iron fence. A gray flight
of pigeons rises from the park, the only free living things in sight.

Now the Communists are routed from the bridge entrance. Some
are chased under the monumental, the more than Roman, arches of
the Municipal Building—they lurk there awhile and then return. Others, retreating down Center Street, return to the battle through Elm.

A patrol wagon and an ambulance arrive, a stretcher is carried
out of City Hall. You read the next morning in the papers that the
demonstrators have had their arms broken, their skulls fractured, their
teeth knocked out; an auditor from the Comptroller's office has had
his head cut open against the Municipal Building; a policeman, who
fell into the hands of the demonstrators and got kicked in the stomach
by them, is in the hospital with internal injuries.

The Communists are shouting, "We want bread, not horses' hoofs!"
and trying to rally around speakers on the curbs. But the speakers get
dislodged, the groups dwindle. Among the passers-by behind the
park, a small plump sharp-beaked Jewish woman in red—great wrath
in a tiny body, like one of Virgil's bees—is wandering by herself and
screaming, "Down with the police!"

At the corner of Center Street, a dingy little man who is walking
by, pauses as a spattering on the sidewalk turns out to be too thick,
too red and too profuse for spit. He says in a foolish way to nobody
in particular, with a mixture of surprise and awe: "Blood!"

Now the streets are completely cleared—the great suction pumps
of downtown New York have pulled up their populations again. The
people are coming out of the subway unimpeded, going up the steps

to Brooklyn Bridge—the taxis are on their way down to Wall Street, the trucks on their way to the docks. The pretzel man with his basket and the roast-chestnut man have come out again. The battle has been obliterated. No one passing has even heard of it. Many of the people who witnessed it or in some way became involved in it never knew what it was about. They are neither sympathetic with the Communists nor particularly indignant with them—they are not even particularly angry at having been chased by the police. They feel no real stake in the city in the sense of its being their community, and they consequently take very little interest in abuses of administration which do not vitally affect themselves. If they have jobs in these hard times, they are glad enough to hang on to them, without worrying about the unemployed. And they have all long ago gone about their business.

Communist parade in Union Square, May Day, 1930.

Waiting for Lefty*

BY CLIFFORD ODETS

CHARACTERS

FATT	CLAYTON
JOE	AGATE KELLER
EDNA	HENCHMAN
MILLER	REILLY
FAYETTE	DR. BARNES
IRV	DR. BENJAMIN
FLORRIE	A MAN
SID	

As the curtain goes up we see a bare stage. On it are sitting six or seven men in a semi-circle. Lolling against the proscenium down left is a young man chewing a toothpick: a gunman. A fat man of porcine appearance is talking directly to the audience. In other words he is the head of a union and the men ranged behind him are a committee of workers. They are now seated in interesting different attitudes and present a wide diversity of type, as we shall soon see. The fat man is hot and heavy under the collar, near the end of a long talk, but not too hot: he is well fed and confident. His name is HARRY FATT.

Of the many proletarian works of the thirties which deal with strikes, Clifford Odets' *Waiting for Lefty* was by far the most popular. Odets wrote the play in three days, then submitted it to the New Theatre League, which had offered a prize for the best one-act play that workers could perform at their own meeting places. *Waiting for Lefty* won the prize, and was produced by the Group Theatre on January 5, 1935; overnight it made Odets one of the best known figures of the decade. Harold Clurman, one of the leaders of the Group Theatre, wrote in *The Fervent Years* that "When the audience at the end of the play responded to the militant question from the stage: 'Well, what's the answer?' with a spontaneous roar of 'Strike! Strike!' it was something more than a tribute to the play's effectiveness, more even than a testimony of the audience's hunger for constructive social action. It was the birth cry of the thirties."

FATT: You're so wrong I ain't laughing. Any guy with eyes to read knows it. Look at the textile strike—out like lions and in like lambs. Take the San Francisco tie-up—starvation and broken heads. The steel boys wanted to walk out too, but they changed their minds. It's the trend of the times, that's what it is. All we workers got a good man behind us now. He's top man of the country—looking out for our interests—the man in the White House is the one I'm referrin' to. That's why the times ain't ripe for a strike. He's working day and night—

VOICE (*from the audience*): For who? (*The* GUNMAN *stirs himself.*)

FATT: For you! The records prove it. If this was the Hoover régime, would I say don't go out, boys? Not on your tin-type! But things is different now. You read the papers as well as me. You know it. And that's why I'm against the strike. Because we gotta stand behind the man who's standin' behind us! The whole country—

ANOTHER VOICE: Is on the blink! (*The* GUNMAN *looks grave.*)

FATT: Stand up and show yourself, you damn red! Be a man, let's see what you look like! (*Waits in vain.*) Yellow from the word go! Red and yellow makes a dirty color, boys. I got my eyes on four or five of them in the union here. What the hell'll they do for you? Pull you out and run away when trouble starts. Give those birds a chance and they'll have your sisters and wives in the whore houses, like they done in Russia. They'll tear Christ off his bleeding cross. They'll wreck your homes and throw your babies in the river. You think that's bunk? Read the papers! Now listen, we can't stay here all night. I gave you the facts in the case. You boys got hot suppers to go to and—

ANOTHER VOICE: Says you!

GUNMAN: Sit down, Punk!

ANOTHER VOICE: Where's Lefty? (*Now this question is taken up by the others in unison.* FATT *pounds with gavel.*)

FATT: That's what I wanna know. Where's your pal, Lefty? You elected him chairman—where the hell did he disappear?

VOICES: We want Lefty! Lefty! Lefty!

FATT (*pounding*): What the hell is this—a circus? You got the committee here. This bunch of cowboys you elected. (*Pointing to man on extreme right end.*)

MAN: Benjamin.

FATT: Yeah, Doc Benjamin. (*Pointing to other men in circle in seated order*): Benjamin, Miller, Stein, Mitchell, Phillips, Keller. It ain't my fault Lefty took a run-out powder. If you guys—

A GOOD VOICE: What's the committee say?

OTHERS: The committee! Let's hear from the committee! *(FATT tries to quiet the crowd, but one of the seated men suddenly comes to the front. The GUNMAN moves over to center stage, but FATT says:)*

FATT: Sure, let him talk. Let's hear what the red boys gotta say! *(Various shouts are coming from the audience. FATT insolently goes back to his seat in the middle of the circle. He sits on his raised platform and relights his cigar. The GUNMAN goes back to his post. JOE, the new speaker, raises his hand for quiet. Gets it quickly. He is sore.)*

JOE: You boys know me. I ain't a red boy one bit! Here I'm carryin' a shrapnel that I picked up in the war. And maybe I don't know it when it rains! Don't tell me red! You know what we are? The black and blue boys! We been kicked around so long we're black and blue from head to toes. But I guess anyone who says straight out he don't like it, he's a red boy to the leaders of the union. What's this crap about goin' home to hot suppers? I'm asking to your faces how many's got hot suppers to go home to? Anyone who's sure of his next meal, raise your hand! A certain gent sitting behind me can raise them both. But not in front here! And that's why we're talking strike—to get a living wage!

VOICE: Where's Lefty?

JOE: I honest to God don't know, but he didn't take no run-out powder. That Wop's got more guts than a slaughter house. Maybe a traffic jam got him, but he'll be here. But don't let this red stuff scare you. Unless fighting for a living scares you. We gotta make up our minds. My wife made up my mind last week, if you want the truth. It's plain as the nose on Sol Feinberg's face we need a strike. There's us comin' home every night—eight, ten hours on the cab. "God," the wife says, "eighty cents ain't money—don't buy beans almost. You're workin' for the company," she says to me, "Joe! you ain't workin' for me or the family no more!" She says to me, "If you don't start . . ."

I. JOE AND EDNA

The lights fade out and a white spot picks out the playing space within the space of seated men. The seated men are very dimly visible in the outer dark, but more prominent is FATT smoking his cigar and often blowing the smoke in the lighted circle.

A tired but attractive woman of thirty comes into the room, drying her hands on an apron. She stands there sullenly as JOE comes in from the other side, home from work. For a moment they stand and look at each other in silence.

JOE: Where's all the furniture, honey?

EDNA: They took it away. No installments paid.

JOE: When?

EDNA: Three o'clock.

JOE: They can't do that.

EDNA: Can't? They did it.

JOE: Why, the palookas, we paid three-quarters.

EDNA: The man said read the contract.

JOE: We must have signed a phoney. . . .

EDNA: It's regular contract and you signed it.

JOE: Don't be so sour, Edna. . . . *(Tries to embrace her.)*

EDNA: Do it in the Movies, Joe—they pay Clark Gable big money for it.

JOE: This is a helluva house to come home to. Take my word!

EDNA: Take MY word! Whose fault is it?

JOE: Must you start that stuff again?

EDNA: Maybe you'd like to talk about books?

JOE: I'd like to slap you in the mouth!

EDNA: No you won't.

JOE *(Sheepishly)*: Jeez, Edna, you get me sore some time. . . .

EDNA: But just look at me—I'm laughing all over!

JOE: Don't insult me. Can I help it if times are bad? What the hell do you want me to do, jump off a bridge or something?

EDNA: Don't yell. I just put the kids to bed so they won't know they missed a meal. If I don't have Emmy's shoes soled tomorrow, she can't go to school. In the meantime let her sleep.

JOE: Honey, I rode the wheels off the chariot today. I cruised around five hours without a call. It's conditions.

EDNA: Tell it to the A & P!

JOE: I booked two-twenty on the clock. A lady with a dog was lit . . . she gave me a quarter tip by mistake. If you'd only listen to me— we're rolling in wealth.

EDNA: Yeah? How much?

JOE: I had "coffee and—" in a beanery. *(Hands her silver coins.)* A buck four.

EDNA: The second month's rent is due tomorrow.

JOE: Don't look at me that way, Edna.

EDNA: I'm looking through you, not at you. . . . Everything was gonna be so ducky! A cottage by the waterfall, roses in Picardy. You're a four-star-bust! If you think I'm standing for it much longer, you're crazy as a bedbug.

JOE: I'd get another job if I could. There's no work—you know it.

EDNA: I only know we're at the bottom of the ocean.

JOE: What can I do?

EDNA: Who's the man in the family, you or me?

JOE: That's no answer. Get down to brass tacks. Christ, gimme a break, too! A coffee and java all day. I'm hungry, too, Babe. I'd work my fingers to the bone if—

EDNA: I'll open a can of salmon.

JOE: Not now. Tell me what to do!

EDNA: I'm not God!

JOE: Jeez, I wish I was a kid again and didn't have to think about the next minute.

EDNA: But you're not a kid and you do have to think about the next minute. You got two blondie kids sleeping in the next room. They need food and clothes. I'm not mentioning anything else—But we're stalled like a flivver in the snow. For five years I laid awake at night listening to my heart pound. For God's sake, do something, Joe, get wise. Maybe get your buddies together, maybe go on strike for better money. Poppa did it during the war and they won out. I'm turning into a sour old nag.

JOE *(defending himself):* Strikes don't work!

EDNA: Who told you?

JOE: Besides that means not a nickel a week while we're out. Then when it's over they don't take you back.

EDNA: Suppose they don't! What's to lose?

JOE: Well, we're averaging six-seven dollars a week now.

EDNA: That just pays for the rent.

JOE: That is something, Edna.

EDNA: It isn't. They'll push you down to three and four a week before you know it. Then you'll say, "That's somethin'," too!

JOE: There's too many cabs on the street, that's the whole damn trouble.

EDNA: Let the company worry about that, you big fool! If their cabs didn't make a profit, they'd take them off the streets. Or maybe you think they're in business just to pay Joe Mitchell's rent!

JOE: You don't know a-b-c, Edna.

EDNA: I know this—your boss is making suckers outa you boys every minute. Yes, and suckers out of all the wives and the poor innocent kids who'll grow up with crooked spines and sick bones. Sure, I see it in the papers, how good orange juice is for kids. But damnit our kids get colds one on top of the other. They look like little ghosts. Betty never saw a grapefruit. I took her to the store last week and she pointed to a stack of grapefruits. "What's that!" she said. My God, Joe—the world is supposed to be for all of us.

JOE: You'll wake them up.

EDNA: I don't care, as long as I can maybe wake you up.

JOE: Don't insult me. One man can't make a strike.

EDNA: Who says one? You got hundreds in your rotten union!

JOE: The union ain't rotten.

EDNA: No? Then what are they doing? Collecting dues and patting your back?

JOE: They're making plans.

EDNA: What kind?

JOE: They don't tell us.

EDNA: It's too damn bad about you. They don't tell little Joey what's happening in his bitsie witsie union. What do you think it is—a ping pong game?

JOE: You know they're racketeers. The guys at the top would shoot you for a nickel.

EDNA: Why do you stand for that stuff?

JOE: Don't you wanna see me alive?

EDNA (after a deep pause): No . . . I don't think I do, Joe. Not if you can lift a finger to do something about it, and don't. No, I don't care.

JOE: Honey, you don't understand what—

EDNA: And any other hackie that won't fight . . . let them all be ground to hamburger!

JOE: It's one thing to—

EDNA: Take your hand away! Only they don't grind me to little pieces! I got different plans. (Starts to take off her apron.)

JOE: Where are you going?

EDNA: None of your business.

JOE: What's up your sleeve?

EDNA: My arm'd be up my sleeve, darling, if I had a sleeve to wear. (Puts neatly folded apron on back of chair.)

JOE: Tell me!

EDNA: Tell you what?

JOE: Where are you going?

EDNA: Don't you remember my old boy friend?

JOE: Who?

EDNA: Bud Haas. He still has my picture in his watch. He earns a living.

JOE: What the hell are you talking about?

EDNA: I heard worse than I'm talking about.

JOE: Have you seen Bud since we got married?

EDNA: Maybe.

JOE: If I thought . . . (He stands looking at her.)

EDNA: See much? Listen, boy friend, if you think I won't do this it just means you can't see straight.

JOE: Stop talking bull!

EDNA: This isn't five years ago, Joe.

JOE: You mean you'd leave me and the kids?

EDNA: I'd leave *you* like a shot!

JOE: No. . . .

EDNA: Yes! (JOE *turns away, sitting in a chair with his back to her. Outside the lighted circle of the playing stage we hear the other seated members of the strike committee. "She will . . . she will . . . it happens that way," etc. This group should be used throughout for various comments, political, emotional and as general chorus. Whispering. . . . The fat boss now blows a heavy cloud of smoke into the scene.*)

JOE *(finally):* Well, I guess I ain't got a leg to stand on.

EDNA: No?

JOE *(suddenly mad):* No, you lousy tart, no! Get the hell out of here. Go pick up that bull-thrower on the corner and stop at some cushy hotel downtown. He's probably been coming here every morning and laying you while I hacked my guts out!

EDNA: You're crawling like a worm!

JOE: You'll be crawling in a minute.

EDNA: You don't scare me that much! *(Indicates a half inch on her finger.)*

JOE: This is what I slaved for!

EDNA: Tell it to your boss!

JOE: He don't give a damn for you or me!

EDNA: That's what I say.

JOE: Don't change the subject!

EDNA: This is the subject, the *exact subject!* Your boss makes this subject. I never saw him in my life, but he's putting ideas in my head a mile a minute. He's giving your kids that fancy disease called the rickets. He's making a jelly-fish outa you and putting wrinkles in my face. This is the subject every inch of the way! He's throwing me into Bud Haas' lap. When in hell will you get wise—

JOE: I'm not so dumb as you think! But you are talking like a red.

EDNA: I don't know what that means. But when a man knocks you down you get up and kiss his fist! You gutless piece of boloney.

JOE: One man can't—

EDNA *(with great joy):* I don't say one man! I say a hundred, a thousand, a whole million, I say. But start in your own union. Get those hack boys together! Sweep out those racketeers like a pile of dirt! Stand

up like men and fight for the crying kids and wives. Goddamnit!
I'm tired of slavery and sleepless nights.

JOE *(with her):* Sure, sure! . . .

EDNA: Yes, Get brass toes on your shoes and know where to kick!

JOE *(suddenly jumping up and kissing his wife full on the mouth):* Listen,
Edna, I'm goin' down to 147th Street to look up Lefty Costello.
Left was saying the other day . . . *(He suddenly stops.)* How about
this Haas guy?

EDNA: Get out of here!

JOE: I'll be back! *(Runs out. For a moment* EDNA *stands triumphant.
There is a blackout and when the regular lights come up,* JOE
MITCHELL *is concluding what he has been saying):*

JOE: You guys know this stuff better than me. We gotta walk out!
(Abruptly he turns and goes back to his seat.)

Blackout

II. LAB ASSISTANT EPISODE

Discovered: MILLER, *a lab assistant, looking around; and* FAYETTE, *an
industrialist.*

FAY: Like it?

MILLER: Very much. I've never seen an office like this outside the movies.

FAY: Yes, I often wonder if interior decorators and bathroom fixture
people don't get all their ideas from Hollywood. Our country's
extraordinary that way. Soap, cosmetics, electric refrigerators—
just let Mrs. Consumer know they're used by the Crawfords and
Garbos—more volume of sale than one plant can handle!

MILL: I'm afraid it isn't that easy, Mr. Fayette.

FAY: No, you're right—gross exaggeration on my part. Competition is
cutthroat today. Market's up flush against a stone wall. The astron-
omers had better hurry—open Mars to trade expansion.

MILL: Or it will be just too bad!

FAY: Cigar?

MILL: Thank you, don't smoke.

FAY: Drink?

MILL: Ditto, Mr. Fayette.

FAY: I like sobriety in my workers . . . the trained ones, I mean. The
pollacks and niggers, they're better drunk—keeps them out of
mischief. Wondering why I had you come over?

MILL: If you don't mind my saying—very much.

FAY *(patting him on the knee):* I like your work.

MILL: Thanks.

FAY: No reason why a talented young man like yourself shouldn't string along with us—a growing concern. Loyalty is well repaid in our organization. Did you see Siegfried this morning?

MILL: He hasn't been in the laboratory all day.

FAY: I told him yesterday to raise you twenty dollars a month. Starts this week.

MILL: You don't know how happy my wife'll be.

FAY: Oh, I can appreciate it. (He laughs.)

MILL: Was that all, Mr. Fayette?

FAY: Yes, except that we're switching you to laboratory A tomorrow. Siegfried knows about it. That's why I had you in. The new work is very important. Siegfried recommended you very highly as a man to trust. You'll work directly under Dr. Brenner. Make you happy?

MILL: Very. He's an important chemist!

FAY (leaning over seriously): We think so, Miller. We think so to the extent of asking you to stay within the building throughout the time you work with him.

MILL: You mean sleep and eat in?

FAY: Yes . . .

MILL: It can be arranged.

FAY: Fine. You'll go far, Miller.

MILL: May I ask the nature of the new work?

FAY (looking around first): Poison gas. . . .

MILL: Poison!

FAY: Orders from above. I don't have to tell you from where. New type poison gas for modern warfare.

MILL: I see.

FAY: You didn't know a new war was that close, did you?

MILL: I guess I didn't.

FAY: I don't have to stress the importance of absolute secrecy.

MILL: I understand.

FAY: The world is an armed camp today. One match sets the whole world blazing in forty-eight hours. Uncle Sam won't be caught napping!

MILL (addressing his pencil): They say 12 million men were killed in that last one and 20 million more wounded or missing.

FAY: That's not our worry. If big business went sentimental over human life there wouldn't be big business of any sort!

MILL: My brother and two cousins went in the last one.

FAY: They died in a good cause.

MILL: My mother says "no!"

FAY: She won't worry about you this time. You're too valuable behind the front.

MILL: That's right.

FAY: All right, Miller. See Siegfried for further orders.

MILL: You should have seen my brother—he could ride a bike without hands. . . .

FAY: You'd better move some clothes and shaving tools in tomorrow. Remember what I said—you're with a growing organization.

MILL: He could run the hundred yards in 9:8 flat. . . .

FAY: Who?

MILL: My brother. He's in the Meuse-Argonne Cemetery. Mama went there in 1926. . . .

FAY: Yes, those things stick. How's your handwriting, Miller, fairly legible?

MILL: Fairly so.

FAY: Once a week I'd like a little report from you.

MILL: What sort of report?

FAY: Just a few hundred words once a week on Dr. Brenner's progress.

MILL: Don't you think it might be better coming from the Doctor?

FAY: I didn't ask you that.

MILL: Sorry.

FAY: I want to know what progress he's making, the reports to be purely confidential—between you and me.

MILL: You mean I'm to watch him?

FAY: Yes!

MILL: I guess I can't do that. . . .

FAY: Thirty a month raise . . .

MILL: You said twenty. . . .

FAY: Thirty!

MILL: Guess I'm not built that way.

FAY: Forty. . . .

MILL: Spying's not in my line, Mr. Fayette!

FAY: You use ugly words, Mr. Miller!

MILL: For ugly activity? Yes!

FAY: Think about it, Miller. Your chances are excellent. . . .

MILL: No.

FAY: You're doing something for your country. Assuring the United States that when those goddamn Japs start a ruckus we'll have offensive weapons to back us up! Don't you read your newspapers, Miller?

MILL: Nothing but Andy Gump.

FAY: If you were on the inside you'd know I'm talking cold sober truth!

Now, I'm not asking you to make up your mind on the spot. Think about it over your lunch period.

MILL: No.

FAY: Made up your mind already?

MILL: Afraid so.

FAY: You understand the consequences?

MILL: I lose my raise—

Simultaneously: {MILL: And my job!
FAY: And your job!
MILL: You misunderstand—

MILL: Rather dig ditches first!

FAY: That's a big job for foreigners.

MILL: But sneaking—and making poison gas—that's for Americans?

FAY: It's up to you.

MILL: My mind's made up.

FAY: No hard feelings?

MILL: Sure hard feelings! I'm not the civilized type, Mr. Fayette. Nothing suave or sophisticated about me. Plenty of hard feelings! Enough to want to bust you and all your kind square in the mouth! *(Does exactly that.)*

Blackout

III. THE YOUNG HACK AND HIS GIRL

Opens with girl and brother. FLORENCE *waiting for* SID *to take her to a dance.*

FLOR: I gotta right to have something out of life. I don't smoke, I don't drink. So if Sid wants to take me to a dance, I'll go. Maybe if you was in love you wouldn't talk so hard.

IRV: I'm saying it for your good.

FLOR: Don't be so good to me.

IRV: Mom's sick in bed and you'll be worryin' her to the grave. She don't want that boy hanging around the house and she don't want you meeting him in Crotona Park.

FLOR: I'll meet him anytime I like!

IRV: If you do, yours truly'll take care of it in his own way. With just one hand, too!

FLOR: Why are you all so set against him?

IRV: Mom told you ten times—it ain't him. It's that he ain't got nothing. Sure, we know he's serious, that he's stuck on you. But that don't cut no ice.

FLOR: Taxi drivers used to make good money.

IRV: Today they're makin' five and six dollars a week. Maybe you wanta raise a family on that. Then you'll be back here living with us again and I'll be supporting two families in one. Well . . . over my dead body.

FLOR: Irv, I don't care—I love him!

IRV: You're a little kid with half-baked ideas!

FLOR: I stand there behind the counter the whole day. I think about him—

IRV: If you thought more about Mom it would be better.

FLOR: Don't I take care of her every night when I come home? Don't I cook supper and iron your shirts and . . . you give me a pain in the neck, too. Don't try to shut me up! I bring a few dollars in the house, too. Don't you see I want something else out of life. Sure, I want romance, love, babies. I want everything in life I can get.

IRV: You take care of Mom and watch your step!

FLOR: And if I don't?

IRV: Yours truly'll watch it for you!

FLOR: You can talk that way to a girl. . . .

IRV: I'll talk that way to your boy friend, too, and it won't be with words! Florrie, if you had a pair of eyes you'd see it's for your own good we're talking. This ain't no time to get married. Maybe later—

FLOR: "Maybe Later" never comes for me, though. Why don't we send Mom to a hospital? She can die in peace there instead of looking at the clock on the mantelpiece all day.

IRV: That needs money. Which we don't have!

FLOR: Money, Money, Money!

IRV: Don't change the subject.

FLOR: This is the subject!

IRV: You gonna stop seeing him? *(She turns away.)* Jesus, kiddie, I remember when you were a baby with curls down your back. Now I gotta stand here yellin' at you like this.

FLOR: I'll talk to him, Irv.

IRV: When?

FLOR: I asked him to come here tonight. We'll talk it over.

IRV: Don't get soft with him. Nowadays is no time to be soft. You gotta be hard as a rock or go under.

FLOR: I found that out. There's the bell. Take the egg off the stove I boiled for Mom. Leave us alone Irv. (SID *comes in—the two men look at each other for a second.* IRV *exits.*)

SID *(enters):* Hello, Florrie.

FLOR: Hello, Honey. You're looking tired.

SID: Naw, I just need a shave.

FLOR: Well, draw your chair up to the fire and I'll ring for brandy and soda . . . like in the movies.

SID: If this was the movies I'd bring a big bunch of roses.

FLOR: How big?

SID: Fifty or sixty dozen—the kind with long, long stems—big as that. . . .

FLOR: You dope. . . .

SID: Your Paris gown is beautiful.

FLOR (acting grandly): Yes, Percy, velvet panels are coming back again. Madame La Farge told me today that Queen Marie herself designed it.

SID: Gee . . . !

FLOR: Every princess in the Balkans is wearing one like this. (Poses grandly.)

SID: Hold it. (Does a nose camera—thumbing nose and imitating grinding of camera with other hand. Suddenly she falls out of the posture and swiftly goes to him, to embrace him, to kiss him with love. Finally):

SID: You look tired, Florrie.

FLOR: Naw, I just need a shave. (She laughs tremulously.)

SID: You worried about your mother?

FLOR: No.

SID: What's on your mind?

FLOR: The French and Indian War.

SID: What's on your mind?

FLOR: I got us on my mind, Sid. Night and day, Sid!

SID: I smacked a beer truck today. Did I get hell! I was driving along thinking of US, too. You don't have to say it—I know what's on your mind. I'm rat poison around here.

FLOR: Not to me. . . .

SID: I know to who . . . and I know why. I don't blame them. We're engaged now for three years. . . .

FLOR: That's a long time. . . .

SID: My brother Sam joined the navy this morning—get a break that way. They'll send him down to Cuba with the hootchy-kootchy girls. He don't know from nothing, that dumb basketball player!

FLOR: Don't you do that.

SID: Don't you worry, I'm not the kind who runs away. But I'm so tired of being a dog, Baby, I could choke. I don't even have to ask what's going on in your mind. I know from the word go, 'cause I'm thinking the same things, too.

FLOR: It's yes or no—nothing in between.

SID: The answer is no—a big electric sign looking down on Broadway!

FLOR: We wanted to have kids. . . .

SID: But that sort of life ain't for the dogs which is us. Christ, Baby! I get like thunder in my chest when we're together. If we went off together I could maybe look the world straight in the face, spit in its eye like a man should do. Goddamnit, it's trying to be a man on the earth. Two in life together.

FLOR: But something wants us to be lonely like that—crawling alone in the dark. Or they want us trapped.

SID: Sure, the big shot money men want us like that.

FLOR: Highly insulting us—

SID: Keeping us in the dark about what is wrong with us in the money sense. They got the power and mean to be damn sure they keep it. They know if they give in just an inch, all the dogs like us will be down on them together—an ocean knocking them to hell and back and each singing cuckoo with stars coming from their nose and ears. I'm not raving, Florrie—

FLOR: I know you're not, I know.

SID: I don't have the words to tell you what I feel. I never finished school. . . .

FLOR: I know. . . .

SID: But it's relative, like the professors say. We worked like hell to send him to college—my kid brother Sam, I mean—and look what he done—joined the navy! The damn fool don't see the cards is stacked for all of us. The money man dealing himself a hot royal flush. Then giving you and me a phony hand like a pair of tens or something. Then keep on losing the pots 'cause the cards is stacked against you. Then he says, what's the matter you can't win—no stuff on the ball, he says to you. And kids like my brother believe it 'cause they don't know better. For all their education, they don't know from nothing. But wait a minute! Don't he come around and say to you—this millionaire with a jazz band—listen Sam or Sid or what's-your-name, you're no good, but here's a chance. The whole world'll know who you are. Yes sir, he says, get up on that ship and fight those bastards who's making the world a lousy place to live in. The Japs, the Turks, the Greeks. Take this gun—kill the slobs like a real hero, he says, a real American. Be a hero! And the guy you're poking at? A real louse, just like you, 'cause they don't let him catch more than a pair of tens, too. On that foreign soil he's a guy like me and Sam, a guy who wants his baby like you and hot sun on his face! They'll teach Sam to point the guns the wrong way, that dumb basketball player!

FLOR: I got a lump in my throat, Honey.

SID: You and me—we never even had a room to sit in somewhere.

FLOR: The park was nice . . .

SID: In winter? The hallways . . . I'm glad we never got together. This way we don't know what we missed.

FLOR (*in a burst*): Sid, I'll go with you—we'll get a room somewhere.

SID: Naw . . . they're right. If we can't climb higher than this together —we better stay apart.

FLOR: I swear to God I wouldn't care.

SID: You would, you would—in a year, two years, you'd curse the day. I seen it happen.

FLOR: Oh, Sid. . . .

SID: Sure, I know. We got the blues, Babe—the 1935 blues. I'm talkin' this way 'cause I love you. If I didn't, I wouldn't care. . . .

FLOR: We'll work together, we'll—

SID: How about the backwash? Your family needs your nine bucks. My family—

FLOR: I don't care for them!

SID: You're making it up, Florrie. Little Florrie Canary in a cage.

FLOR: Don't make fun of me.

SID: I'm not, Baby.

FLOR: Yes, you're laughing at me.

SID: I'm not. (*They stand looking at each other, unable to speak. Finally, he turns to a small portable phonograph and plays a cheap, sad, dance tune. He makes a motion with his hand; she comes to him. They begin to dance slowly. They hold each other tightly, almost as though they would merge into each other. The music stops, but the scratching record continues to the end of the scene. They stop dancing. He finally looses her clutch and seats her on the couch, where she sits, tense and expectant.*)

SID: Hello, Babe.

FLOR: Hello. (*For a brief time they stand as though in a dream.*)

SID (*finally*): Good-bye, Babe. (*He waits for an answer, but she is silent. They look at each other.*)

SID: Did you ever see my Pat Rooney imitation? (*He whistles Rosy O'Grady and soft-shoes to it. Stops. He asks:*)

SID: Don't you like it?

FLOR (*finally*): No. (*Buries her face in her hands. Suddenly he falls on his knees and buries his face in her lap.*)

Blackout

IV. LABOR SPY EPISODE

FATT: You don't know how we work for you. Shooting off your mouth won't help. Hell, don't you guys ever look at the records like me? Look in your own industry. See what happened when the hacks walked out in Philly three months ago! Where's Philly? A thousand miles away? An hour's ride on the train.

VOICE: Two hours!!

FATT: Two hours . . . what the hell's the difference. Let's hear from someone who's got the practical experience to back him up. Fellers, there's a man here who's seen the whole parade in Philly, walked out with his pals, got knocked down like the rest—and blacklisted after they went back. That's why he's here. He's got a mighty interestin' word to say. *(Announces): Tom Clayton! (As* CLAYTON *starts up from the audience,* FATT *gives him a hand which is sparsely followed in the audience.* CLAYTON *comes forward.)*

Fellers, this is a man with practical strike experience—Tom Clayton from little ole Philly.

CLAYTON *a thin, modest individual:* Fellers, I don't mind your booing. If I thought it would help us hacks get better living conditions, I'd let you walk all over me, cut me up to little pieces. I'm one of you myself. But what I wanna say is that Harry Fatt's right. I only been working here in the big town five weeks, but I know conditions just like the rest of you. You know how it is—don't take long to feel the sore spots, no matter where you park.

CLEAR VOICE *(from audience):* Sit down!

CLAYTON: But Fatt's right. Our officers is right. The time ain't ripe. Like a fruit don't fall off the tree until it's ripe.

CLEAR VOICE: Sit down, you fruit!

FATT *(on his feet):* Take care of him, boys.

VOICE *(in audience, struggling):* No one takes care of me. *(Struggle in house and finally the owner of the voice runs up on stage, says to speaker):*

SAME VOICE: Where the hell did you pick up that name! Clayton! This rat's name is Clancy, from the old Clancys, way back! Fruit! I almost wet myself listening to that one!

FATT *(gunman with him):* This ain't a barn! What the hell do you think you're doing here!

SAME VOICE: Exposing a rat!

FATT: You can't get away with this. Throw him the hell outa here.

VOICE *(preparing to stand his grounds):* Try it yourself. . . . When this bozo throws that slop around. You know who he is? That's a company spy.

FATT: Who the hell are you to make—

VOICE: I paid dues in this union for four years, that's who's me! I gotta right and this pussy-footed rat ain't coming in here with ideas like that. You know his record. Lemme say it out—

FATT: You'll prove all this or I'll bust you in every hack outfit in town!

VOICE: I gotta right. I gotta right. Looka *him*, he don't say boo!

CLAYTON: You're a liar and I never seen you before in my life!

VOICE: Boys, he spent two years in the coal fields breaking up any organization he touched. Fifty guys he put in jail. He's ranged up and down the east coast—shipping, textiles, steel—he's been in everything you can name. Right now—

CLAYTON: That's a lie!

VOICE: Right now he's working for that Bergman outfit on Columbus Circle who furnishes rats for any outfit in the country, before, during, and after strikes. *(The man who is the hero of the next episode goes down to his side with other committee men.)*

CLAYTON: He's trying to break up the meeting, fellers!

VOICE: We won't search you for credentials. . . .

CLAYTON: I got nothing to hide. Your own secretary knows I'm straight.

VOICE: Sure. Boys, you know who this sonovabitch is?

CLAYTON: I never seen you before in my life!!

VOICE: Boys, I slept with him in the same bed sixteen years. HE'S MY OWN LOUSY BROTHER!!

FATT *(after pause):* Is this true? *(No answer from* CLAYTON.*)*

VOICE *(to* CLAYTON*):* Scram, before I break your neck! *(*CLAYTON *scrams down center aisle.* VOICE *says, watching him:* Remember his map— he can't change that—Clancy! *(Standing in his place says):* Too bad you didn't know about this, Fatt! *(After a pause.)* The Clancy family tree is bearing nuts! *(Standing isolated clear on the stage is the hero of the next episode.)*

Blackout

V. INTERNE EPISODE

Dr. Barnes, an elderly distinguished man, is speaking on the telephone. He wears a white coat.

DR. BARNES: No, I gave you my opinion twice. You outvoted me. You did this to Dr. Benjamin yourself. That is why you can tell him yourself. *(Hangs up phone, angrily. As he is about to pour himself a drink from a bottle on the table, a knock is heard.)*

BARNES: Who is it?

BENJAMIN *(without):* Can I see you a minute, please?

BARNES *(hiding the bottle):* Come in, Dr. Benjamin, come in.

BENJ: It's important—excuse me—they've got Leeds up there in my place—He's operating on Mrs. Lewis—the historectomy—it's my job. I washed up, prepared . . . they told me at the last minute. I don't mind being replaced, Doctor, but Leeds is a damn fool! He shouldn't be permitted—

BARNES *(dryily):* Leeds is the nephew of Senator Leeds.

BENJ: He's incompetent as hell.

BARNES *(obviously changing subject, picks up lab. jar):* They're doing splendid work in brain surgery these days. This is a very fine specimen. . . .

BENJ: I'm sorry, I thought you might be interested.

BARNES *(still examining jar):* Well, I am, young man, I am! Only remember it's a charity case!

BENJ: Of course. They wouldn't allow it for a second, otherwise.

BARNES: Her life is in danger?

BENJ: Of course! You know how serious the case is!

BARNES: Turn your gimlet eyes elsewhere, Doctor. Jigging around like a cricket on a hot grill won't help. Doctors don't run these hospitals. He's the Senator's nephew and there he stays.

BENJ: It's too bad.

BARNES: I'm not calling you down either. *(Plopping down jar suddenly.)* Goddamnit, do you think it's my fault?

BENJ *(about to leave):* I know . . . I'm sorry.

BARNES: Just a minute. Sit down.

BENJ: Sorry, I can't sit.

BARNES: Stand then!

BENJ *(sits):* Understand, Dr. Barnes, I don't mind being replaced at the last minute this way, but . . . well, this flagrant bit of class distinction—because she's poor—

BARNES: Be careful of words like that—"class distinction." Don't belong here. Lots of energy, you brilliant young men, but idiots. Discretion! Ever hear that word?

BENJ: Too radical?

BARNES: Precisely. And some day like in Germany, it might cost you your head.

BENJ: Not to mention my job.

BARNES: So they told you?

BENJ: Told me what?

BARNES: They're closing Ward C next month. I don't have to tell you the hospital isn't self-supporting. Until last year that board of trustees met deficits. . . . You can guess the rest. At a board meeting Tuesday, our fine feathered friends discovered they couldn't meet the last quarter's deficit—a neat little sum well over $100,000. If the hospital is to continue at all, its damn—

BENJ: Necessary to close another charity ward!

BARNES: So they say. . . . (*A wait.*)

BENJ: But that's not all?

BARNES (*ashamed*): Have to cut down on staff too. . . .

BENJ: That's too bad. Does it touch me?

BARNES: Afraid it does.

BENJ: But after all I'm top man here. I don't mean I'm better than others, but I've worked harder.

BARNES: And shown more promise. . . .

BENJ: I always supposed they'd cut from the bottom first.

BARNES: Usually.

BENJ: But in this case?

BARNES: Complications.

BENJ: For instance? (BARNES *hesitant.*)

BARNES: I like you, Benjamin. It's one ripping shame.

BENJ: I'm no sensitive plant—what's the answer?

BARNES: An old disease, malignant, tumescent. We need an antitoxin for it.

BENJ: I see.

BARNES: What?

BENJ: I met that disease before—at Harvard first.

BARNES: You have seniority here, Benjamin.

BENJ: But I'm a Jew! (BARNES *nods his head in agreement.* BENJ *stands there a moment and blows his nose.*)

BARNES (*blows his nose*): Microbes!

BENJ: Pressure from above?

BARNES: Don't think Kennedy and I didn't fight for you!

BENJ: Such discrimination, with all those wealthy brother Jews on the board?

BARNES: I've remarked before—doesn't seem to be much difference between wealthy Jews and rich Gentiles. Cut from the same piece!

BENJ: For myself I don't feel sorry. My parents gave up an awful lot to get me this far. They ran a little dry goods shop in the Bronx until their pitiful savings went in the crash last year. Poppa's peddling neckties. . . . Saul Ezra Benjamin—a man who's read Spinoza all his life.

BARNES: Doctors don't run medicine in this country. The men who know their jobs don't run anything here, except the motormen on trolley cars. I've seen medicine change—plenty—anesthesia, sterilization—but not because of rich men—in *spite* of them! In a rich man's country your true self's buried deep. Microbes! Less. . . . Vermin! See this ankle, this delicate sensitive hand? Four hundred years to breed that. Out of a revolutionary background! Spirit of '76! Ancestors froze at Valley Forge! What's it all mean! Slops! The honest workers were sold out then, in '76. The Constitution's for rich men then and now. Slops! *(The phone rings.)*

BARNES *(angrily):* Dr. Barnes. *(Listens a moment, looks at* BENJAMIN.*)* I see. *(Hangs up, turns slowly to the younger Doctor.)* They lost your patient. *(*BENJ *stands solid with the shock of this news but finally hurls his operation gloves to the floor.)*

BARNES: That's right . . . that's right. Young, hot, go and do it! I'm very ancient, fossil, but life's ahead of you, Dr. Benjamin, and when you fire the first shot say, "This one's for old Doc Barnes!" Too much dignity—bullets. Don't shoot vermin! Step on them! If I didn't have an invalid daughter—

*(*BARNES *goes back to his seat, blows his nose in silence):* I have said my piece, Benjamin.

BENJ: Lots of things I wasn't certain of. Many things these radicals say . . . you don't believe theories until they happen to you.

BARNES: You lost a lot today, but you won a great point.

BENJ: Yes, to know I'm right? To really begin believing in something? Not to say, "What a world!", but to say, "Change the world!" I wanted to go to Russia. Last week I was thinking about it—the wonderful opportunity to do good work in their socialized medicine—

BARNES: Beautiful, beautiful!

BENJ: To be able to work—

BARNES: Why don't you go? I might be able—

BENJ: Nothing's nearer what I'd like to do!

BARNES: Do it!

BENJ: No! Our work's here—America! I'm scared. . . . What future's ahead, I don't know. Get some job to keep alive—maybe drive a cab—and study and work and learn my place—

BARNES: And step down hard!

BENJ: Fight! Maybe get killed, but goddamn! We'll go ahead! *(*BENJAMIN *stands with clenched fist raised high.)*

Blackout

AGATE: *Ladies and Gentlemen,* and don't let anyone tell you we ain't got some ladies in this sea of upturned faces! Only they're wearin' pants. Well, maybe I don't know a thing; maybe I fell outa the cradle when I was a kid and ain't been right since—you can't tell!

VOICE: Sit down, cockeye!

AGATE: Who's paying you for those remarks, Buddy?—Moscow Gold? Maybe I got a *glass eye,* but it come from working in a factory at the age of eleven. They hooked it out because they didn't have a shield on the works. But I wear it like a medal 'cause it tells the world where I belong—deep down in the working class! We had delegates in the union there—all kinds of secretaries and treasurers . . . walkin' delegates, but not with blisters on their feet! Oh no! On their fat little ass from sitting on cushions and raking in mazuma. (SECRETARY *and* GUNMAN *remonstrate in words and actions here.*) Sit down, boys. I'm just sayin' that about unions in general. I know it ain't true here! Why no, our officers is all aces. Why, I seen our own secretary Fatt walk outa his way not to step on a cockroach. No boys, don't think—

FATT *(breaking in):* You're out of order!

AGATE *(to audience):* Am I outa order?

ALL: No, no. Speak. Go on, etc.

AGATE: Yes, our officers is all aces. But I'm a member here—and no experience in Philly either! Today I couldn't wear my union button. The damnest thing happened. When I take the old coat off the wall, I see she's smoking. I'm a sonovagun if the old union button isn't on fire! Yep, the old celluloid was makin' the most god-awful stink: the landlady come up and give me hell! You know what happened? That old union button just blushed itself to death! Ashamed! Can you beat it?

FATT: Sit down, Keller! Nobody's interested!

AGATE: Yes they are!

GUNMAN: Sit down like he tells you!

AGATE *(continuing to audience):* And when I finish— *(His speech is broken by* FATT *and* GUNMAN *who physically handle him. He breaks away and gets to other side of stage. The two are about to make for him when some of the committee men come forward and get in between the struggling parties.* AGATE'S *shirt has been torn.)*

AGATE *(to audience):* What's the answer boys? The answer is, if we're reds because we wanna strike, then we take over their salute too! Know how they do it? *(Makes Communist salute.)* What is it? An uppercut! The good old uppercut to the chin! Hell, some of us boys ain't even got a shirt to our backs. What's the boss class tryin' to do

—make a nudist colony outa us? (*The audience laughs and suddenly* AGATE *comes to the middle of the stage so that the other cabmen back him up in a strong clump.*)

AGATE: Don't laugh! Nothing's funny! This is your life and mine! It's skull and bones every incha the road! Christ, we're dyin' by inches! For what? For the debutant-ees to have their sweet comin' out parties in the Ritz! Poppa's got a daughter she's gotta get her picture in the papers. Christ, they make 'em with our blood, Joe said it. Slow death or fight. It's war! (*Throughout this whole speech* AGATE *is backed up by the other six workers, so that from their activity it is plain that the whole group of them are saying these things. Several of them may take alternate lines out of this long last speech.*)

You Edna, God love your mouth! Sid and Florrie, the other boys, old Doc Barnes—fight with us for right! It's war! Working class, unite and fight! Tear down the slaughter house of our old lives! Let freedom really ring.

These slick slobs stand there telling us about bogeymen. That's a new one for the kids—the reds is bogeymen! But the man who got me food in 1932, he called me Comrade! The one who picked me up where I bled—he called me Comrade too! What are we waiting for. . . . Don't wait for Lefty! He might never come. Every minute — (*This is broken into by a man who has dashed up the center aisle from the back of the house. He runs up on stage, says*):

MAN: Boys, they just found Lefty!

OTHERS: What? What? What?

SOME: Shhh. . . . Shhh. . . .

MAN: They found Lefty. . . .

AGATE: Where?

MAN: Behind the car barns with a bullet in his head!

AGATE (*crying*): Hear it, boys, hear it? Hell, listen to me! Coast to coast! HELLO AMERICA! HELLO. WE'RE STORM-BIRDS OF THE WORKING-CLASS. WORKERS OF THE WORLD. . . . OUR BONES AND BLOOD! And when we die they'll know what we did to make a new world! Christ, cut us up to little pieces. We'll die for what is right! put fruit trees where our ashes are!

(*To audience*): Well, what's the answer?

ALL: STRIKE!

AGATE: LOUDER!

ALL: STRIKE!

AGATE and OTHERS on Stage: AGAIN!

ALL: STRIKE, STRIKE, STRIKE!! *Curtain*

"Rider of the Apocalypse" by George Grosz.

Let Us Have Madness

Let us have madness openly, O men
Of my generation. Let us follow
The footsteps of this slaughtered age . . .
KENNETH PATCHEN

WITH America's entry into the second World War, the Great Depression came to an end. Yet if it had not been for the depression, there might never have been a war. Prosperity had come to most of America in the twenties, but not to Europe. With the depression, all hopes of attaining economic security were crushed, and in desperation many Europeans turned their back on democratic principles. Some turned to Communism; many more sought solace in the Fascism of Mussolini and Hitler. The Nazi party offered the Jew and the Versailles Treaty as scapegoats for Germany's economic crisis; the bourgeoisie and the unemployed could not resist. On February 27, 1933, the Reichstag building in Berlin went up in flames. Hitler proclaimed the burning as "a sign from heaven," and had one hundred Communist deputies arrested on a trumped-up charge. As a result, the March 5 election for the chancellorship was meaningless. The Nazi party took control of the country, and not long afterward the German Republic was crushed. In its place rose the Third Reich, with Adolph Hitler as supreme dictator. The world, as Goebbels correctly noted, was about to witness *Die Zeit Ohne Beispiel*—an age without parallel —but it was to be an age of unparalleled madness.

In America Hitler and Mussolini had only a handful of adherents, but demagoguery and fascism exerted a strong influence in this country all the same. As the economic and political systems began to change under the New Deal, and as America became the haven for Jewish exiles, anti-Semitism and fascism began to spread, and the followers of Father Charles Coughlin, Dr. Francis Townsend, and Huey Long increased in number. For the most part, the followers of these demagogues came from the lower-middle classes, were self-employed, and had evangelic backgrounds. But fascism also proved to be appealing to a few educated men who wanted to revive what they felt was the true spirit of America. Seward Collins, a Princeton graduate, announced that "We are offered our choice of Communist collectivism or personal liberty under fascism"; to Collins, as to Ezra Pound, Mussolini was one of the most constructive statesmen of the age. Lawrence Dennis, who had gone to Exeter and Harvard, expressed his admiration for Huey Long, whom he considered "the nearest approach to a national fascist leader" the country had seen. "It takes a man like Long to lead the masses," Dennis wrote in 1935. "I think Long's smarter than Hitler." And in October of the same year, William Randolph Hearst offered the following observation: "Whenever you hear a prominent American called a "Fascist," you can usually make up your mind that the man is simply a LOYAL CITIZEN WHO STANDS FOR AMERICANISM." Such sentiments, together with the establishment of

Fritz Kuhn's German-American Bund and William Dudley Pelley's Silver Shirts, make it all to clear that the bases of such literary warnings as Sinclair Lewis' *It Can't Happen Here* and Edward Dahlberg's *Those Who Perish* were terrifyingly accurate.

Fascism has always been most appealing to the Babbits; it has had little to offer the intellectual. Thus, in the thirties, the idealist in search of a better world turned not to fascism, but to socialism and communism. Although only a few men of letters actually joined the Communist Party, many were sympathetic with its aims. In 1932, for example, more than fifty artists and intellectuals—including Sherwood Anderson, Malcolm Cowley, John Dos Passos, Waldo Frank, Sidney Hook, Lincoln Steffens, and Edmund Wilson—endorsed a pamphlet entitled *Culture and Crisis,* in which they declared their support for William Z. Foster and James W. Ford, the Presidential candidates of the Communist Party. Disenchantment, though, gradually set in. Most of the Americans who expressed sympathy with the Communist cause were disillusioned idealists who, as a result of the depression, believed that the planned economy and classless society of the Soviet Union was perhaps the only way to achieve economic order. But the Moscow Trials of 1936, 1937, and 1938, and the signing of the Stalin-Hitler pact in 1939, convinced almost all the friends of the Party that the cause of the Soviet Union was not just. Lines were being drawn, as John Dewey said in "Truth Is On The March," between devotion to justice and adherence to a faction, "between fair play and a love of darkness that is reactionary in effect no matter what banner it flaunts." Stalin had betrayed a noble dream; it was no longer possible to ignore his contempt for freedom and dignity. "How," James T. Farrell wrote to Lionel Trilling, "can liberty and intellectual integrity be preserved against the abuse of power?"

Many of the men and women who hitched their wagon to the star of the Soviet Union were to be hounded for their dreams; others were to seek forgiveness in the confines of the *Reader's Digest,* the Book-of-the-Month Club, and the Radical Right. But in the thirties, while most of America watched with indifferent eyes, these intellectuals joined with the Soviet Union in forming a bulwark against Fascism. In April of 1933 the *New Masses* published Joseph Freeman's manifesto against the Nazis, as well as statements by Newton Arvin, Heywood Broun, and Scott Nearing, among many others, who agreed that the American intellectual had to set up "an anti-Fascist front of intellectual workers in America."

The concern with the menacing power of Fascism reached its culmination in 1936 with the outbreak of the Spanish Civil War. Theodore

Dreiser may have been unable to find an American capitalist who would support the Loyalist relief program, but writers and intellectuals throughout the world rallied to the side of the anti-Fascists. Arthur Koestler, Andre Malraux, Christopher Caudwell, Stephen Spender, Ernest Hemmingway: all went to lend their support. In America, the League of American Writers charged the American press with presenting "an utterly false and misleading picture of the military revolt in Spain." The struggle was not a civil war between Fascism and Communism, but "an attempt by reactionaries of all sorts—fascists, militarists, royalists, and ultra-royalists—to overthrow a democratic government elected and supported by the broad masses of people." The war not only embodied the class struggle; it was also a testing ground for the battle against fascism in general. "Better a life for loving life proudly," Robert McAlmon wrote in "Spanish Resolve," than living submission to causes/not of man's dignity."

Before the way was over, much of the initial fervor turned to confusion and disillusionment; too often the essential issues were lost in the maze of Communist propaganda. But initially the cause had been just, and the intelligentsia had responded. Soon, all of America would be shocked into awareness. In 1935, Hitler reintroduced compulsory military service; three years later his army was on the move. First it was Austria; then Czechoslovakia and Poland. On June 24, 1941 the pact with Stalin was broken and the Nazis invaded Russia. Pearl Harbor was only a few months away. Madness had come openly; we were about to find, in Kenneth Patchen's words, "extended hell and fog/ Upon the earth, and within the head/ A rotting bog of lean huge graves."

Cartoon in The Nation *by John Mackey.*

Denouement

BY KENNETH FEARING

I

Sky, be blue, and more than blue; wind, be flesh and blood; flesh and
blood, be deathless;
  walls, streets, be home;
  desire of millions, become more real than warmth and breath and
    strength and bread;
  clock, point to the decisive hour and, hour without name when
    stacked and waiting murder fades, dissolves, stay for-
    ever as the world grows new;

Truth, be known, be kept forever, let the letters, letters, souvenirs,
    documents, snapshots, bills be found at last, be torn
    away from a world of lies, be kept as final evidence,
    transformed forever into more than truth;
  change, change, rows and rows and rows of figures, spindles,
    furrows, desks, change into paid-up rent and let the
    paid-up rent become South Sea music;
  magic film, unwind, unroll, unfold in silver on that million mile
    screen, take us all, bear us again to the perfect denou-
    ment,

The literary left in the 1930's produced three outstanding poets: Muriel Rukeyser, Horace Gregory, and Kenneth Fearing. (Examples of Rukeyser's and
Gregory's work are to be found in the next to last section of the book, *A World
to Win*.) Fearing is one of America's foremost satirical poets. Although his
style—the use of slang and staccato rhythms—shows his indebtedness to Carl
Sandburg, Fearing is more biting and hardboiled than Sandburg. At his best, as
Horace Gregory said, Fearing wrote "a kind of satire in light verse that has
seldom if ever been equaled in America." Fearing's first volume of poems, *Angel
Arms,* was published in 1929; it was followed during the thirties by *Poems*
(1935), and *Dead Reckoning* (1938). Fearing also wrote six novels, the first of
which, *The Hospital,* was published in 1939.

Where everything lost, needed, each forgotten thing, all that never
happens,
gathers at last into a dynamite triumph, a rainbow peace, a thun-
derbolt kiss,
for you, the invincible, and I, grown older, and he, the shipping
clerk, and she, an underweight blond journeying home
in the last express.

II

But here is the body found lying face down in a burlap sack, strangled
in the noose jerked shut by these trussed and twisted
and frantic arms;
but here are the agents come to seize the bed;
but here is the vase holding saved-up cigarstore coupons, and here
is a way to save on cigars and to go without meat;
but here is the voice that strikes around the world, "My friends
. . . my friends," issues from the radio and thunders
"My friends" in newsreel close-ups, explodes across
headlines, "Both rich and poor, my friends, must sacrifice," re-echoes, murmuring, through hospitals, death-
cells, "My friends . . . my friends . . . my friends
. . . my friends . . . my friends . . ."

And who, my friend, are you?
Are you the one who leaped to the blinds of the cannonball
express? Or are you the one who started life again with
three dependents and a pack of cigarettes?

But how can these things be made finally clear in a post-mortem room
with the lips taped shut and the blue eyes cold, wide,
still, blind, fixed beyond the steady glare of electric
lights, through the white-washed ceiling and the cross-
mounted roof, past the drifting clouds?

Objection, over-ruled, exception, proceed:

Was yours the voice heard singing one night in a flyblown, sootbeamed,
lost and forgotten Santa Fe saloon? Later bellowing in
rage? And you boiled up a shirt in a Newark furnished
room? Then you found another job, and pledged not to
organize or go on strike?

We offer this union book in evidence. We offer these rent receipts in
    evidence. We offer in evidence this vacation card marked,
    "This is the life. Regards to all."

You, lodge member, protestant, crossborn male, the placenta discolored,
    at birth, by syphilis, you, embryo four inches deep in the
    seventh month,
  among so many, many sparks struck and darkened at conception,
  which were you,
  you, six feet tall on the day of death?

Then you were at no time the senator's son? Then you were never the
    beef king's daughter, married in a storm of perfume and
    music and laughter and rice?
  And you are not now the clubman who waves and nods and
    vanishes to Rio in a special plane?
  But these are your lungs, scarred and consumed? These are your
    bones, still marked by rickets? These are your pliers?
    These are your fingers, O master mechanic, and these
    are your cold, wide, still, blind eyes?

The witness is lying, lying, an enemy, my friends, of Union Gas and the
    home:

But how will you know us, wheeled from the icebox and stretched upon
    the table with the belly slit wide and the entrails removed,
    voiceless as the clippers bite through ligaments and
    flesh and nerves and bones,
  but how will you know us, attentive, strained, before the director's
    desk, or crowded in line in front of factory gates,
  but how will you know us through ringed machinegun sights as
    we run and fall in gasmask, steel helmet, flame-tunic,
    uniform, bayonet, pack,
  but how will you know us, crumbled into ashes, lost in air and
    water and fire and stone,
  how will you know us, now or any time, who will ever know that
    we have lived or died?

And this is the truth? So help you God, this is the truth? The truth in
    full, so help you God? So help you God?
  But the pride that was made of iron and could not be broken,
    what has become of it, what has become of the faith

that nothing could destroy, what has become of the
    deathless hope,
you, whose ways were yours alone, you, the one like no one else,
    what have you done with the hour you swore to remem-
    ber, where is the hour, the day, the achievement that
    would never die?

Morphine. Veronal. Veronal. Morphine. Morphine. Morphine.
    Morphine.

III

Leaflets, scraps, dust, match-stubs strew the linoleum that leads up-
    stairs to the union hall; the walls of the basement work-
    ers' club are dim and cracked and above the speaker's
    stand Vanzetti's face shows green, behind closed doors the
    committeeroom is a fog of smoke,

Who are these people?

All day the committee fought like cats and dogs and twelve of Mr.
    Kelly's strongarm men patrolled the aisles that night,
    them blackjack guys get ten to twenty bucks a throw,
    the funds were looted, sent to Chicago, at the meeting
    the section comrade talked like a fool, more scabs came
    through in trucks guarded by police,
workers of the world, workers of the world, workers of the world,

Who are these people and what do they want, can't they be decent,
    can't they at least be calm and polite,
besides the time is not yet ripe, it might take years, like Mr.
    Kelly said, years,

Decades black with famine and red with war, centuries on fire, ripped
    wide,

Who are these people and what do they want, why do they walk back
    and forth with signs that say "Bread Not Bullets," what
    do they mean "They Shall Not Die" as they sink in
    clouds of poison gas and fall beneath clubs, hooves,
    rifles, fall and do not arise, arise, unite,
never again these faces, arms, eyes, lips,

Not unless we live, and live again,
    return, everywhere alive in the issue that returns, clear as light
        that still descends from a star long cold, again alive and
        everywhere visible through and through the scene that
        comes again, as light on moving water breaks and
        returns, heard only in the words, as millions of voices
        become one voice, seen only in millions of hands that
        move as one,

Look at them gathered, raised, look at their faces, clothes, who are these
        people, who are these people,
    what hand scrawled large in the empty prison cell "I have just
        received my sentence of death. Red Front," whose
        voice screamed out in the silence "Arise"?

And all along the waterfront, there, where rats gnaw into the leading
        platforms, here, where the wind whips at warehouse
        corners, look, there, here,
    everywhere huge across the walls and gates "Your party lives,"
    where there is no life, no breath, no sound, no touch, no warmth,
        no light but the lamp that shines on a trooper's drawn
        and ready bayonet.

"Progress of Humanity" by Daniel Fitzpatrick.

St. Louis Post-Dispatch

The Unknown Soldier

BY WILLIAM MARCH

WE were returning from a wiring party that quiet night and the men were in high spirits. Then two Maxims opened a deadly, enfilading fire, and one of my companions threw his hands up and fell without a sound. I stood there confused at the sudden attack, not knowing which way to turn. Then I heard some one shout: "Look out! Look out for the wire!" and I saw my companions, flat on their frightened bellies, scattering in all directions. I started to run, but at that moment something shoved me, and something took my breath away, and I toppled backward, and the wire caught me.

At first I did not realize that I was wounded. I lay there on the wire, breathing heavily. "I must keep perfectly calm," I thought. "If I move about, I'll entangle myself so badly that I'll never get out." Then a white flare went up and in the light that followed I saw my belly was ripped open and that my entrails hung down like a badly arranged bouquet of blue roses. The sight frightened me and I began to struggle, but the more I twisted about, the deeper the barbs sank in. Finally I could not move my legs any more and I knew, then, that I was going to die. So I lay stretched quietly, moaning and spitting blood.

I could not forget the faces of the men and the way they had scurried off when the machine guns opened up. I remembered a time when I was a little boy and had gone to visit my grandfather, who lived on a farm. Rabbits were eating his cabbages that year, so grandfather had

---

Caught in a world which had not yet recovered from its first world war, but which was already moving toward its second one, the Communist and non-Communist writer alike found in the horrors of war a subject about which they were equally impassioned. Kay Boyle's short stories, Irwin Shaw's play, *Bury the Dead,* and the three major anti-war novels of the decade—Humphrey Cobb's *Paths of Glory,* Dalton Trumbo's *Johnny Got His Gun,* and William March's *Company K*—all concentrated on the brutality and madness of war. Probably nothing written during the thirties was a more impressive anti-war statement than the chapter here reprinted from *Company K.*

closed all the entrances to his field except one, and he baited that one
with lettuce leaves and young carrots. When the field was full of rabbits,
the fun began. Grandfather opened the gate and let in the dog, and the
hired man stood at the gap, a broomstick in his hand, breaking the
necks of the rabbits as they leaped out. I had stood to one side, I
remembered, pitying the rabbits and thinking how stupid they were to
let themselves be caught in such an obvious trap.—And now as I lay
on the wire, the scene came back to me vividly. . . . *I* had pitied the
rabbits!—I, of all people . . .

I lay back, my eyes closed, thinking of that. Then I heard the mayor
of our town making his annual address in the Soldiers' Cemetery at
home. Fragments of his speech kept floating through my mind: "These
men died gloriously on the Field of Honor! . . . Gave their lives gladly
in a Noble Cause! . . . What a feeling of exaltation was theirs when
Death kissed their mouths and closed their eyes for an Immortal
Eternity! . . ." Suddenly I saw myself, too, a boy in the crowd, my
throat tight to keep back the tears, listening enraptured to the speech
and believing every word of it; and at that instant I understood clearly
why I now lay dying on the wire. . . .

The first shock had passed and my wounds began to pain me. I had
seen other men die on the wire and I had said if it happened to me, I
would make no sound, but after a while I couldn't stand the pain
any longer and I began to make a shrill, wavering noise. I cried like
that for a long time. I couldn't help it. . . .

Towards daybreak a German sentry crawled out from his post and
came to where I lay. "Hush!" he said in a soft voice. "Hush, please!"

He sat on his haunches and stared at me, a compassionate look in
his eyes. Then I began to talk to him: "It's all a lie that people tell
each other, and nobody really believes," I said. . . . "And I'm a part
of it, whether I want to be or not.—I'm more a part of it now than ever
before: In a few years, when war is over, they'll move my body back
home to the Soldiers' Cemetery, just as they moved the bodies of the
soldiers killed before I was born. There will be a brass band and speech
making and a beautiful marble shaft with my name chiseled on its
base. . . . The mayor will be there also, pointing to my name with
his thick, trembling forefinger and shouting meaningless words about
glorious deaths and fields of honor. . . . And there will be other little
boys in that crowd to listen and believe him, just as I listened and
believed!"

"Hush," said the German softly. "Hush! . . . Hush!"

I began to twist about on the wire and to cry again. "I can't stand the
thought of that! I can't stand it! . . . I never want to hear military

music or high sounding words again: I want to be buried where nobody will ever find me.—I want to be wiped out completely . . ."

Then, suddenly, I became silent, for I had seen a way out. I took off my identification tags and threw them into the wire, as far as I could. I tore to pieces the letters and the photographs I carried and scattered the fragments. I threw my helmet away, so that no one could guess my identity from the serial number stamped on the sweatband. Then I lay back exultant!

The German had risen and stood looking at me, as if puzzled. . . . "I've beaten the orators and the wreath layers at their own game!" I said. . . . "I've beaten them all!—Nobody will ever use me as a symbol. Nobody will ever tell lies over my dead body now! . . ."

"Hush," said the German softly. "Hush! . . . Hush!"

Then my pain became so unbearable that I began to choke and bite at the wire with my teeth. The German came closer to me, touching my head with his hand. . . .

"Hush," he said. . . . "Hush, please. . . ."

But I could not stop. I thrashed about on the wire and cried in a shrill voice. The German took out his pistol and stood twisting it in his hand, not looking at me. Then he put his arm under my head, lifting me up, and kissed me softly on my cheek, repeating phrases which I could not understand. I saw, then, that he too, had been crying for a long time. . . .

"Do it quickly!" I said. "Quickly! . . . Quickly!"

He stood with trembling hands for a moment before he placed the barrel of his pistol against my temple, turned his head away, and fired. My eyes fluttered twice and then closed; my hands clutched and relaxed slowly.

"I have broken the chain," I whispered. "I have defeated the inherent stupidity of life."

"Hush," he said. "Hush! . . . Hush! . . . Hush! . . ."

"Spain" by William Gropper.

Dispatch from Spain

BY ERNEST HEMINGWAY

From *The New York Times,* April 25, 1937

MADRID, APRIL 24—The window of the hotel is open and, as you lie in bed, you hear the firing in the front line seventeen blocks away. There is a rifle fire all night long. The rifles go "tacrong, carong, craang, tacrong," and then a machine gun opens up. It has a bigger caliber and is much louder—"rong, cararibong, rong, rong."

Then there is the incoming boom of a trench-mortar shell and a burst of machine-gun fire. You lie and listen to it, and it is a great thing to be in a bed with your feet stretched out gradually warming the cold foot of the bed and not out there in University City or Carabanchel. A man is singing hard-voiced in the street below and three drunks are arguing when you fall asleep.

In the morning, before your call comes from the desk, the roaring burst of a high-explosive shell wakes you. You go to the window and look out to see a man, his head down, his coat collar up, sprinting desperately across the paved square. There is the acrid smell of high explosive you hoped you'd never smell again.

In a bathrobe and bathroom slippers, you hurry down to the marble stairs and almost into a middle-aged woman, wounded in the abdomen, who is being helped into the hotel entrance by two men in blue workmen's smocks.

"Politically," Ernest Hemingway wrote to his biographer Carlos Baker, "I was always on the side of the Spanish Republic from the day it was declared and for a long time before." (By the end of 1936, Hemingway had raised $40,000 to help equip the Loyalists with ambulances and medical supplies; in January 1937, he became chairman of the Ambulance Committee, Medical Bureau, American Friends of Spanish Democracy.) Artistically, Hemingway was also on the side of the Republic: "There is only one form of government that cannot produce good writers," he told the second American Writers' Congress, "and that system is fascism. For fascism is a lie told by bullies." Hemingway reported the war for the North American Newspaper Alliance, and a year after the Loyalist defeat he published *For Whom the Bell Tolls.* This account first appeared in the *New York Times* on April 25, 1937.

On the corner, twenty yards away, is a heap of rubble, smashed cement, and thrown-up dirt, a single dead man, his torn clothes dusty, and a great hole in the sidewalk from which the gas from a broken main is rising, looking like a heat mirage in the cold morning air.

"How many dead?" you ask a policeman.

"Only one," he says. "It went through the sidewalk and burst below. If it had burst on the solid stone of the road there might have been fifty."

A policeman covers the body; they send for someone to repair the gas main, and you go in to breakfast. A charwoman, her eyes red, is scrubbing the blood off the marble floor of the corridor. The dead man wasn't you nor anyone you know, and everyone is very hungry in the morning after a cold night and a long day the day before up at the Guadalajara front.

"Did you see him?" asked someone else at breakfast.

"Sure," you say.

"That's where we pass a dozen times a day—right on that corner." But everyone has the feeling that characterizes war. It wasn't me, see? It wasn't me.

The Italian dead up on the Guadalajara weren't you, although Italian dead, because of where you had spent your boyhood, always seemed, still, like our dead. No. You went to the front early in the morning in a miserable little car with a more miserable little chauffeur who suffered visibly the closer he came up to the fighting. But at night, sometimes late, without lights, with the big trucks roaring past, you came on back to sleep in a bed with sheets in a good hotel, paying a dollar a day for the best rooms on the front.

The smaller rooms in the back, on the side away from the shelling, were considerably more expensive. After the shell that lighted on the sidewalk in front of the hotel, you got a beautiful double corner room on that side, twice the size of the one you had had, for less than a dollar. It wasn't me they killed. See? No. Not me. It wasn't me any more.

Then, in a hospital given by the American Friends of Spanish Democracy, located out behind the Morata front along the road to Valencia, they said, "Raven wants to see you."

"Do I know him?"

"I don't think so," they said, "but he wants to see you."

"Where is he?"

"Upstairs."

In the room upstairs they were giving a blood transfusion to a man with a very gray face who lay on a cot with his arm out, looking away from the gurgling bottle and moaning in a very impersonal way. He moaned mechanically and at regular intervals, and it did not seem to be he that made the sound. His lips did not move.

"Where's Raven?" I asked.

"I'm here," said Raven.

The voice came from a high mound covered by a shoddy gray blanket. There were two arms crossed on the top of the mound with a wide blanket across the eyes.

"Who is it?" asked Raven.

"Hemingway," I said. "I came up to see how you were doing."

"My face was pretty bad," he said. "It got sort of burned from the grenade, but it's peeled a couple of times and it's doing better."

"It looks swell," I said. "It's doing fine."

I wasn't looking at it when I spoke.

"How are things in America?" he asked. "What do they think of us over there?"

"Sentiment's changed a lot," I said. "They're beginning to realize the government is going to win the war."

"Do you think so?"

"Sure," I said.

"I'm awfully glad," he said. "You know, I wouldn't mind any of this if I could just watch what was going on. I don't mind the pain, you know. It never seemed important really. But I was always awfully interested in things and I really wouldn't mind the pain at all if I could just sort of follow things intelligently. I could even be of some use. You know, I didn't mind the war at all. I did all right in the war. I got hit once before and I was back and rejoined the battalion in two weeks. I couldn't stand to be put away. Then I got this."

He had put his hand in mine. It was not a worker's hand. There were no calluses and the nails on the long, spatulate fingers were smooth and rounded.

"How did you get it?" I asked.

"Well, there were some troops that were routed and we went over to sort of re-form them, and we did; and then we had quite a fight with the Fascists, and we beat them. It was quite a bad fight, you know, but we beat them and then someone threw this grenade at me."

Holding his hand and hearing him tell it, I did not believe a word of it. What was left of him did not sound like the wreckage of a soldier, somehow. I did not know how he had been wounded, but the story did not sound right. It was the sort of way everyone would like to have been wounded. But I wanted him to think I believed it.

"Where did you come from?" I asked.

"From Pittsburgh. I went to the university there."

"What did you do before you joined up here?"

"I was a social worker," he said.

Then I knew it couldn't be true, and I wondered how he had really been so frightfully wounded; and I didn't care. In the war that I had known, men often lied about the manner of their wounding. Not at first; but later. I'd lied a little myself in my time, especially late in the evening. But I was glad he thought I believed it, and we talked about books. He wanted to be a writer, and I told him about what had happened north of Guadalajara and promised to bring some things from Madrid next time we got out that way. I hoped maybe I could get a radio.

"They tell me John Dos Passos and Sinclair Lewis are coming over, too," he said.

"Yes," I said. "And when they come I'll bring them up to see you."

"Gee, that will be great," he said. "You don't know what that will mean to me."

"I'll bring them," I said.

"Will they be here pretty soon?"

"Just as soon as they come I'll bring them."

"Good boy, Ernest," he said. "You don't mind if I call you Ernest, do you?"

The voice came very clear and gentle.

"Hell, no," I said. "Please. Listen, old-timer, you're going to be fine. You'll be a lot of good, you know. You can talk on the radio."

"Maybe," he said. "You'll be back?"

"Sure," I said. "Absolutely."

"Good-bye, Ernest," he said.

"Good-bye," I told him.

Downstairs they told me he'd lost both eyes and was also badly wounded all through the legs and in the feet.

"He's lost some toes, too," the doctor said, "but he doesn't know that."

"I wonder if he'll ever know it."

"Oh, sure he will," the doctor said. "He's going to get well."

And it still isn't you that gets hit, but it is your countryman now. Your countryman from Pennsylvania, where once we fought at Gettysburg.

Then, walking along the road, with his left arm in an airplane splint, walking with the gamecock walk of the professional British soldier that neither ten years of militant party work nor the projecting metal wings of the splint could destroy, I met Raven's commanding officer, Jock Cunningham, who had three fresh rifle wounds through his upper left arm (I looked at them, one was septic) and another rifle bullet under his shoulder blade that had entered his left chest, passed through, and lodged there.

He told me, in military terms, the history of the attempt to rally retiring troops on his battalion's right flank, of his bombing raid down a trench which was held at one end by the Fascists and at the other end by the government troops, of the taking of this trench and, with six men and a Lewis gun, cutting off a group of some eighty Fascists from their own lines, and of the final desperate defense of their impossible position his six men put up until the government troops came up and, attacking, straightened out the line again.

He told it clearly, completely convincingly, and with a strong Glasgow accent. He had deep, piercing eyes, sheltered like an eagle's; and, hearing him talk, you could tell the sort of soldier he was. For what he had done he would have had a VC in the last war. In this war there are no decorations. Wounds are the only decorations, and they don't award wound stripes.

"Raven was in the same show," he said. "I didn't know he'd been hit. Ay, he's a good mon. He got his after I got mine. The Fascists we'd cut off were very good troops. They never fired a useless shot when we were in that bad spot. They waited in the dark there until they had us located and then opened with volley fire. That's how I got four in the same place."

We talked for a while, and he told me many things. They were all important, but nothing was as important as that what Jay Raven, the social worker from Pittsburgh with no military training, had told me was true. This is a strange new kind of war where you learn just as much as you are able to believe.

First Franco soldiers to enter Barcelona, Spain.

Dispatch from Spain

BY HERBERT L. MATTHEWS

From *The New York Times,* March 18, 1938

BARCELONA, MARCH 17—Barcelona has lived through twelve air raids in less than twenty-four hours, and the city is shaken and terror-struck. Human beings have seldom had to suffer as these people are suffering under General Francisco Franco's determined effort to break their spirit and induce their government to yield.

I have just come back from the principal morgue, which is at the Clinical Hospital, and there I counted 328 dead lying side by side. Those were more or less whole bodies. Then there are the others in hospitals and, above all, those who lie in the ruins of dozens of buildings and whose bodies never will be recovered.

The destruction is in one sense haphazard, for the bombs are dropped anywhere at all, without any attempt at specific objectives. However, there is an obvious plan, that every part of the city, from the richest to the poorest, shall get its full measure of tragedy.

Spaniards are meeting this trial—and it is the greatest that their people have had to bear in the whole war—with the stoicism and the dignity of their race, but they are only human, and this is terribly hard to bear. Foreigners are deserting their hotels for the frontier as fast as they can get conveyance, for there is a genuine sense of impending disaster here among those who have escaped so far.

One sees such occurrences as a British newspaperman giving his wife some money in case "something silly happens." A chambermaid said to me this morning:

"We are all going to be killed—all."

A clerk at a drugstore sighed as he handed over some headache medicine.

Herbert L. Matthews covered the Spanish Civil War for the *New York Times.* Earlier, he had watched Mussolini's forces destroy the Negus in Ethiopia and commented: "The right or wrong of it did not interest me greatly." But the Spanish Civil War was different; it convinced Matthews that Fascism had to be stopped. Such was not to be the case in Spain. Barcelona fell in January 1939, and Madrid in March; deserted by the Western democracies, the Loyalist cause collapsed. Matthews' account of the bombardment of Barcelona first appeared in the *New York Times* on March 18, 1938.

"Oh, for a plane to fly to France," he said. "I don't want to die."

7:40, 10:25, 1:55—those were tragic moments during the day. It was not necessary to send many planes each time. Fearful damage done in the last-mentioned raid required only five heavy bombers.

The account of what happened today is an unmitigated succession of horrors, and one feels helpless trying to convey the horror of all this in cold print, which people read and throw away.

One comes back from the scenes dazed: men, women, and children buried alive, screaming in the wreckage of their houses like trapped animals. *I have never seen so many weeping women.*

This bombing is meant to strike terror, demoralize the rear guard, and weaken resistance, because human beings are not built to withstand such horror. It is true they are stricken by terror all right—terror that freezes the blood and makes one either hysterical or on the verge of hysteria. But then, too, one would not be human if it did not cause rage—deep, burning rage. These people would like to return the compliment.

A tram was wrecked and everyone in it killed or wounded. A truck was still burning, and something black that had been a human being had just been taken out. And there was the noise—ambulances dashing up with whistles blowing, women screaming and struggling hysterically, men shouting. Up the block a house was burning fiercely.

And all around, everywhere we went, were wrecked houses, dead and wounded, and those intangibles of fear, horror, and fury.

I watched them take two wounded persons from a building in the first bombing this morning. Both had been completely buried. A woman was screaming so weakly that we thought she was a child until they extricated her limp body. She seemed dead then, but they rushed her away to a hospital.

The other was a fifteen-year-old boy. By some miracle he had not been crushed, although I could see from his hair down to his bare feet he had been completely buried. His body did not seem to be hurt, but something else was, for he could not control his muscles—the twitching of his face or shuddering.

There are those freakish things which happen to intensify the horror. There is that house where nothing remains on the fifth floor except some clothes hanging on a rack. In another place a corner of the kitchen has somehow escaped, and we could see that the housewife had not had time to wash the dishes. Once a funeral passed along a street where bombs had fallen. There could have been no fitter symbol.

But life must go on. They have been repairing car tracks and clearing wreckage. After each raid they do it. Then they wait for the next.

It is surely the most savage and most ruthless punishment any modern city has taken.

The raid at 1:55 this afternoon left Barcelona shaking under the strain.

The writer was in a restaurant, eating lunch. All of us got up hastily to dash toward the back as the building shook, and I watched in amazement as the windows bent inward under the strain without breaking.

One takes what humor one can out of this tragedy; otherwise it would be hard to remain sane. For my own part I did not find it amusing to see a great hulking fellow who was eating with his girl jump up and beat her to the kitchen by three strides. Another thing, at which everybody laughs ruefully today, is the way everybody jumps at any unusual noise—the horns of cars that sound sirenlike, the banging of doors, the roar of automobile motors. I even saw a cat jump as if it had an electric shock when a shopkeeper suddenly lowered his blinds.

There is one remark I heard this afternoon that sticks, for it was not said in jest:

"It may not be the end of the war, but it feels like the end of the world!"

In a Madrid subway, 1938. Robert Capa.

Say That We Saw Spain Die

BY EDNA ST. VINCENT MILLAY

Say that we saw Spain die. O splendid bull, how well you fought!
Lost from the first.
    . . . the tossed, the replaced, the watchful *torero*
      with gesture elegant and spry,
Before the dark, the tiring but the unglazed eye deploying the bright
    cape,
Which hid for once not air, but the enemy indeed, the authentic shape,
A thousand of him, interminably into the ring released . . . the turning
    beast at length between converging colours caught.

Save for the weapons of its skull, a bull
Unarmed, considering, weighing, charging
Almost a world, itself without ally.

Say that we saw the shoulders more than the mind confused, so profusely
Bleeding from so many more than the accustomed barbs, the game gone
    vulgar, the rules abused.

Say that we saw Spain die from loss of blood, a rustic reason, in a
    reinforced
And proud punctilious land, no *espada*—
A hundred men unhorsed,

A hundred horses gored, and the afternoon aging, and the crowd growing
    restless (all, all so much later than planned),
And the big head heavy, sliding forward in the sand, and the tongue
    dry with sand,—no *espada*
Toward that hot neck, for the delicate and final thrust, having dared
    thrust forth his hand.

Edna St. Vincent Millay's concern with social issues was life-long. In 1919 she wrote the successfully produced anti-war play, *Aria de Capo;* and, shortly after, she became one of the foremost champions of Sacco and Vanzetti. Although she was opposed to war, the crisis in Europe convinced her that there were times when it was necessary to oppose evil with force. "Say that We Saw Spain Die" is reprinted from her 1939 collection of poems, *Huntsman, What Quarry?*

"Moonlight" by Joseph Hirsch.

Litany for Dictatorships

BY STEPHEN VINCENT BENET

For all those beaten, for the broken heads,
The fosterless, the simple, the oppressed,
The ghosts in the burning city of our time . . .

For those taken in rapid cars to the house and beaten
By the skilful boys, the boys with the rubber fists,
—Held down and beaten, the table cutting their loins,
Or kicked in the groin and left, with the muscles jerking
Like a headless hen's on the floor of the slaughter-house
While they brought the next man in with his white eyes staring.
For those who still said "Red Front!" or "God Save the Crown!"
And for those who were not courageous
But were beaten nevertheless.
For those who spit out the bloody stumps of their teeth
Quietly in the hall,
Sleep well on stone or iron, watch for the time
And kill the guard in the privy before they die,
Those with the deep-socketed eyes and the lamp burning.

For those who carry the scars, who walk lame—for those
Whose nameless graves are made in the prison-yard
And the earth smoothed back before morning and the lime scattered.

For those slain at once. For those living through months and years
Enduring, watching, hoping, going each day

Stephen Vincent Benét was awarded the Pulitzer Prize in 1929 for his long narrative poem, *John Brown's Body*, and in 1933 received the Roosevelt Medal for his contribution to American literature. Although Benét's fame rests primarily on those works which glorify the American past (*John Brown's Body, Western Star,* and *The Devil and Daniel Webster*), many of his poems written during the 1930's deal with the increasing menace of Fascism. "Litany for Dictatorships" is reprinted from Benét's 1936 collection of poems, *Burning City*.

To the work or the queue for meat or the secret club,
Living meanwhile, begetting children, smuggling guns,
And found and killed at the end like rats in a drain.

For those escaping
Incredibly into exile and wandering there.
For those who live in the small rooms of foreign cities
And who yet think of the country, the long green grass,
The childhood voices, the language, the way wind smelt then,
The shape of rooms, the coffee drunk at the table,
The talk with friends, the loved city, the waiter's face,
The gravestones, with the name, where they will not lie
Nor in any of that earth. Their children are strangers.

For those who planned and were leaders and were beaten
And for those, humble and stupid, who had no plan
But were denounced, but grew angry, but told a joke,
But could not explain, but were sent away to the camp,
But had their bodies shipped back in the sealed coffins,
"Died of pneumonia." "Died trying to escape."

For those growers of wheat who were shot by their own wheat-stacks,
For those growers of bread who were sent to the ice-locked wastes,
And their flesh remembers their fields.

For those denounced by their smug, horrible children
For a peppermint-star and the praise of the Perfect State,
For all those strangled or gelded or merely starved
To make perfect states; for the priest hanged in his cassock,
The Jew with his chest crushed in and his eyes dying,
The revolutionist lynched by the private guards
To make perfect states, in the names of the perfect states.

For those betrayed by the neighbours they shook hands with
And for the traitors, sitting in the hard chair
With the loose sweat crawling their hair and their fingers restless
As they tell the street and the house and the man's name.

And for those sitting at table in the house
With the lamp lit and the plates and the smell of food,
Talking so quietly; when they hear the cars
And the knock at the door, and they look at each other quickly

And the woman goes to the door with a stiff face,
Smoothing her dress.
                       "We are all good citizens here.
We believe in the Perfect State."
                                 And that was the last
Time Tony or Karl or Shorty came to the house
And the family was liquidated later.
It was the last time.
                    We heard the shots in the night
But nobody knew next day what the trouble was
And a man must go to his work. So I didn't see him
For three days, then, and me near out of my mind
And all the patrols on the streets with their dirty guns
And when he came back, he looked drunk, and the blood was on him.

For the women who mourn their dead in the secret night,
For the children taught to keep quiet, the old children,
The children spat-on at school.
                         For the wrecked laboratory,
The gutted house, the dunged picture, the pissed-in well,
The naked corpse of Knowledge flung in the square
And no man lifting a hand and no man speaking.

For the cold of the pistol-butt and the bullet's heat,
For the rope that chokes, the manacles that bind,
The huge voice, metal, that lies from a thousand tubes
And the stuttering machine-gun that answers all.

For the man crucified on the crossed machine-guns
Without name, without resurrection, without stars,
His dark head heavy with death and his flesh long sour
With the smell of his many prisons—John Smith, John Doe,
John Nobody—oh, crack your mind for his name!
Faceless as water, naked as the dust,
Dishonored as the earth the gas-shells poison
And barbarous with portent.
                              This is he.
This is the man they ate at the green table
Putting their gloves on ere they touched the meat.
This is the fruit of war, the fruit of peace,
The ripeness of invention, the new lamb,
The answer to the wisdom of the wise.

And still he hangs, and still he will not die,
And still, on the steel city of our years
The light fails and the terrible blood streams down.

We thought we were done with these things but we were wrong.
We thought, because we had power, we had wisdom.
We thought the long train would run to the end of Time.
We thought the light would increase.
Now the long train stands derailed and the bandits loot it.
Now the boar and the asp have power in our time.
Now the night rolls back on the West and the night is solid.
Our fathers and ourselves sowed dragon's teeth.
Our children know and suffer the armed men.

Anti-Fascist demonstration in Union Square.

From You Can't Go Home Again

BY THOMAS WOLFE

It was the season of the great Olympic games, and almost every day George and Else went to the stadium in Berlin. George observed that the organizing genius of the German people, which has been used so often to such noble purpose, was now more thrillingly displayed than he had ever seen it before. The sheer pageantry of the occasion was overwhelming, so much so that he began to feel oppressed by it. There seemed to be something ominous in it. One sensed a stupendous concentration of effort, a tremendous drawing together and ordering in the vast collective power of the whole land. And the thing that made it seem ominous was that it so evidently went beyond what the games themselves demanded. The games were overshadowed, and were no longer merely sporting competitions to which other nations had sent their chosen teams. They became, day after day, an orderly and overwhelming demonstration in which the whole of Germany had been schooled and disciplined. It was as if the games had been chosen as a symbol of the new collective might, a means of showing to the world in concrete terms what this new power had come to be.

With no past experience in such affairs, the Germans had constructed a mighty stadium which was the most beautiful and most perfect in its design that had ever been built. And all the accessories of this monstrous plant—the swimming pools, the enormous halls, the lesser stadia—had been laid out and designed with this same cohesion

---

Offered $150 worth of free passage by the German magazine *The Seven Seas* in exchange for a couple of articles about Germany, Thomas Wolfe left for Berlin on July 23, 1936 to spend the royalties from *Of Time and the River* and to watch the Olympic games. Wolfe's attitude toward Nazi Germany was mixed. It was the place where he felt he was liked best and where he had the most friends; but, slowly, he began to understand the meaning of Hitler's oppression. By the time he returned to the United States, Wolfe was an ardent anti-Fascist. "Europe this summer," he wrote on October 23, 1936, "was a volcano of poisonous and constricted hatred which threatened to erupt at any moment. The great engines of war are ready, are on the rails, are being constantly enlarged and magnified . . . It is good to be back home and to feel that, whatever we may lack, we are free of these constricting national hatreds, that we still have space and air to move in." The experiences of his trip were incorporated in *You Can't Go Home Again*, published posthumously in 1940. We have reprinted part of the chapter entitled "The Dark Messiah."

of beauty and of use. The organization was superb. Not only were the events themselves, down to the minutest detail of each competition, staged and run off like clockwork, but the crowds—such crowds as no other great city has ever had to cope with, and the like of which would certainly have snarled and maddened the traffic of New York beyond hope of untangling—were handled with a quietness, order, and speed that was astounding.

The daily spectacle was breath-taking in its beauty and magnificence. The stadium was a tournament of color that caught the throat; the massed splendor of the banners made the gaudy decorations of America's great parades, presidential inaugurations, and World's Fairs seem like shoddy carnivals in comparison. And for the duration of the Olympics, Berlin itself was transformed into a kind of annex to the stadium. From one end of the city to the other, from the Lustgarten to the Brandenburger Tor, along the whole broad sweep of Unter den Linden, through the vast avenues of the faëry Tiergarten, and out through the western part of Berlin to the very portals of the stadium, the whole town was a thrilling pageantry of royal banners—not merely endless miles of looped-up bunting, but banners fifty feet in height, such as might have graced the battle tent of some great emperor.

And all through the day, from morning on, Berlin became a mighty Ear, attuned, attentive, focused on the stadium. Everywhere the air was filled with a single voice. The green trees along the Kurfürstendamm began to talk: from loud-speakers concealed in their branches an announcer in the stadium spoke to the whole city—and for George Webber it was a strange experience to hear the familiar terms of track and field translated into the tongue that Goethe used. He would be informed now that the *Vorlauf* was about to be run—and then the *Zwischenlauf*—and at length the *Endlauf*—and the winner:

"Owens—Oo Ess Ah!"

Meanwhile, through those tremendous banner-laden ways, the crowds thronged ceaselessly all day long. The wide promenade of Unter den Linden was solid with patient, tramping German feet. Fathers, mothers, children, young folks, old—the whole material of the nation was there, from every corner of the land. From morn to night they trudged, wide-eyed, full of wonder, past the marvel of those banner-laden ways. And among them one saw the bright stabs of color of Olympic jackets and the glint of foreign faces: the dark features of Frenchmen and Italians, the ivory grimace of the Japanese, the straw hair and blue eyes of the Swedes, and the big Americans, natty in straw hats, white flannels, and blue coats crested with the Olympic seal.

And there were great displays of marching men, sometimes ungunned but rhythmic as regiments of brown shirts went swinging through the streets. By noon each day all the main approaches to the games, the embannered streets and avenues of the route which the Leader would take to the stadium, miles away, were walled in by the troops. They stood at ease, young men, laughing and talking with each other—the Leader's bodyguards, the Schutz Staffel units, the Storm Troopers, all the ranks and divisions in their different uniforms—and they stretched in two unbroken lines from the Wilhelm-strasse up to the arches of the Brandenburger Tor. Then, suddenly, the sharp command, and instantly there would be the solid smack of ten thousand leather boots as they came together with the sound of war.

It seemed as if everything had been planned for this moment, shaped to this triumphant purpose. But the people—they had not been planned. Day after day, behind the unbroken wall of soldiers, they stood and waited in a dense and patient throng. These were the masses of the nation, the poor ones of the earth, the humble ones of life, the workers and the wives, the mothers and the children—and day after day they came and stood and waited. They were there because they did not have money enough to buy the little cardboard squares that would have given them places within the magic ring. From noon till night they waited for just two brief and golden moments of the day: the moment when the Leader went out to the stadium, and the moment when he returned.

At last he came—and something like a wind across a field of grass was shaken through that crowd, and from afar the tide rolled up with him, and in it was the voice, the hope, the prayer of the land. The Leader came by slowly in a shining car, a little dark man with a comic-opera mustache, erect and standing, moveless and unsmiling, with his hand upraised, palm outward, not in Nazi-wise salute, but straight up, in a gesture of blessing such as the Buddha or Messiahs use.

From the beginning of their relationship, and straight through to the end, Else refused to discuss with George anything even remotely connected with the Nazi regime. That was a closed subject between them. But others were not so discreet. The first weeks passed, and George began to hear some ugly things. From time to time, at parties, dinners, and the like, when George would speak of his enthusiasm for Germany and the German people, various friends that he had made would, if they had had enough to drink, take him aside afterwards and, after looking around cautiously, lean toward him with an air of great secrecy and whisper:

"But have you heard . . . ? And have you heard . . . ?"

He did not see any of the ugly things they whispered about. He did not see anyone beaten. He did not see anyone imprisoned, or put to death. He did not see any men in concentration camps. He did not see openly anywhere the physical manifestations of a brutal and compulsive force.

True, there were men in brown uniforms everywhere, and men in black uniforms, and men in uniforms of olive green, and everywhere in the streets there was the solid smack of booted feet, the blare of brass, the tootling of fifes, and the poignant sight of young faces shaded under iron helmets, with folded arms and ramrod backs, precisely seated in great army lorries. But all of this had become so mixed in with his joy over his own success, his feeling for Else, and the genial temper of the people making holiday, as he had seen and known it so many pleasant times before, that even if it did not now seem good, it did not seem sinister or bad.

Then something happened. It didn't happen suddenly. It just happened as a cloud gathers, as fog settles, as rain begins to fall.

A man George had met was planning to give a party for him and asked him if he wanted to ask any of his friends. George mentioned one. His host was silent for a moment; he looked embarrassed; then he said that the person George had named had formerly been the editorial head of a publication that had been suppressed, and that one of the people who had been instrumental in its suppression had been invited to the party, so would George mind—?

George named another, an old friend named Franz Heilig whom he had first met in Munich years before, and who now lived in Berlin, and of whom he was very fond. Again the anxious pause, the embarrassment, the halting objections. This person was—was—well, George's host said he knew about this person and knew he did not go to parties—he would not come if he were invited—so would George mind—?

George next spoke the name of Else von Kohler, and the response to this suggestion was of the same kind. How long had he known this woman? Where, and under what circumstances, had he met her? George tried to reassure his hosts on all these scores. He told the man he need have no fear of any sort about Else. His host was instant, swift, in his apologies: oh, by no means—he was sure the lady was eminently all right—only, nowadays—with a mixed gathering—he had tried to pick a group of people whom George had met and who all knew one another—he had thought it would be much more pleasant that way—strangers at a party were often shy, constrained, and formal—Frau von Kohler would not know anybody there—so would George mind—?

Not long after this baffling experience a friend came to see him. "In a few days," his friend said, "you will receive a phone call from a certain person. He will try to meet you, to talk to you. Have nothing to do with this man."

George laughed. His friend was a sober-minded German, rather on the dull and heavy side, and his face was so absurdly serious as he spoke that George thought he was trying to play some lumbering joke upon him. He wanted to know who this mysterious personage might be who was so anxious to make his acquaintance.

To George's amazement and incredulity, his friend named a high official in the government.

But why, George asked, should this man want to meet him? And why, if he did, should he be afraid of him?

At first his friend would not answer. Finally he muttered circumspectly:

"Listen to me. Stay away from this man. I tell you for your own good." He paused, not knowing how to say it; then: "You have heard of Captain Roehm? You know about him? You know what happened to him?" George nodded. "Well," his friend went on in a troubled voice, "there were others who were not shot in the purge. This man I speak of is one of the bad ones. We have a name for him—it is *'The Prince of Darkness.'* "

George did not know what to make of all this. He tried to puzzle it out but could not, so at last he dismissed it from his mind. But within a few days the official whom his friend had named did telephone, and did ask to meet him. George offered some excuse and avoided seeing the man, but the episode was most peculiar and unsettling.

Both of these baffling experiences contained elements of comedy and melodrama, but those were the superficial aspects. George began to realize now the tragedy that lay behind such things. There was nothing political in any of it. The roots of it were much more sinister and deep and evil than politics or even racial prejudice could ever be. For the first time in his life he had come upon something full of horror that he had never known before—something that made all the swift violence and passion of America, the gangster compacts, the sudden killings, the harshness and corruption that infested portions of American business and public life, seem innocent beside it. What George began to see was a picture of a great people who had been psychically wounded and were now desperately ill with some dread malady of the soul. Here was an entire nation, he now realized, that was infested with the contagion of an ever-present fear. It was a kind of creeping paralysis which twisted and blighted all human relations.

The pressures of a constant and infamous compulsion had silenced this whole people into a sweltering and malignant secrecy until they had become spiritually septic with the distillations of their own self-poisons, for which now there was no medicine or release.

As he began to see and understand the true state of affairs, George wondered if anyone could be so base as to exult at this great tragedy, or to feel hatred for the once-mighty people who were the victims of it. Culturally, from the eighteenth century on, the German was the first citizen of Europe. In Goethe there was made sublimely articulate a world spirit which knew no boundary lines of nationality, politics, race, or religion, which rejoiced in the inheritance of all mankind, and which wanted no domination or conquest of that inheritance save that of participating in it and contributing to it. This German spirit in art, literature, music, science, and philosophy continued in an unbroken line right down to 1933, and it seemed to George that there was not a man or woman alive in the world who was not, in one way or another, the richer for it.

When he first visited Germany, in 1925, the evidence of that spirit was manifest everywhere in the most simple and unmistakable ways. For example, one could not pass the crowded window of a bookshop in any town without instantly observing in it a reflection of the intellectual and cultural enthusiasm of the German people. The contents of the shop revealed a breadth of vision and of interest that would have made the contents of a French bookshop, with its lingual and geographic constrictions, seem paltry and provincial. The best writers of every country were as well known in Germany as in their own land. Among the Americans, Theodore Dreiser, Sinclair Lewis, Upton Sinclair, and Jack London had particularly large followings; their books were sold and read everywhere. And the work of America's younger writers was eagerly sought out and published.

Even in 1936 this noble enthusiasm, although it had been submerged and mutilated by the regime of Adolph Hitler, was still apparent in the most touching way. George had heard it said that good books could no longer be published and read in Germany. This, he found, was not true, as some of the other things he had heard about Germany were not true. And about Hitler's Germany he felt that one must be very true. And the reason one needed to be very true was that the thing in it which every decent person must be against was false. You could not turn the other cheek to wrong, but also, it seemed to him, you could not be wrong about wrong. You had to be right about it. You could not meet lies and trickery with lies and trickery, although there were some people who argued that you should.

So it was not true that good books could no longer be published and read in Germany. And because it was not true, the tragedy of the great German spirit was more movingly evident, in the devious and distorted ways in which it now manifested itself, than it would have been if it were true. Good books were still published if their substance did not, either openly or by implication criticize the Hitler regime or controvert its dogmas. And it would simply be stupid to assert that any book must criticize Hitler and controvert his doctrines in order to be good.

For these reasons, the eagerness, curiosity, and enthusiasm of the Germans for such good books as they were still allowed to read had been greatly intensified. They wanted desperately to find out what was going on in the world, and the only way they had left was to read whatever books they could get that had been written outside of Germany. This seemed to be one basic explanation of their continued interest in American writing, and that they *were* interested was a fact as overwhelming as it was pathetic. Under these conditions, the last remnants of the German spirit managed to survive only as drowning men survive—by clutching desperately at any spar that floated free from the wreckage of their ship.

So the weeks, the months, the summer passed, and everywhere about him George saw the evidences of this dissolution, this shipwreck of a great spirit. The poisonous emanations of suppression, persecution, and fear permeated the air like miasmic and pestilential vapors, tainting, sickening, and blighting the lives of everyone he met. It was a plague of the spirit—invisible, but as unmistakable as death. Little by little it sank in on him through all the golden singing of that summer, until at last he felt it, breathed it, lived it, and knew it for the thing it was.

Hess, Von Papen, Schacht, and Goering. Cartoon by John Mackey in the New Masses.

From **Those Who Perish**

BY EDWARD DAHLBERG

ELI MELAMED had made his third round of Woodrow Wilson Park. His face, wind-burnt and hollowed out with tiredness, he decided that he would go to see the Briarcliffs for an hour's rest. Noticing the few finger-like trees, their embryonic buds of leaves—spring buds in reverse gear, for they had been wrinkled and corrugated by the death-fumes of automobile gasoline—he felt the need to get near to something human and warmly domesticated. Already eager to be inside the Briarcliffs' apartment and to shake hands with Edgar, he thought, with renewed courage: "We Jews do not know who we are, or from whence we come. The blood of all nations and races flows through our veins —from feudal times onward, our women have been defiled by Christians, and the offspring of these acts of rapine have passed as 'pure Jews.' " He repeated this, saying to himself: "Perhaps there is the blood of French or Italians, of the Romance Language peoples in my veins; after all, I'm a Sephardic type, and my Palestinian forebears must have been in Spain during the Inquisition." All this he said with the same kind of racial reasoning and inferiority complex that prompts Jews to call a Hitler or an Ivy Lee a Jew.

As Melamed stepped under the pseudo-beachish canopy outside the apartment house entrance, a thin rain began to canter lightly against the sidewalk. Suddenly he turned back, took off his hat and stood under it for a moment, lifting up his chin and face as though he were taking a shower. Melamed wanted to get wet so that it would appear that he had run in on the Briarcliffs for refuge. The rain grew swifter, galloping against the curbs, and Melamed ducked under the canopy again. The elevator took him up to the eighth floor.

Less well-known than Sinclair Lewis' *It Can't Happen Here* (1935), Edward Dahlberg's *Those Who Perish* was published a year before Lewis' anti-fascist novel, and was the first American novel to concern itself with Nazism in the United States. It is still among the best of its kind. Dahlberg was in Germany during the rise of the Nazi régime, and upon returning to the United States became a member of the executive board of the National Committee for the Defense of Political Prisoners. Prior to *Those Who Perish,* Dahlberg wrote *Bottom Dogs* (1930) and *From Flushing to Calvary* (1932), which Edmund Wilson called "some of the only specimens of original proletarian literature we have yet had in this country."

Standing in front of the Briarcliffs' door, he turned up his coat collar, unthinkingly shivered for a second, his arms and legs rippling against his suit, as though he were at large and not inside of it, and touched the bell, sotto voce. When Mrs. Briarcliff came to the door, he was wiping the back of his neck and swobbing his face with gymnastic phews and clucks. As he took hold of Mrs. Briarcliff's hand, he shut his eyes, vigorously shook it up and down, piston-like, as if he had to reach up to seize it, and greeted her in a high, off-pitch voice: "So awfully glad to see you, Jenny!" He had never called her Jenny before, and he was appalled by his over-familiarity. "Just ran in out of the rain . . . hope I'm not . . ." He stopped short here, for he heard voices inside, felt that he was intruding, and was afraid that she would give him one of those straight looks that would indicate that he was.

There was something thin-lipped about Mrs. Briarcliff's body. She was one of those women, with long sharp noses and paper-thin throats that readily crease, whom handsome men so often marry. Frequently taken for a Jewess, or suspected of being one because of her nose, she was, as a matter of fact, of old New England stock. Melamed had always been a little afraid of her, because he thought she was Jewish and was hiding it, and because he believed she knew that he thought so. In one of his nasty moments he had had fleeting pictures of her as the wooden American Indian in front of the cigar store, but as he disliked harboring any sort of unkind thoughts about other human beings, he had summarily exorcised this mental photograph of Jenny Briarcliff.

The Briarcliffs' apartment, whose fake medieval wooded panels and electric candle-bulbs made it resemble the interior of Schrafft's restaurant, was filled with people standing around a ping-pong table. Three or four people were seated in chairs behind them drinking cocktails; some were sipping from their glasses and standing. Edgar Briarcliff, who had a clean-cut Arrow collar physiognomy and the Gentile retroussé nose, which American Jews admire, was serving. His opponent was a somewhat hefty woman whose green silk dress noisily rustled against her bust. She had a squat Slavonic nose, and her name was Evelyn Syracuse Beach.

Edgar Briarcliff was cutting the ball low over the net, and Miss Evelyn Syracuse Beach was having considerable difficulty in gauging and returning the serve. While the ping-pong balls sped back and forth across the green table with the clicking precision of typewriter keys, jibes and japes constantly came from the spectators. "Say, Edgar," said a heavily begoggled, gawky Freudian, "a little less sadism in those returns—save that for the wife!" "Oh, Evelyn, put a postage stamp on that last one, and no return address," said another.

When the game was over, Edgar Briarcliff approached Eli Melamed and introduced him, and Melamed shook hands with each one. After a colored maid had brought him a cocktail, Edgar left him.

The spectators were now watching the new game. The man who was serving held the paddle upright against his stomach. His opponent was his wife, and this set in motion the stenciled marital remarks. As the server sprung the paddle so as to release the ball, the psychoanalyst called: "Say, Burt, where did you get that umbilical serve, or what have you?" Melamed also let out a small, guttural he-heh-huh, which sounded like a slender stick being lightly run across a wooden picket fence. He had been admiring the faces around him, and listening with esthetic attentiveness and pleasure to their Aryan, fiscal names. Finally, he had gotten up enough courage to make a complete semicircular smile, showing all his white teeth, for Miss Evelyn Syracuse Beach, but she did not notice him.

The Negro maid came around again with a tray of ice-clinking glasses. Mrs. Briarcliff moved from one couple to the other, and Edgar was seated on a cushion on the floor in the next room, holding a serious theosophical discussion with Mrs. Van Cortland Dinwiddie. Shortly afterwards, Edgar came over and said, "How about a set, Mel-ah-mede?" and Melamed emotionally bubbled over this intimacy.

Melamed went toward one end of the table and picked up his paddle, and Edgar moved toward the other. Eli Melamed, who had played a good deal of ping-pong at the Phoenix Physical Culture Club of New Jersey, now for the first time felt sure of himself.

He had a short, inching, sniping serve, which Edgar was unable to pick up. Melamed won the first five points. The people standing around the table stopped talking and began to watch. Edgar corkscrewed his serve which twisted and landed in an askew cut. But Melamed coolly waited for it to hit the table and then slammed it back across the net with the speed of a football player. Melamed, whenever Edgar returned the ball, ran from one part of the rim of the table to the other, picking up the ball, and lunging in after it with quarterback alacrity and the confidence of good fleshly poundage across his shoulders. As his bowing collar touched his neck, he felt as if it were a strong leathern headgear. Melamed took the next three points, and pausing for a second, examined his small feet with glowing sartorial satisfaction.

"Really, you're not the man you were," said Melamed, in a friendly non-competitive spirit, but without looking at Edgar. As he took the ninth point Melamed accidentally caught a vague cross-section of Edgar Briarcliff's countenance, which seemed to have become plaque-like. Looking again to make certain, Melamed missed the next one. The two men changed sides. Melamed laid his paddle down to adjust his suspenders and to catch Edgar's eye, and to soften him with a warm glance. But Briarcliff did not see and was impatient to continue the game.

Melamed then turned to the guests, and parting his lips he imagined that he had smiled at them. No one returned his greetings. However, this slight movement of the lips was more of an unprinted negative in Melamed's mind than an objective salutation. Melamed sent the next three balls wildly off the table, and did not see the following one which Briarcliff lightly popped over the net. His trousers hanging in a wretched defeatist sag, his suspenders loosening again and sprawling over his suspiciously gray shirt, Melamed fumbled another shot. Troubled and unhinged by the silent, tense faces around the table, Melamed felt like an oppressed minority people engulfed by a hostile imperialistic power.

By now Melamed had entirely lost his intuitive and photographic sense of time and place, which had made him so uncannily precise in his serves and returns at the beginning of the game. When Melamed hit the ball off the table again, and both men stooped over to pick it up off the floor, Edgar said: "Too bad, old man, I know how it feels." These words of non-competitive sympathy filled Melamed with gratitude. And when they both stepped forward and bent over to get another ball, Briarcliff patted Melamed's shoulder. Melamed closed his eyes, which simmered with quiescent emotions. His face was covered with the light pink marks of happiness that a lover might have playfully put there with his teeth. He was enormously thankful that it was Edgar Briarcliff and not he who was winning. Melamed gazed at Briarcliff's aristocratic Nordic eyes, mouth, teeth, and cravat, which were of one piece, and felt this was as it should be.

After the game was ended, Briarcliff having won, Melamed thought he had better leave. He had the same unmistakable sense of time now, the precise time for leaving, that he had had at the beginning of the game when he had served and returned each separate, atomic ping-pong ball with an historic intuition of time and place. But he wanted to slip out of the room without leaving, so that there should be no interruption, no gap, no empty and fatuous space between him and the onlooking guests.

But someone began to discuss the German situation. Everyone trailed into the next room, taking chairs or sitting on cushions on the carpeted floor. "Do you think Hitler will last?" someone asked. "I feel that the whole Nazi Youth Movement has a homosexual basis," said the bespectacled Freudian, whose snub Tyrolese nose looked as though it were pressed up against a windowpane. "The only way to approach the whole situation is psychoanalytically," he continued.

"I must tell you of a little experience I had," said Mrs. Van Cortlandt Dinwiddie, who was related to the Astors and Bismarck, and who, genealogically speaking, had a Wotan-like bust. Otherwise, she had Samoan brown eyes and resembled the Phoenician Jack of Spades. "I had dinner with Charmian London, the wife of Jack London, at the Bohemian Club in San Francisco. She told me—and incidentally, I am using this in my memoirs—that she believed that certain meteorological changes which had taken place in 1914 had so unhinged people's nerves that they brought on the World War. I have since developed this thesis as a kind of undertone in my autobiography, which I was going to call *I Have Only Myself to Blame* until I discovered that the title had already been copyrighted and used for another book. Fancy my disappointment. . . . Anyway, it is my opinion that we are compelled to interpret Fascism in terms of neurones and meteorology. I think that the Versailles Treaty had such a devastating effect upon the nervous system of the German people."

"Don't you think," interrupted Mr. Monte Lorrimer, who had stout Arabic thighs, "that it was the stomach rather than the nerves?"

"I think that the Versailles Treaty," pursued Mrs. Van Cortlandt Dinwiddie with more resolution than before, "had such an exhausting effect upon the nervous system of the German nation that it turned them into lunatics; so what we have in Germany today is an insane asylum, with the only difference that the few sane people left are straitjacketed and kept in the protective custody of the crazy who are the wardens."

"I think that's a brilliant analysis, Mrs. Dinwiddie," exclaimed the young Freudopath. "Just think what superb endocrine portraits Modigliani could do of Hitler and Rosenberg if he were alive today. Why, the League of Nations would actually sanction intervention so that they could be committed."

"I don't think we'll ever solve the European situation until Germany is wiped off the map. They're always getting us into trouble," stated an intellectual Anglo-American in a dreary adenoidal tone.

"Now take Goering," went on the Psychoanalyst.

"No, *you* take him," popped up Melamed who had been waiting for such an opportunity. Everyone laughed and Melamed's eyes glistened. He had been anxious to be included in the conversation, not because he had anything specific to say, but because he felt unhappily isolated. A Dakota Western-pulp type, with a Semitic Tom Mix proboscis, was so tickled over this bit of repartee that he pulled out his handkerchief and began to loudly boo-hoo into it. He was as shaken up as a large fleshy woman, and Melamed fetched a glass of water from a tray, brought it to him, and sort of held his arm as he drank it down.

"Well, Goering's a drug-addict and a dangerous paranoiac," continued the psychoanalytic student. "He was in an asylum in Stockholm in 1925."

"I don't think it's paranoia, but race," uttered Edgar Briarcliff.

"You're absolutely right," supported Mrs. Briarcliff. "Edgar, it is race."

"You-you—will p-pardon me," stuttered Monmouth Hightower, turning to Melamed. "I didn't get your name."

"Oh, this is Mr. Mel-ah-mede," spoke up Edgar Briarcliff. "Terribly sorry."

"We—ell," continued Monmouth Hightower, who had a dark smutty Mediterranean complexion and was the son of a D.A.R., "I—I have the—the great—greatest fancy for pe—people—of your race. You are Hebrew, aren't you?" Melamed nodded. He was beginning to feel deeply united with these persons and to derive a jubilant aesthetic experience from their Anglican names and countenances. Seeing Monmouth Hightower in a happily weepy haze he thought his soiled maple hair was the mane of Siegfried.

"But—but I—I be—believe," said Monmouth Hightower, "that the an—antagonism between different nationalities, as—as well as the—the attraction, is chemical. Take—take intermarriage." By this time his mouth had become a nervous hoop out of which the words rolled askew. "And—and just go back to Goethe's *Elective Affinities,* and—and—"

"Well—ah, per—perhaps there's something in what you say," interrupted Melamed, also stammering, because he felt very sensitive and high-keyed at that moment, and because he believed there was a certain wonderful non-Jewish quality about Monmouth Hightower's Aryan stuttering.

"I—I don't wan—want you to mis—misunderstand me, Mr. Mel —mel—ah—ah—mede. I think your people have gifts of genius, and —and—that accounts for—for my opinion, no doubt, but don't— don't you think the Hebrew people are—are a little difficult?"

"Well—ah, per—perhaps there's a certain amount of truth in what you say," answered Melamed. "Of course, if you—you mean some of the pushing aggressive type," added Melamed, feeling that it would be in good taste to be a little anti-Semitic in order to show them how objective and impartial a Jew could be, "I must admit, I find that kind just as objectionable as you do."

"And—and don't you think—think the—the Hebrew people are a little too sensi—sensitive?" pursued Monmouth Hightower.

To prove how outside of it he was, Melamed replied: "Maybe Jews are—to borrow the information Mr. Burt Webb has been so good as to give us—as paranoiac as Goering."

"I think," stated a tallish woman, with a Hittite beak and charcoal Armenian hair, who came from the Arran Islands and who spoke as though it were high time for a little political housecleaning, "that the German-Jews are getting what's coming to them. They not only lorded it over," she sped on in a shrill and impassioned prose, "the poor Russian and Lithuanian Jews who migrated into Eastern Germany, but it was actually German-Jewish money that supported and kept in power the Czar so that he was able to carry on his pogroms. Don't you think that's right, Mr. Mel-ah-mede?" Melamed, who was still occupied tying emotional bonds with these new acquaintances, and who had not been listening attentively, attempted to shuttle back to the conversation.

"Of course, eh, but you know my mother and father were born in Palestine. But then, what you say is . . . Well, I guess it is true the German-Jews were a little impatient about becoming Germans, and no doubt they did lose their heads in the excitement."

"What's your opinion on Russia?" asked Mr. Monte Lorrimer, whose nose, which looked like the toe of Italy, seemed racially at loggerheads with his Ottoman thighs. By now everybody was directing questions at Melamed, presupposing that he as a Jew naturally knew all about Germany, Communism, and the Soviet Union.

"We—well," interrupted the Son of the D.A.R., "I'm in fa—favor of the R—Russian Bol—Bolsheviks, but I don't like—like the Com—com—communists."

"Is—is it true," went on Monmouth Hightower, "that—that Jewish bankers financed Lenin?"

Melamed looked blank, and, weighing his words, he answered: "I —I'd be willing to look that up for you."

"What is the Communist situation in this country?" asked Mr. Lorrimer. He looked with kind eyes at Melamed as he added: "I'm really very interested and would be grateful if you'd tell me."

"Well, I can't say off-hand," asseverated Melamed, "but I'd be willing to look that up too."

"What do you think of the German Terror?" asked Miss Evelyn Syracuse Beach.

"I think it ought to stop," replied Melamed snappily and getting his bearings for a moment.

Three people simultaneously shot questions at him, after which Monmouth Hightower asked: "Mr. Me-mel-ah-ah-mede, what is your opinion of the Com-Com-Communist International?"

"Well, I don't know whether they do or don't," replied Melamed, who now was so harassed that he had become psychologically stone-deaf. And like a deaf person, who pretends he is hearing every word spoken, Melamed replied.

"I believe we should have nothing to do with the boycott," blurted forth Mrs. Briarcliff. "I think it's positively wrong and immoral for one country to attempt to interfere in the affairs of another." Melamed's voice twittered, then died. He said nothing.

There was a pause, and then Melamed said: "I guess I must be going," but as no one noticed him, he remained. Finally, he said good-by, and sort of waved at every one as though he were running for a street-car, but the others were talking. He got his hat and coat, and as he started to move toward the door, Edgar Briarcliff ran up to him: "Must you be going, old man?" Whereupon those present stopped talking and looked up at him. Mr. Monte Lorrimer smiled at him, and Melamed, beaming, took a tiny step forward and then hurried back to shake hands with Mr. Lorrimer. Looking at the others, whom he did not wish to offend, he shook hands with each one, repeating each time, "So awfully glad to have met you"—falling into that Nordic Bostonese vocabulary. By the time he reached Mrs. Jenny Briarcliff, he was bubbling again with emotion. His eyes half-shut, he grasped Mrs. Briarcliff's wrist, and pressing his fingers hard against it, broke the crystal of her watch. She screamed, and Melamed was so alarmed that he bent down, picked up the pieces of glass, and handed them back to her. Looking at him in amazement, she said, with fingernails in her voice, "Thank you."

After Edgar Briarcliff had shut the door, Melamed stood outside, wondering whether to ring the bell, go in, and apologize all over again to make amends for his clumsiness. He put his finger out, pressed the elevator bell, and then went down the steps, emptily sliding from one side of his suit to the other.

Outside the rain was still thinly scribbling against the curbs. Gazing at the trees, which looked like skeletal umbrella frames without covers, he turned up his coat collar, and, reminding himself that he was without employment and alone, he no longer wondered whether the blood of the Romance Language peoples flowed through his veins.

WAKE UP AMERICANS!
DO YOU WANT THIS?

Clean up America! Break the Red Plague!
BOYCOTT the JEW!

*Above, anti-Semitic poster in Oregon, 1938.
Above right, Fritz Kuhn, president
of the German-American Volksbund,
addresses his followers in 1937. Below, still
from Chaplin's "The Great Dictator,"
produced by United Artists.*

From Jefferson and/or Mussolini

BY EZRA POUND

POWER

THE millenniar habit of slavery and the impulse toward enslaving others is very strong in the race. By the time chattel-slavery was driven out by the American Civil War, it had been discovered that paid labour probably cost less to the employer.

Some men are now struggling to convince the mob that the machine is ready to replace the slave.

The greatest obstacle may well be just simple bossiness, bos, bovis, the bull, likes to order some fellow-human about.

The "will to power" (admired and touted by the generation before my own) was literatureifyed by an ill-balanced hysterical teuto-pollak. Nothing more vulgar, in the worst sense of the word, has ever been sprung on a dallying intelligentsia.

Power is necessary to some acts, but neither Lenin nor Mussolini show themselves primarily as men thirsting for power.

The great man is filled with a very different passion, the will toward *order*.

Hence the mysteries and the muddles in inferior minds.

The superior passion is incompatible with Dogberry and the local bully. The second line of inferiority complex (professorial) toddles in

Ezra Pound is the most controversial literary figure of our time. A life-long fighter for creative freedom, he became obsessed with what he considered to be the failure of American capitalism and, living in Italy, began to transfer his aesthetic belief in Confucian order to a political and economic belief in Fascist order. He wrote in the conclusion to *Jefferson and/or Mussolini* (1935): "I assert again my own firm belief that the Duce will stand not with despots and the lovers of power but with the lovers of ORDER." During the war, Pound made propaganda speeches supporting Mussolini and was arrested for treason in 1945. He was committed to a mental institution "in a paranoid state of psychotic proportions," where he remained until 1958.

with its twaddle about insanity and genius, and "the man must be mad."

Five or six years ago the Roman barflies and social idiots were waiting for Mussolini to go mad.

The brittle mind, living on prejudice or privilege, as a last refuge plays ostrich. Something is NOT what its mamma or schoolmarm told it, and it simply can't readjust itself.

When Mussolini has expressed any satisfaction it has been with the definite act performed, the artwork in the civic sense, the leading the Romans back to the sea, for example, by the wide new road into Ostia.

So Shu, king of Soku, built roads. What sort of shouting would the Chinese have raised for the release of the Lake of Abano, an exhilaration that might perfectly well have upset a considerable equanimity?

FREUD OR. . .

As one of the Bloomsbury weepers once remarked, "Freud's writings may not shed much light on human psychology but they tell one a good deal about the private life of the Viennese."

They are flower of a deliquescent society going to pot. The average human head is less in need of having something removed from it, than of having something inserted.

The freudized ex-neurasthenic, oh well, pass it for the neurasthenic, but the general results of Freud are Dostoievskian duds, worrying about their own unimportant innards with the deep attention of Jim drunk occupied with the crumb on his weskit.

I see no advantage in this system over the ancient Roman legion, NO individual worth saving is likely to be wrecked by a reasonable and limited obedience practised to given ends and for limited periods. So much for commandments to the militia as superior to psychic sessions for the debilitated.

That which makes a man forget his bellyache (physical or psychic) is probably as healthy as concentration of his attention on the analysis of the products or educts of a stomach-pump.

Modern ignorance, fostered and intensified by practically all university systems, has succeeded in obliterating or in dimming the old distinction in Rodolpho Agricola's *De Dialectica*.

Verbal composition is committed, "ut doceat, ut moveat, ut delectet."

Verbal composition exists to three ends, to teach, to move and to please. You do not aid either literary or philosophical discussion by criticizing one sort with criteria properly applied to the other.

We know that the German university system was perverted from the search for truth (material truth in natural research) into a vast machine for conducting the mental segment of the nation AWAY from actual problems, getting them embedded and out of the way of the tyrants.

American subsidized universities have become anodyne in the departments that "don't matter," i.e. those where the subject has not or need not have any direct incidence on life.

When it comes to economic study the interference of the controllers is less covered.

I am no longer "in touch." I know that professors are occasionally "fired." I have heard that the ladies' Vassar once had a curiosity in the form of a heavy endowment "for as long as nothing contrary to protective tariff was taught there."

The instinct of self-preservation, obviously THE great passion in the bureaucratic booZUM, leads often towards the anodyne. Such is the nature of bureaucracy. Once IN, it is hardly possible to be ousted for incompetence. So long as you aren't noticed you STAY there, promotion is in any case slow. Soft paws, quiet steps, look and listen.

This has even bred the careerist in scholarship, the man who carefully studies WHAT KIND of anodyne bunk will lead him upward in the system, or best assure his income.

I have met various specimens, one definitely producing bunk to "get ahead," another mildly discontented with the dullness of work which was at any rate safe, and couldn't by any stretch of fancy lead one into an opinion on anything save its own dullness and, by comparison with any intellectual pursuit, its lack of use. Naturally he felt the need of his income.

Thus ultimately the makers of catalogues, etc., undeniably useful but undeniably giving a very low YIELD in intellectual life, or to the intellectual life of the nation.

In fact the idea of intellectual life IN an American University is usually presented as a joke by people with what is called a sense of humour.

When an experiment is made or advocated it is usually attributed (often correctly) to "cranks."

A crank in "this pragmatical pig of a world" as Wm. Yeats has ultimately come to designate the Celto-Saxon segments of the planet, is any man having ANY other ambition save that of saving his own skin from the tanners.

An inventor stops being a crank when he has made, i.e. acquired, money, or when he has been exploited by someone who has.

Henry Ford is the best possible type of crank (taken in his *fort intérieur*), Henry himself was visible in his early days, but once inside the caterpillared tank of success his mental make-up is forgotten.

The fact that it often takes a series of two, three, or four cranks to get a thing done blinds the general reader to the utility of the successive components.

"C'est beau," said Fernand Léger in the best defence of the French republic I have ever heard. "C'est beau, it is good to look at because it works without there being anyone of interest or importance, any 'great man' necessary to make it function."

It's "beau" all right, but dear old Fernand wasn't looking at the Comité des Forges, which might appear to come nearer to being the real government of France than the gents in the Deputés and the figurehead at the Elysées. The Comité has got its dictatorship and its one-party system.

All without public responsibility. Our own country when finally betrayed by Wilson also showed from its secret internal workings, not only the financiers who had some sort of responsibility, private if not public, but the *louche* figure of State Militia "Colonel" House skulking from here to there with no responsibility whatsodamnever.

Disgust with Wilson, unimpeached, bred a reaction against having "a strong man in the White House" and we suffered the three deficients, and Heaven knows what the present (as H. Mencken defines him) "weak sister" will offer us.

The problem of democracy is whether its alleged system, its *de jure* system, can still be handled by the men of good will; whether real issues as distinct from red herrings CAN be forced into the legislatures (House and Senate), and whether a sufficiently active segment of the public can be still persuaded to combine and compel its elected delegates to act decently in an even moderately intelligent manner.

Damn the bolsheviki as much as you like, the Russian *projects* have served as stimuli BOTH to Italy and to America. Our democratic system is, for the first time, on trial against systems professing greater care for national welfare.

It becomes increasingly difficult to show WHY great schemes, Muscle Shoals etc., should be exploited for the benefit of someone in particular instead of for the nation as a whole.

It becomes, in fact it has become, utterly impossible to show that the personal resilience of the individual is less, or the scope of individual action, his fields of initiative, is any more limited, under Mussolini than under our pretendedly republican system.

The challenge of Mussolini to America is simply:

Do the driving ideas of Jefferson, Quincy Adams, Van Buren, or whoever else there is in the creditable pages of our history, FUNCTION actually in the America of this decade to the extent that they function in Italy under the DUCE?

The writer's opinion is that they DON'T, and that nothing but vigorous realignment will make them, and that if, or when, they are made so to function, Mussolini will have acted as stimulus, will have entered into American history, as Lenin has entered into world history.

That don't, or don't necessarily, mean an importation of the details of mechanisms and forms more adapted to Italy or to Russia than to the desert of Arizona or to the temperament of farms back of Baaaston. But it does definitely mean an orientation of will.

The power lust of Wilson was that of a diseased and unbalanced man who before arriving at the White House had had little experience of the world. The job of being a college president in a freshwater town, the petty hypocrisies necessary to being an example to the young, are about as good preparation for political life as that of being abbot in a monastery.

"The Eternal City" by Peter Blume.

September 1, 1939

BY W. H. AUDEN

I sit in one of the dives
On Fifty-second Street
Uncertain and afraid
As the clever hopes expire
Of a low dishonest decade:
Waves of anger and fear
Circulate over the bright
And darkened lands of the earth,
Obsessing our private lives;
The unmentionable odour of death
Offends the September night.

Accurate scholarship can
Unearth the whole offence
From Luther until now
That has driven a culture mad,
Find what occurred at Linz,
What huge imago made
A psychopatic god:
I and the public know
What all schoolchildren learn,
Those to whom evil is done
Do evil in return.

W. H. Auden came to the United States from England at the very end of the thirties, by which time he was widely recognized as the leading Marxist poet of his generation. It was Auden's deep concern for the political issues of the time that prompted Dylan Thomas to write that Auden "makes Mr. Yeats's isolation guilty as a trance." Recently, Auden has expressed his dissatisfaction with many of his poems of the thirties, including "September 1, 1939." It nevertheless remains one of the best known of all war-time poems.

Exiled Thucydides knew
All that a speech can say
About Democracy,
And what dictators do,
The elderly rubbish they talk
To an apathetic grave;
Analysed all in his book,
The enlightenment driven away,
The habit-forming pain,
Mismanagement and grief:
We must suffer them all again.

Into this neutral air
Where blind skyscrapers use
Their full height to proclaim
The strength of Collective Man,
Each language pours its vain
Competitive excuse:
But who can live for long
In an euphoric dream;
Out of the mirror they stare,
Imperialism's face
And the international wrong.

Faces along the bar
Cling to their average day:
The lights must never go out,
The music must always play,
All the conventions conspire
To make this fort assume
The furniture of home;
Lest we should see where we are,
Lost in a haunted wood,
Children afraid of the night
Who have never been happy or good.

The windiest militant trash
Important Persons shout
Is not so crude as our wish:
What mad Nijinsky wrote
About Diaghilev
Is true of the normal heart;

For the error bred in the bone
Of each woman and each man
Craves what it cannot have,
Not universal love
But to be loved alone.

From the conservative dark
Into the ethical life
The dense commuters come,
Repeating their morning vow;
"I *will* be true to the wife,
I'll concentrate more on my work,"
And helpless governors wake
To resume their compulsory game:
Who can release them now,
Who can reach the deaf,
Who can speak for the dumb?

Defenceless under the night
Our world in stupor lies;
Yet, dotted everywhere,
Ironic points of light
Flash out wherever the Just
Exchange their messages:
May I, composed like them
Of Eros and of dust,
Beleaguered by the same
Negation and despair,
Show an affirming flame.

PART TWO

The Social Muse

THE heated controversies which were to be such a dominant part of the literary world in the 1930's began before the first year of the decade had come to a close. On October 22, 1930, The New Republic printed Michael Gold's scathing attack on Thornton Wilder, "Wilder: Prophet of the Genteel Christ," in which Gold accused Wilder of being the poet of the "genteel bourgeoisie." Two months later, Sinclair Lewis addressed the Swedish Academy as the first American to be awarded the Nobel Prize for Literature and shocked the staid members—as well as the American press—by being, as he said, "a little impolite regarding certain institutions and persons of my own greatly beloved land." Lewis caustically attacked the "astonishing circus" known as the New Humanism. To Lewis, as to Michael Gold, the Humanism of Paul Elmer More, Irving Babbitt, and Stuart Sherman was a doctrine of the "blackest reaction introduced into a stirring revolutionary world."

The attack on Humanism, which was taken up by many of the leading liberal writers of the period, was the first of the literary wars to be fought in the thirties and was indicative of both the cause and the nature of the coming battles. At issue was the role the artist was to assume in his society. The Humanists were essentially conservative, religious, and erudite; they were also antidemocratic and antiscientific. As such, Humanism, as Malcolm Cowley declared, had no validity "for the mill hands of New Bedford and Gastonia, for the beet-toppers of Colorado, for the men who tighten a single screw in the automobiles that march along Mr. Ford's assembly belt." For many of the writers who were moving toward the left, the coming of a new society demanded the creation of a new art. Thus the editors of Partisan Review proclaimed in the magazine's first issue (1934): "We propose to concentrate on creative and critical literature, but we shall maintain a definite viewpoint—that of the revolutionary working class." No longer was the artist to be separated from society; the value of the revolutionary writer, as Waldo Frank told the first American Writers' Congress in 1935, was to be his ability to coordinate his art with "the political-economic aspects of the recreation of mankind." And for this reason, the principal achievement of the first Congress was considered to be the beginning of a new literary movement "which springs from an alliance of writers and artists with the working class."

Not all writers, however, regarded art primarily as a weapon. There were those who, although greatly concerned with the moral issues of the time, refused to use their art to further the cause of Marxism. Writers as different as James T. Farrell and Wallace Stevens took issue with the programmatic tendencies of the literary left and insisted upon preserving the integrity of their mind and art. But the thirties were dominated by a revolutionary fervor, and the writer who denied the importance of proletarian art frequently found that in left-wing circles the price he had to pay for his independence was social ostracism and critical disdain. The battles, as the following selections will show, were often bitter and hard-fought. The wedding of politics and literature meant that personalities were often involved and attacked along with the writing. In many cases, the wounds have still not healed.

NEW MASSES

SEPTEMBER, 1932   **15 CENTS**

In This Issue:

SHERWOOD ANDERSON
CLIFTON B. FADIMAN
LANGSTON HUGHES
ENGELS ON GOETHE
GRANVILLE HICKS
EDMUND WILSON
JOHN L. SPIVACK
UPTON SINCLAIR
MAURICE DOBB
WALDO FRANK
MICHAEL GOLD
A. B. MAGIL
MOE BRAGIN

Book Reviews
Features
Cartoons

Free Trip to the
Soviet Union!

MICHAEL GOLD AND THE GENTEEL SPIRIT

Michael Gold was one of the leading figures of the thirties. He was an editor of both the *Masses* and *New Masses;* and by 1930 he was able to say with considerable justification that he was "the first American writer to herald the advent of a world proletarian literature as a concomitant to the rise of the world proletariat." From the time he joined Max Eastman's *The Liberator* in 1921 and implored his readers to "fling all we are into the cauldron of the Revolution," Gold was generally regarded to be the "outstanding proletarian."

His review in *The New Republic* on October 22, 1930 of four novels and a volume of plays by Thornton Wilder was premised on his belief that a writer's obligation was to the Cause, not his craft. Gold had, in fact, made the same point in an earlier attack on Wilder which appeared in *New Masses.* Although both cases against Wilder were substantially the same, the *New Masses* article aroused little excitement. The readers of *The New Republic,* on the other hand, responded to Gold's review by beseiging the magazine with heated letters until, on December 17, the editors were forced to announce that the Gold-Wilder controversy was "hereby called on account of darkness." Wilder himself took no part in the argument (although many years later he was to tell Daniel Aaron that despite the fact that he had been interested in social justice and had joined a number of organizations which were eventually blacklisted, he understood why Gold had made him the object of his attack on Humanism: "In those days," Wilder wrote to Aaron in March 25, 1959, "didn't I seem very 'humanist'? I was bookish (and how!) and genteel . . . I was not interested in communism as such—never read Marx. . . .").

It remained for Edmund Wilson to point out the historical significance of the controversy. Wilson had himself become involved in the dispute when, in an unsigned editorial in *The New Republic* of November 26, 1930, he justified Gold's position by noting that Wilder was in actuality a "popularizer of Proust," whose exotic themes offered a "sedative for sick Americans." More than a year later, looking at Gold's essay and the reaction to it, Wilson summed up its importance in a two-part essay which appeared in *The New Republic* on May 4 and May 11, 1932, by referring to the controversy as the beginning of the literary class war. "There is no question," Wilson wrote, "that the Gold-Wilder row marked definitely the eruption of the Marxist issues out of the literary circles of the radicals into the field of general criticism. After that, it became very plain that the economic crisis was to be accompanied by a literary one."

Wilder: Prophet of the Genteel Christ

BY MICHAEL GOLD

"HERE'S a group of people losing sleep over a host of notions that the rest of the world has outgrown several centuries ago: one duchess's right to enter a door before another; the word order in a dogma of the Church; the divine right of Kings, especially of Bourbons."

In these words Thornton Wilder describes the people in his first book, "The Cabala." They are some eccentric old aristocrats in Rome, seen through the eyes of a typical American art "pansy" who is there as a student.

Marcantonio is the sixteen-year-old son of one of the group; he i₅ burned out with sex and idleness, and sexualizes with his sister, and then commits suicide. Another character is a beautiful, mad Princess who hates her dull Italian husband, falls in love with many Nordics and is regularly rejected by them. Others are a moldy old aristocrat woman who "believes," and a moldy old Cardinal who doesn't, and some other fine worm-eaten authentic specimens of the rare old Italian antique.

Wilder views these people with tender irony. He makes no claim as to their usefulness to the world that feeds them; yet he hints that their palace mustiness is a most important fact in the world of today. He writes with a brooding seriousness of them as if all the gods were watching their little lavender tragedies. The style is a diluted Henry James.

Wilder's second novel was "The Bridge of San Luis Rey." This famous and vastly popular yarn made a bold leap backward in time. Mr. Wilder, by then, had evidently completed his appraisal of our own age. The scene is laid in Lima, Peru; the time is Friday noon, July 20, 1714. In this volume Wilder perfected the style which is now probably permanent with him; the diluted and veritable Anatole France.

Among the characters of San Luis Rey are: (1) A sweet old duchess who loves her grown daughter to madness, but is not loved in return; (2) A beautiful unfortunate genius of an actress who after much sexualizing turns nun; (3) Her tutor, a jolly old rogue, but a true worshipper of literature; (4) Two strange brothers who love each other with a passion and delicacy that again brings the homosexual bouquet into a Wilder book, and a few other minor sufferers.

Some of the characters in this novel die in the fall of a Bridge. Our author points out the spiritual lessons imbedded in this Accident; viz: that God is Love.

The third novel is the recent "The Woman of Andros." This marks a still further masterly retreat into time and space. The scene is one of the lesser Greek islands, the hour somewhere in B. C.

The fable: a group of young Greeks spend their evenings in alternate sexual bouts and lofty Attic conversations with the last of the Aspasias. One young man falls in love with her sister, who is "pure." His father objects. Fortunately, the Aspasia dies. The father relents. But then the sister dies, too. Wistful futility and sweet soft sadness of Life. Hints of the coming of Christ: "and in the East the stars shone tranquilly down upon the land that was soon to be called Holy and that even then was preparing its precious burden." (Palestine.)

Then Mr. Wilder has published some pretty, tinkling, little three-minute playlets. These are on the most erudite and esoteric themes one could ever imagine; all about Angels, and Mozart, and King Louis, and Fairies, and a Girl of the Renaissance, and a whimsical old Actress (1780) and her old Lover; Childe Harold to the Dark Tower Came; Proserpina and the Devil; The Flight into Egypt; a Venetian Prince and a Mermaid; Shelley, Judgment Day, Centaurs, God, The Woman in the Chlamys, Christ; Brigomeide, Leviathan, Ibsen; every waxwork in Wells's Outline, in fact, except Buffalo Bill.

And this, to date, is the garden cultivated by Mr. Thornton Wilder. It is a museum, it is not a world. In this devitalized air move the wan ghosts he has called up, each in "romantic" costume. It is an historic junkshop over which our author presides.

Here one will not find the heroic archaeology of a Walter Scott or Eugene Sue. Those men had social passions, and used the past as a weapon to affect the present and future. Scott was the poet of feudalism. The past was a glorious myth he created to influence the bourgeois anti-feudal present. Eugene Sue was the poet of the proletariat. On every page of history he traced the bitter, neglected facts of the working-class martyrdom. He wove these into an epic melodrama to strengthen the heart and hand of the revolutionary workers, to inspire them with a proud consciousness of their historic mission.

That is how the past should be used; as a rich manure, as a springboard, as a battle cry, as a deepening, clarifying and sublimation of the struggles in the too-immediate present. But Mr. Wilder is the poet of the genteel bourgeoisie. They fear any such disturbing lessons out of the past. Their goal is comfort and status quo. Hence, the vapidity of these little readings in history.

Mr. Wilder, in a foreword to his book of little plays, tells himself and us the object of his esthetic striving:

"I hope," he says, "through many mistakes, to discover that spirit that is not unequal to the elevation of the great religious themes, yet which does not fall into a repellent didacticism. Didacticism is an attempt at the coercion of another's free mind, even though one knows that in these matters beyond logic, beauty is the only persuasion. Here the schoolmaster enters again. He sees all that is fairest in the Christian tradition made repugnant to the new generations by reason of the diction in which it is expressed. . . . So that the revival of religion is almost a matter of rhetoric. The work is difficult, perhaps impossible (perhaps all religions die out with the exhaustion of the language), but it at least reminds us that Our Lord asked us in His work to be not only gentle as doves, but as wise as serpents."

Mr. Wilder wishes to restore, he says, through Beauty and Rhetoric, the Spirit of Religion in American Literature. One can respect any writer in America who sets himself a goal higher than the usual racketeering. But what is this religious spirit Mr. Wilder aims to restore? Is it the crude self-torture of the Holy Rollers, or the brimstone howls and fears of the Bapists, or even the mad, titanic sincerities and delusions of a Tolstoy or Dostoievsky?

No, it is that newly fashionable literary religion that centers around Jesus Christ, the First British Gentleman. It is a pastel, pastiche, dilettante religion, without the true neurotic blood and fire, a daydream of homesexual figures in graceful gowns moving archaically among the lilies. It is Anglo-Catholicism, that last refuge of the American literary snob.

This genteel spirit of the new parlor-Christianity pervades every phase of Mr. Wilder's rhetoric. What gentle theatrical sighs! what lovely, well composed deaths and martyrdoms! what languishings and flutterings of God's sinning doves! what little jewels of Sunday-school wisdom, distributed modestly here and there through the softly flowing narrative like delicate pearls, diamonds and rubies on the costume of a meek, wronged Princess gracefully drowning herself for love, (if my image is clear).

Wilder has concocted a synthesis of all the chambermaid literature, Sunday-school tracts and boulevard piety there ever were. He has added a dash of the prep-school teacher's erudition, then embalmed all this in the speciously glamorous style of the late Anatole France. He talks much of art, of himself as Artist, of style. He is a very conscious craftsman. But his is the most irritating and pretentious style pattern I have read in years. It has the slick, smug finality of the lesser Latins; that shallow clarity and tight little good taste that remind one of nothing so much as the conversation and practice of a veteran cocotte.

Mr. Wilder strains to be spiritual; but who could reveal any real agonies and exaltations of spirit in this neat, tailor-made rhetoric? It is a great lie. It is Death. Its serenity is that of the corpse. Prick it, and it will bleed violet ink and *apéritif*. It is false to the great stormy music of Anglo-Saxon speech. Shakespeare is crude and disorderly beside Mr. Wilder. Neither Milton, Fielding, Burns, Blake, Byron, Chaucer nor Hardy could ever receive a passing mark in Mr. Wilder's classroom of style.

And this is the style with which to express America? Is this the speech of a pioneer continent? Will this discreet French drawing-room hold all the blood, horror and hope of the world's new empire? Is this the language of the intoxicated Emerson? Or the clean, rugged Thoreau, or vast Whitman? Where are the modern streets of New York, Chicago and New Orleans in these little novels? Where are the cotton mills, and the murder of Ella May and her songs? Where are the child slaves of the beet fields? Where are the stockbroker suicides, the labor racketeers or passion and death of the coal miners? Where are Babbitt, Jimmy Higgins and Anita Loos's Blonde? Is Mr. Wilder a Swede or a Greek, or is he an American? No stranger would know from these books he has written.

But is it right to demand this "nativism" of him? Yes, for Mr. Wilder has offered himself as a spiritual teacher; therefore one may say: Father, what are your lessons? How will your teaching help the "spirit" trapped in American capitalism? But Wilder takes refuge in the rootless cosmopolitanism which marks every *emigré* trying to flee the problems of his community. Internationalism is a totally different spirit. It begins at home. Mr. Wilder speaks much of the "human heart" and its eternal problems. It is with these, he would have us believe, that he concerns himself; and they are the same in any time and geography, he says. Another banal evasion. For the human heart, as he probes it in Greece, Peru, Italy and other remote places, is only the "heart" of a small futile group with whom few Americans have the faintest kinship.

For to repeat, Mr. Wilder remains the poet of a small sophisticated class that has recently arisen in America—our genteel bourgeoisie. His style is their style; it is the new fashion. Their women have taken to wearing his Greek chlamys and faintly indulge themselves in his smart Victorian pieties. Their men are at ease in his Paris and Rome.

America won the War. The world's wealth flowed into it like a red Mississippi. The newest and greatest of all leisure classes was created. Luxury-hotels, golf, old furniture and Vanity Fair sophistication were some of their expressions.

Thorstein Veblen foretold all this in 1899, in an epoch-making book that every American critic ought to study like a Bible. In "The Theory of the Leisure Class" he painted the hopeless course of most American culture for the next three decades. The grim, ironic prophet has been justified. Thornton Wilder is the perfect flower of the new prosperity. He has all the virtues Veblen said this leisure class would demand; the air of good breeding, the decorum, priestliness, glossy high finish as against intrinsic qualities, conspicuous inutility, caste feeling, love of the archaic, etc. . . .

All this is needed to help the parvenu class forget its lowly origins in American industrialism. It yields them a short cut to the aristocratic emotions. It disguises the barbaric sources of their income, the billions wrung from American workers and foreign peasants and coolies. It lets them feel spiritually worthy of that income.

Babbitt made them ashamed of being crude American climbers. Mr. Wilder, "gentle as the dove and wise as the serpent," is a more constructive teacher. Taking them patiently by the hand, he leads them into castles, palaces and far-off Greek islands, where they may study the human heart when it is nourished by blue blood. This Emily Post of culture will never reproach them; or remind them of Pittsburgh or the breadlines. He is always in perfect taste; he is the personal friend of Gene Tunney.

"For there is a land of the living and a land of the dead, and the bridge is love, the only survival, the only meaning." And nobody works in a Ford plant, and nobody starves looking for work, and there is nothing but Love in God's ancient Peru, Italy, Greece, if not in God's capitalist America 1930!

Let Mr. Wilder write a book about modern America. We predict it will reveal all his fundamental silliness and superficiality, now hidden under a Greek chlamys.

ARCHIBALD MACLEISH AND THE SOCIAL MUSE

Archibald MacLeish, perhaps more than any other writer in the early 1930's, came under the attack of the left-wing press. To MacLeish, the artist had no obligation to become involved with the problems of the state. If ultimately he preferred a capitalistic society, it was only because such a system was more favorable than either fascism or communism to the writer's artistic and intellectual freedom. The poet, MacLeish warned in "Invocation to the Social Muse," must remain alone; to be true to his art he must be apolitical and antisocial.

The reaction to the "Invocation" was generally hostile, and MacLeish's rebuttal to his critics in *The New Republic* on December 21, 1932, only intensified the controversy: "So long as the critics write and read and think in the vocabulary of Marxian dialectic, they will fumble the meaning of poetry written in the vocabulary of poetry." The following year MacLeish published "Frescoes for Mr. Rockefeller's City," and the controversy grew more heated and more personal. Mike Gold resented the "vulgar dialect" which MacLeish had given to "Comrade Levine" and decided that MacLeish was exhibiting clear symptoms of "the fascist unconscious." When Carl Sandburg tried to defend the "Frescoes" by pointing out that MacLeish had merely indulged in the "genial custom" of imitating dialects, Gold replied that Sandburg had never found it necessary to "write poems in phony Yiddish dialect to make a joke of the idea that men were brothers."

Matters were not made any better when, in 1934, MacLeish published his "Preface to an American Manifesto," in which he announced that "No man really concerned with the failure of the revolutionary movement in America need deceive himself as to the cause. The cause is obvious. The American revolutionary movement has stalled because it is a movement conceived, delivered,

and nurtured in negatives. Its impulse is hatred." The next year, however, Mac-
Leish published *Panic*, the first of his anti-Fascist works, and was embraced by
the Left. (As Malcolm Cowley wrote, MacLeish had come down from his ivory
tower and had decided "to write about the life of his own time.") But in 1940
another storm of controversy arose over the publication of MacLeish's *The Ir-
responsibles: A Declaration.* The official Marxian position in 1940 regarding
the war was one of nonintervention. To MacLeish, however, as to Waldo Frank
and Lewis Mumford, nonintervention was a mistake; Hitler had to be stopped. No
longer was MacLeish the defender of the Muse; the scholar and writer, he felt,
had become irresponsible in a world which was threatened by Fascism. "Both
writers and scholars," MacLeish wrote, "freed themselves of the subjective passions, the emotional preconceptions which color conviction and judgment. Both
writers and scholars freed themselves of the responsibility associated with personal choice. They emerged free, pure and single into the antiseptic air of ob-
jectivity. And by that sublimation of the mind they prepared the mind's disaster."

Of the many controversies in which Archibald MacLeish was involved, the
one surrounding "Invocation to the Social Muse" was the first and perhaps
the most pertinent. The poem appeared in *The New Republic* on October
26, 1932; the replies were printed in the issues of December 14, 1932 and
February 8, 1933.

Invocation to the Social Muse

BY ARCHIBALD MACLEISH

Señora, it is true the Greeks are dead.

It is true also that we here are Americans:
That we use the machines: that a sight of the god is unusual:
That more people have more thoughts: that there are

Progress and science and tractors and revolutions and
Marx and the wars more antiseptic and murderous
And music in every home: there is also Hoover.

Does the lady suggest we should write it out in The Word?
Does Madame recall our responsibilities? We are
Whores, Fräulein: poets, Fräulein, are persons of

Known vocation following troops: they must sleep with
Stragglers from either prince and of both views.
The rules permit them to further the business of neither.

It is also strictly forbidden to mix in maneuvers.
Those that infringe are inflated with praise on the plazas—
Their bones are resultantly afterwards found under newspapers.

Preferring life with the sons to death with the fathers,
We also doubt on the record whether the sons
Will still be shouting around with the same huzzas—

For we hope Lady to live to lie with the youngest.
There are only a handful of things a man likes,
Generation to generation, hungry or

Well fed: the earth's one: life's
One: Mister Morgan is not one.

There is nothing worse for our trade than to be in style.

He that goes naked goes further at last than another.
Wrap the bard in a flag or a school and they'll jimmy his
Door down and be thick in his bed—for a month:

(Who recalls the address now of the Imagists?)
But the naked man has always his own nakedness.
People remember forever his live limbs.

They may drive him out of the camps but one will take him.
They may stop his tongue on his teeth with a rope's argument—
He will lie in a house and be warm when they are shaking.

Besides, Tovarishch, how to embrace an army?
How to take to one's chamber a million souls?
How to conceive in the name of a column of marchers?

The things of the poet are done to a man alone
As the things of love are done—or of death when he hears the
Step withdraw on the stair and the clock tick only.

Neither his class nor his kind nor his trade may come near him
There where he lies on his left arm and will die,
Nor his class nor his kind nor his trade when the blood is jeering

And his knee's in the soft of the bed where his love lies.
I remind you, Barinya, the life of the poet is hard—
A hardy life with a boot as quick as a fiver:

Is it just to demand of us also to bear arms?

The Social Muse Replies:
Letters to The New Republic

AENEAS AT NEW YORK

To Archibald MacLeish

You have Sir said it well but I have if
Not knowledge a long memory of arms
The dates the various implements of war
Is it just to demand of us also to bear arms?
It is just: what manner of man was he
Sinon who swore at Neptune's priest, swearing
When the hard spear betrayed the horse's belly?
First we are priests second we are not whores
We are those who have arranged the auguries
And in dangerous youth made the good battle
I think Sir that you honoring our trade
(And nothing is lost save its honor)
And wishing us our own integrity and calm
Fall, if I may say it with respect, in error:
Is it just to demand of us also to bear arms
It is just and it is chiefly the nice question
Of the period of life and of whose arms:
You will remember the name of the poet fighting,
The young man at Salamis. Was he a whore?
The poet is he who fights on the passionate
Side and whoever loses he wins; when he
Is defeated it is hard to say who wins
Appreciation of victory contains no views
Neither views nor princes nor are there rules
There is the infallible instinct for the right battle
On the passionate side. With whose arms
Not arms of Mister J. P. Morgan: he is not one:
With one's own arms when necessity detects
The fir-built horse inside the gates of Troy
We have nothing to do with Aulis nor intrigues
At Mycenae. I cannot of course prescribe
For other cities. Here (I merely suggest it)
Is what we did at Troy: there was no column
Of marchers there were myself and sad Hector
Have you Penates have you altars, have

You your great-great-grandfather's breeches?
Do not I do not attempt to wear the greaves
The moths are fed; our shanks too thin. Have you
His flintlock or had he none have you bought
A new Browning? The use of arms is ownership
Of the appropriate gun. It is ownership that brings
Victory that is not hinted at in "Das Kapital."
I think there is never but one true war
So let us as you desire perfect our trade.

ALLEN TATE.

SIR: Archibald MacLeish's "Invocation to the Social Muse" is an admirable poem. Furthermore, it says something that needed very much to be said at this time when every force, including a fear for his own skin, urges the poet to take political sides. It is too often assumed that if a poet does not mix in politics, he is refusing in some cowardly fashion to face life, and that, if once engaged, he does not take up an extreme position, he is not only a poltroon, but an ignoramus. The truth is, a poet has shown enough courage if he can face his own life. And it requires a great ignorance of literary history not to be aware that politics is the besetting sin of poets and one which has done them and their craft more harm than all forms of drunkenness and debauchery put together.

For having yielded to that temptation, the Tuscans suffered exile, the Tudor poets decapitation and the liberal poets of the nineteenth century extinction through rhetoric. Think of what "Paradise Lost" might have been had John Milton not attached himself to the warty Cromwell and wasted the best years of his life! Nor are recent examples more edifying. Louis Aragon has only yielded to his own already excessive love of violence in putting himself at the service of the revolution, and I notice that Yessenin and Mayakovsky found that once on the extreme left there was no place to go but toward suicide. Nor is it recorded that politics has benefited much by their intrusion.

There is a way for the poet, as there is for the novelist, to write of political events. There is "Coriolanus," there is "The Possessed." The one is a dramatic poem, the other a novel. They have no immediate interest. Mr. MacLeish deserves the highest praise for his stand that a poet should attend to his business, which is writing poems, at a time when so many have deserted literature to engage in polemics. For it would be, I think, a mistake to describe the American Communists as engaged in political activity when what they are really doing is indulging themselves in an intellectual coma and letting two other men, both dead, do their thinking for them.

Orgeval, France.   JOHN PEALE BISHOP.

SIR: Mr. MacLeish's "Invocation to the Social Muse" has drawn responses whose content is scarcely commensurate with the indignation of the correspondents. Mr. MacLeish said that the poets were whores, and even though he explicitly included himself in this modest profession, he gave great offense. It seems that the poets do not like to be called whores, and some of them have written to the editor.

Mr. Tate says that the poets are not whores, and presents his views in a remarkably fine poem whose classical allusions and punctuation are equally unintelligible, and whose statements are nothing so much as adroitly oracular. However, Mr. Tate claims that the poets are neither *femmes de guerre* nor *hors de combat;* moreover, they are sometimes priests. Mr. Platt does not comprehend the abrupt sexual metamorphosis that overtakes one of Mr. MacLeish's bards, and in truth Mr. MacLeish is much from the past, no matter how ardently his conscious activity struggles to be free of its influence. A poet of past revolution is a member of the established order; whereas revolutions in process abolish leisure. That leaves the poet the revolution of the future to set down, if he can manage to see it. If the vision of the prophet is strong enough upon him, if he can maintain his own ecstasy without succumbing to the prophet's aim to excite, he may accomplish a *tour de force.* But even if he does thus succeed in wearing his rue with a difference, he will trail clouds of glory from the unregenerate past. Thus we see that a pure revolutionary art is impossible. Q. E. D.

The generals of the revolution are perfectly aware of these considerations (v. Trotsky "Literature and Revolution"), and it is not their fault if the far-flung sergeants in the province are less subtle. Whether the latter are well advised to comb the literary field in search of recruits is a debatable question. The poets are intelligent and articulate; moreover, in their own way, they are disciplined and brave. *Create* is a word so worn by fools' misuse that there is little sense left in it; let us say that the poets can see, hear, think, feel, talk, write. But these special aptitudes handicap rather than qualify them for service in the line, and they are mainly thought to be useful as auxiliaries, to hearten the troops or harangue the civilian population. If they are enlisted on these terms, the military arm should bear in mind that there is no camp-follower for whom the soldier has a more hearty detestation.

These peculiarities do not make them draft-exempt. Artists are not sacrosanct; too much nonsense has been sung to that score. Moreover, nobody is an artist all the time. It is just to ask them to bear arms or to shovel snow—only it is not remarkably astute. They abrogate their proper functions when you recruit them for the wars: do not delude yourself that they bring cantonments a talent capable of transfer.

New York City.   ROLFE HUMPHRIES.

A POSTCARD TO THE SOCIAL MUSE

Madam, since you choose
To call yourself a Muse,
I will not be too nice
To give advice.

Passion is hard of speech,
Wisdom exact of reach;
Poets have studied verse;
And wit is terse.

Change or repose is wrought
By steady arm and thought:
The fine indignant sprawl
Confuses all.

Than to engage with those
Of small verse and less prose
'Twas better far to play
At bouts-rimés.

Stanford University, Calif.   YVOR WINTERS.

THE WRITER ON MIDDLE GROUND

In 1935 the Communist Party officially announced its policy of a Popular Front. No longer would the Party follow a hard line; it was agreed at the Seventh World Congress of the Communist International held in Moscow in 1935 that the Party would pursue a policy of collaboration with all enemies of Fascism. This meant, among other things, that an attempt would be made to gain the support of those writers who were on the "middle-ground." No one would be rejected, Stanley Burnshaw wrote in the *New Masses* of April 30, 1935, who might be turned into a friend of the revolutionary movement. This did not mean, though, that "middle-ground" writers would not continue to be taken to task for failing to instill their art with Marxist doctrine. On October 1, 1935, *New Masses* printed Burnshaw's review of two books by "middle-ground" poets, Haniel Long's *Pittsburgh Memoranda* and Wallace Steven's *Ideas of Order*. Entitled "Turmoil in the Middle Ground," Burnshaw's review acknowledged that Long and Stevens were "poets whose artistic stature have long been recognized," but criticized them for not realizing that "If mankind's fulfillment is his supreme desire, where else can he turn for real hope except Marxism?" The review angered Stevens, who wrote to Ronald L. Latimer on October 9, 1935: "I hope I am headed left, but there are lefts and lefts, and certainly I am not headed for the ghastly left of the *Masses*. The rich man and the comfortable man of the imagination of people like Mr. Burnshaw are not nearly so rich nor nearly so comfortable as he believes them to be." The following year, when Stevens' *Owl Clover* was published, it became clear just how angry he was; the second section of the volume, "Mr. Burnshaw and the Statue," was one of Stevens' few ventures into political satire. Years later, Stevens was to refer to Communism as a "grubby faith" which "promises a practicable earthly paradise," while Burnshaw was to observe that in 1936 Stevens cut the poem and changed the title to "The Statue at the World's End," then made other revisions for the version in *The Man with the Blue Guitar*, and finally omitted the poem altogether from *Collected Poems*. The original version of "Mr. Burnshaw and the Statue" appears in *Opus Posthumous*, from which it has been reprinted in its entirety; only the latter half of Burnshaw's review, that part which deals with *Ideas of Order*, has been reprinted.

Turmoil in the Middle Ground

BY STANLEY BURNSHAW

CONFUSED as it is, *Pittsburgh Memoranda* is a marvel of order alongside Wallace Stevens' volume; and yet to many readers it is something of a miracle that Stevens has at all bothered to give us his *Ideas of Order*.

When *Harmonium* appeared a dozen years ago Stevens was at once set down as an incomparable verbal musician. But nobody stopped to ask if he had any ideas. It was tacitly assumed that one read him for pure poetic sensation; if he had "a message" it was carefully buried and would take no end of labor to exhume. Yet he often comes out with flat judgments and certain ideas weave through the book consistently.

> The magnificent cause of being,
> The imagination, the one reality
> In this imagined world

underlies a number of poems. Realists have been bitter at the inanity of Pope's "whatever is is right," but Stevens plunges ahead to the final insolence: "For realists, what is is what should be." And yet it is hard to know if such a line is not Stevens posing in self-mockery. One can rarely speak surely of Stevens' ideas.

But certain general convictions he admits in such a poem as "To the One of Fictive Music." Bound up with the sovereignty of the imagination is his belief in an interfusion of music among the elements and man. And "music is feeling . . . not sound." This trinity of principles makes the business of living to him a matter of searching out the specific harmonies.

Harmonium, then, is mainly sense poetry, but not as Keats' is sense poetry because this serener poet is not driven to suffuse sensuous imagery with powerful subjective emotions. This is "scientific," objectified sensuousness separated from its kernel of fire and allowed to settle, cool off and harden in the poet's mind until it emerges a strange amazing crystal. Reading this poetry becomes a venture in crystallography. It is remembered for its curious humor, its brightness, words and phrases that one rolls on the tongue. It is the kind of verse that people concerned with the murderous world collapse can hardly swallow today except in tiny doses.

And it is verse that Stevens can no longer write. His harmonious cosmos is suddenly screeching with confusion. *Ideas of Order* is the record of a man who, having lost his footing, now scrambles to stand up and keep his balance. The opening poem observes

> . . . This heavy historical sail
> Through the mustiest blue of the lake
> In a really vertiginous boat
> Is wholly the vapidest fake. . . .

And the rest follows with all the ironical logic of such a premise. The "sudden mobs of men" may have the answer

> But what are radiant reason and radiant will
> To warblings early in the hilarious trees. . . .

Sceptical of man's desire in general, there is still much to be said for the ordering power of the imagination. But there remains a yearning —and escape is itself an irony. "Marx has ruined Nature, for the moment," he observes in self-mockery; but he can speculate on the wisdom of turning inward *(vide* Long), and a moment later look upon collective mankind as the guilty bungler of harmonious life, in "a peanut parody for a peanut people." What answer is there in the cosmic law—"everything falls back to coldness"? With apparent earnestness he goes a step beyond his former nature-man interfusing harmony:

> Only we two are one, not you and night,
> Nor night and I, but you and I, alone,
> So much alone, so deeply by ourselves,
> So far beyond the casual solitudes,
> That night is only the background of our selves . . .

And in a long poem he pours out in strange confusion his ideas of order, among them

> If ever the search for a tranquil belief should end,
> The future might stop emerging out of the past,
> Out of what is full of us; yet the search
> And the future emerging out of us seem to be one.

Paraphrase, always a treacherous tool, is especially dangerous when used on so *raffiné* a poet as Stevens. Does he talk of himself when he explains that the "purple bird must have notes for his comfort that he may repeat through the gross tedium of being rare?" Does he make political reference in declaring "the union of the weakest develops strength, not wisdom?"

Asking questions may not be a reviewer's function, but uncertainties are unavoidable when reading such poets as the two under review; for the texture of their thought is made of speculations, questionings, contradictions. Acutely conscious members of a class menaced by clashes between capital and labor, these writers are in the throes of struggle for philosophical adjustment. And their words have intense value and meaning to the sectors within their class whose confusion they articulate. Their books have deep importance for us as well.

Of course, objectively neither poet is weakening the class in power —as yet they are potential allies as well as potential enemies—but one of them looks for a new set of values and the other earnestly propagates (however vaguely) some form of collectivism. Will Long emancipate himself from his paralyzing faith in inner perfection? Will Stevens sweep his contradictory notions into a valid Idea of Order? The answers depend not only on the personal predispositions of these poets but on their full realization of the alternatives facing them as artists.

Mr. Burnshaw and the Statue

BY WALLACE STEVENS

I

The thing is dead . . . Everything is dead
Except the future. Always everything
That is is dead except what ought to be.
All things destroy themselves or are destroyed.

These are not even Russian animals.
They are horses as they were in the sculptor's mind.
They might be sugar or paste or citron-skin
Made by a cook that never rode the back
Of his angel through the skies. They might be mud
Left here by moonlit muckers when they fled
At the burst of day, crepuscular images
Made to remember a life they never lived
In the witching wilderness, night's witchingness,
Made to affect a dream they never had,
Like a word in the mind that sticks at artichoke
And remains inarticulate, horses with cream.
The statue seems a thing from Schwarz's, a thing
Of the dank imagination, much below
Our crusted outlines hot and huge with fact,
Ugly as an idea, not beautiful
As sequels without thought. In the rudest red
Of autumn, these horses should go clattering
Along the thin horizons, nobly more
Than this jotting-down of the sculptor's foppishness
Long after the worms and the curious carvings of
Their snouts.

II

Come, all celestial paramours,
Whether in-dwelling haughty clouds, frigid
And crisply musical, or holy caverns temple-toned,
Entwine your arms and moving to and fro,
Now like a ballet infantine in awkward steps,
Chant sibilant requiems for this effigy.
Bring down from nowhere nothing's wax-like blooms,
Calling them what you will but loosely-named

In a mortal lullaby, like porcelain.
Then, while the music makes you, make, yourselves,
Long autumn sheens and pittering sounds like sounds
On pattering leaves and suddenly with lights,
Astral and Shelleyan, diffuse new day;
And on this ring of marble horses shed
The rainbow in its glistening serpentines
Made by the sun ascending seventy seas.
Agree: the apple in the orchard, round
And red, will not be redder, rounder then
Than now. No: nor the ploughman in his bed
Be free to sleep there sounder, for the plough
And the dew and the ploughman still will best be one.
But this gawky plaster will not be here.

III

The stones
That will replace it shall be carved, *"The Mass
Appoints These Marbles Of Itself To Be
Itself."* No more than that, no subterfuge,
No memorable muffing, bare and blunt.

IV

Mesdames, one might believe that Shelley lies
Less in the stars than in their earthy wake,
Since the radiant disclosures that you make
Are of an eternal vista, manqué and gold
And brown, an Italy of the mind, a place
Of fear before the disorder of the strange,
A time in which the poets' politics
Will rule in a poets' world. Yet that will be
A world impossible for poets, who
Complain and prophesy, in their complaints,
And are never of the world in which they live.
Disclose the rude and ruddy at their jobs
And if you weep for peacocks that are gone
Or dance the death of doves, most sallowly,
Who knows? The ploughman may not live alone
With his plough, the peacock may abandon pride,
The dove's adagio may lose its depth
And change. If ploughmen, peacocks, doves alike
In vast disorder live in the ruins, free,

The charts destroyed, even disorder may,
So seen, have an order of its own, a peace
Not now to be perceived yet order's own.

V

A solemn voice, not Mr. Burnshaw's says:
At some gigantic, solitary urn,
A trash can at the end of the world, the dead
Give up dead things and the living turn away.
There buzzards pile their sticks among the bones
Of buzzards and eat the bellies of the rich,
Fat with a thousand butters, and the crows
Sip the wild honey of the poor man's life,
The blood of his bitter brain; and there the sun
Shines without fire on columns intercrossed,
White slapped on white, majestic, marble heads,
Severed and tumbled into seedless grass,
Motionless, knowing neither dew nor frost.
There lies the head of the sculptor in which the thought
Of lizards, in its eye, is more acute
Than the thought that once was native to the skull;
And there are the white-maned horses' heads, beyond
The help of any wind or any sky:
Parts of the immense detritus of a world
That is completely waste, that moves from waste
To waste, out of the hopeless waste of the past
Into a hopeful waste to come. There even
The colorless light in which this wreckage lies
Has faint, portentous lustres, shades and shapes
Of rose, or what will once more rise to rose,
When younger bodies, because they are younger, rise
And chant the rose-points of their birth, and when
For a little time, again, rose-breasted birds
Sing rose-beliefs. Above that urn two lights
Commingle, not like the commingling of sun and moon
At dawn, nor of summer-light and winter-light
In an autumn afternoon, but two immense
Reflections, whirling apart and wide away.

VI

Mesdames, it is not enough to be reconciled
Before the strange, having wept and having thought

And having said farewell. It is not enough
That the vista retain ploughmen, peacocks, doves,
However tarnished, companions out of the past,
And that, heavily, you move with them in the dust.
It is not enough that you are indifferent,
Because time moves on columns intercrossed
And because the temple is never quite composed,
Silent and turquoised and perpetual,
Visible over the sea. It is only enough
To live incessantly in change. See how
On a day still full of summer, when the leaves
Appear to sleep within a sleeping air,
They suddenly fall and the leafless sound of the wind
Is no longer a sound of summer. So great a change
Is constant. The time you call serene descends
Through a moving chaos that never ends. Mesdames,
Leaves are not always falling and the birds
Of chaos are not always sad nor lost
In melancholy distances. You held
Each other moving in a chant and danced
Beside the statue, while you sang. Your eyes
Were solemn and your gowns were blown and grief
Was under every temple-tone. You sang
A tragic lullaby, like porcelain.
But change composes, too, and chaos comes
To momentary calm, spectacular flocks
Of crimson and hoods of Venezuelan green
And the sound of z in the grass all day, though these
Are chaos and of archaic change. Shall you,
Then, fear a drastic community evolved
From the whirling, slowly and by trial; or fear
Men gathering for a mighty flight of men,
An abysmal migration into a possible blue?

VII

Dance, now, and with sharp voices cry, but cry
Like damsels daubed and let your feet be bare
To touch the grass and as you circle, turn
Your backs upon the vivid statue. Then,
Weaving ring in radiant ring and quickly, fling
Yourselves away and at a distance join
Your hands held high and cry again, but cry,

This time, like damsels captured by the sky,
Seized by that possible blue. Be maidens formed
Of the most evasive hue of a lesser blue,
Of the least appreciable shade of green
And despicable shades of red, just seen,
And vaguely to be seen, a matinal red,
A dewy flashing blanks away from fire,
As if your gowns were woven of the light
Yet were not bright, came shining as things come
That enter day from night, came mirror-dark,
With each fold sweeping in a sweeping play.
Let your golden hands wave fastly and be gay
And your braids bear brightening of crimson bands.
Conceive that while you dance the statue falls,
The heads are severed, topple, tumble, tip
In the soil and rest. Conceive that marble men
Serenely selves, transfigured by the selves
From which they came, make real the attitudes
Appointed for them and that the pediment
Bears words that are the speech of marble men.
In the glassy sound of your voices, the porcelain cries,
The alto clank of the long recitation, in these
Speak, and in these repeat: *To Be Itself,*
Until the sharply-colored glass transforms
Itself into the speech of the spirit, until
The porcelain bell-borrowings become
Implicit clarities in the way you cry
And are your feelings changed to sound, without
A change, until the waterish ditherings turn
To the tense, the maudlin, true meridian
That is yourselves, when, at last, you are yourselves,
Speaking and strutting broadly, fair and bloomed,
No longer of air but of the breathing earth,
Impassioned seducers and seduced, the pale
Pitched into swelling bodies, upward, drift
In a storm blown into glittering shapes, and flames
Wind-beaten into freshest, brightest fire.

ON SOUTHERN CULTURE

The left-wing attack against the anti-collectivism of the Humanists was officially launched in April of 1930. V. F. Calverton, writing in *New Masses,* warned that Humanism was more than a literary disease; it was nothing less than the "venomous spirit of social reaction." And to Mike Gold, writing in the same issue of *New Masses,* Humanism was "the startling and sly introduction of Fascism into this country." Among the important defenders of Humanism was T. S. Eliot, who in 1929 likened communism to fascism, and who admitted that "the fascist form of unreason is less remote from my own than is that of the communists." Eliot followed the lead of his friend Ezra Pound not only in rejecting the idea that art was determined by social and economic conditions, but also in his dislike for capitalism. Although he scorned the young intellectuals in New York who were turning to communism—like Pound, he had little use for "free-thinking Jews"—Eliot welcomed the cause of the twelve Southerners who, in 1930, published their manifesto for a return to the agrarianism of the Old South, *I'll Take My Stand.* Their position was staunchly anti-industrialist: "It is strange," they wrote, "that a majority of men anywhere could ever as with one mind become enamored of individualism. . . . Men are prepared to sacrifice their private dignity and happiness to an abstract social ideal, and without asking whether the social ideal produces the welfare of any individual man whatsoever. But this is absurd. The responsibility of men is for their own welfare and that of their neighbors; not for the hypothetical welfare of some fabulous creature called society." Such a position was bound to be criticized by the Left—as indeed it was—and eventually resulted in the exchange here reprinted between V. F. Calverton and John Crowe Ransom, which originally appeared in the same issue of *Scribner's Magazine* in May 1936. Interestingly enough, Calverton's essay was written three years after he had himself fallen out of favor with the Communist Party, while Ransom's essay represents the last public statement he made on behalf of Agrarianism.

The Bankruptcy of Southern Culture

BY V. F. CALVERTON

THE SOUTH today is two hundred years behind the North in cultural advance. The same religious handicaps which weighed down New England culture in the seventeenth and first half of the eighteenth centuries have now overwhelmed Southern culture. While the South today is not officially governed by a theocracy, as New England was in the seventeenth century, the clergy there at the present time has almost as strong a hold upon the prevailing institutions as the theocrats had upon those in the North two centuries ago. In other words, the North and the South have changed places in the religious cycle, the South having burdened itself with the same incubus from which the North, after a bitter struggle, disencumbered itself generations ago. As a result Southern culture has been brought to an abrupt standstill. Religion-ridden from top to bottom, adoring superstition instead of science, sceptical of the new and credulous of the old, the South today in cultural outlook is scarcely more progressive than a medieval village. In a sense, it is nothing more than a big village in its attitudes and aspirations. In economics, politics, education, and art its religious psychology, with its prying, meddlesome, inquisitorial emphasis, its fanatic self-righteousness and intolerant perfectionism, has penetrated into the heart of the culture and paralyzed the spirit of progress.

In several directions, to be sure, there have been signs of cultural advance in the South in recent days, but at best they have been nothing more than isolated, scattered flags dotting the face of a wilderness. There have been literary and cultural conventions which have resulted in the formation of various literary cliques, one or two of which are not without a kind of pseudo-political cast; several universities have shown sudden spurts of progress; and there have been a number of individual writers who have sprung into prominence, most notably Thomas Wolfe, William Faulkner, Paul Green, T. S. Stribling, Julia Peterkin, DuBose Heyward, Allen Tate, Donald Davidson, Erskine Caldwell, Fielding Burke, and Grace Lumpkin. But have those conventions, those cliques, or those writers destroyed the cultural stagnation of the South? Do they signify any marked advance in the intellectual outlook of the Southern States, which reflects itself in religion, economics, politics, education, the press or the theater? Obviously not. Do they even indicate the growth of a sufficient audience in the South to assure those writers of an adequate prestige and patronage to keep on with their work? No! Because the prestige and financial support which those writers have acquired have been derived from the North and not from the South which has scarcely more than recognized their existence. Even such magazines as *The Virginia Quarterly Review, The Sewanee Review, The Southwest Review,* and *Social Forces,* all of which represent a spirit of advance far superior to the environment in which they exist, rally perhaps as much of their support from the North as from the South—if not more. When we remember that *The Reviewer* had less than fifty subscribers in the whole state of North Carolina, the state in which it was published under Paul Green's able editorship, we should not be surprised at such a condition of affairs. While these writers and these magazines do indicate slight signs of advance they will not have any marked influence upon Southern culture until industry spreads throughout the South and breaks down the provincialism which now prevails. So long as the South remains a community dominated by petty agrarians, the religious tyranny from which it now suffers will continue unabated.

At the present time the religious domination of Southern culture is a far more devastating phenomenon than was the theocratic dictatorship over New England culture. Whatever else one may say of the theocratic dictatorship, one must admit that the theocrats themselves were not inferior minds, unacquainted with the prevailing knowledge of their period. Several of the earlier group were Oxford graduates, and practically all were highly trained men. Implacably opposed though they were to the aristocratic way of life, they did not allow the aristocracy to monopolize the existing wisdom of the day. Shrewd-minded to the extreme, they utilized every opportunity to twist thought in their direction instead of allowing it to twist beyond their reach. Cotton Mather even delved into the eccentric science of his time and encouraged people to record their scientific observations and discoveries. More than that, at a period when such matters had been scarcely freed of the trappings of magic, the New England clergy came out in defense of vaccination, and defied the pre-scientific objections to it which were raised by many medical men of the period.

If we turn to philosophy, it can certainly be said without resort to hyperbole that Jonathan Edwards was not only acquainted with the entire philosophic tradition, but was also one of the outstanding philosophers of the day. The arguments of the New England theocrats, therefore, cannot be flagrantly accused of being backward in terms of their times. That they were backward in terms of today is obvious, but so were most of the other ideas and attitudes of that day. In the South at the present time, on the contrary, the clergy have not kept up with the accumulated knowledge of our day. Their conclusions are based upon the prevailing ignorance instead of upon the prevailing knowledge of our century. Nowhere is there a Cotton Mather among them to effect a necessary conjunction between religion and science, nor a Jonathan Edwards to establish a philosophic justification for religious thought. Instead of cultivating an understanding of science and philosophy in an attempt to harmonize them with religion, they have closed their minds to the scientific and philosophic thought of the day, rejecting its contributions instead of accepting them. As a consequence, scientific and philosophic progress in the South has been deprived of initiative and vigor. The fear of ecclesiastical condemnation has terrorized the spirit of inquiry and has annihilated the possibility of intellectual advance.

ECCLESIASTICAL TERRORISM

Before the Civil War the South had been religious also, but the religion which then prevailed had interfered but little with the growth of ideas and the dissemination of culture. On the contrary, the Episcopal Church, which was the church of the plantation aristocracy, allowed for that elasticity of outlook which was necessary for the spread of culture. It was the evangelical religions which acquired supremacy after the Civil War that destroyed the latitudinarian spirit which had preceded. And it has been these evangelical religions which have assailed intellectual freedom in the South and forced anti-evolution bills through various Southern legislatures and almost forced them through many others. These anti-evolution bills provide one of the most tragic illustrations of the influence of this religious force in the educational field.

The authority of Bishop Candler, whom Corra Harris described in *My Book and Heart* as "the greatest churchman of his time," is typical of this evangelical psychology in its most glaring form. Bishop Candler's opposition to such "freethinking" institutions as Harvard and Yale, and his hostility to independent educational institutions and State universities, is characteristic of this philosophy as it expresses itself in educational thought. Without question there are bishops and parsons in the North who share the views of Bishop Candler, but the difference is that these Northern bishops and parsons have little influence and less power, while Bishop Candler has great influence and enormous power. It was just this influence and power, shaping the cast of Southern culture, which provoked the Dayton fiasco and made the South into a spectacle of stupidity in the eyes of the modern world. This same spirit was manifest in the condemnation of Paul Green's defunct magazine, *The Reviewer,* as "the Devil's Instrument."

Even among the more liberal educators in the South this same religious-tinged attitude persists in slightly adulterated form. Although a new attitude is beginning to poke its head up here and there in the independent colleges and universities in the South, it has not yet been able to free itself from the incubus of religious rule.

Without libraries that are genuinely interested in the promotion of literature, without bookstores to cultivate the sale of books—although there are both individual librarians and individual book-sellers who are doing everything in their power to encourage literature, they find their efforts rendered futile by the pressures of the environment —without publishing houses and magazines to stir up a consciousness of literature in the environment, the condition of culture in the South today is no better than when Sidney Lanier wrote to his brother that, in his soberest moments, he could "perceive no outlook for that land." "Our people," asserted Lanier, "have failed to perceive the deeper movements, under-running the times: they lie wholly off, out of the stream of thought, and whirl their poor dead leaves of recollection, round and round, in a piteous eddy that has all the wear and tear of motion without any of the rewards of progress."

ROSE-RIMMED DIXIE! — THE LORELEI OF THE SOUTHERN MIND

Conscious of the nature of these conditions, cognizant of the tragedy which they imply, progressive minds in the South today are concerned with finding a way out of them, a means of spiritual escape. In fact, as I shall show a little later on, as a result of this concern, which has become almost an obsession, the whole Southern mind has turned into an escape mechanism. Escape to what? To the past! To a South that once was, a pre-Civil-War South—Dixie.

But why should these minds be so concerned with a South that belongs so definitely and irrevocably to the past? What did that South represent which continues to enchant long after its day is gone? In the first place, that South represented the very antithesis of the South of today. It was just as interested in culture at that time as the contemporary South is uninterested in it. It was that pre-Civil-War South which organized the first musical society in America, the Saint Cecilia Society, welcomed the first opera, presented the first orchestra, and staged the first drama. At the same time that the North associated music with sorcery the South came to look upon music as an elevating diversion. It was that same South which possessed virginals, hand lyres, violins, and flutes, and adorned its walls with the canvases of Reynolds, Gainsborough, and Stuart. In that South also Scott, Byron, Bulwer, Campbell, Mrs. Hemans, Addison, Pope and Wycherly, Congreve and, Dryden were revered as well as read. The psychology of the plantation aristocrat dominated and not that of the ecclesiastic, and cultural energy, consequently, was shunted off in the direction of political oratory instead of theological polemics. Politics then was the great art, with religion playing an ever-receding rôle in the administration of the social order. Indeed, the religion of this plantation aristocracy, finding its voice in the Episcopal Church, cultivated virtue without too strongly denouncing vice, exalted form more than faith, and was more willing to condone than to condemn. While the religious leaders in the North were opposed to music and dancing, and even forbade the introduction of organs into their churches, the Episcopalian clergymen were no more averse to musical entertainment than they were to horse-racing or theater-going. It is no wonder, then, that the South in those days represented the gayest life in America.

PURITANISM IN THE SOUTH

It is to that South that so many romantic Southerners still wish to return. What happened to that South many of them still cannot understand. One of the reasons is that they continue to think of that old South as a single unit instead of as a divided entity. There were two Souths before the Civil War, not one. There was a seventeenth-century South which was different from the eighteenth-century and nineteenth-century South. In the seventeenth century, before the plantation aristocracy had established itself as the ruling class, the attitude toward religion and art was not very different in Virginia from that in Massachusetts. The fact of the matter is, the same petty-bourgeois element which settled in New England settled also in the South. Although the petty bourgeoisie in Virginia did not stem from the same Puritan stock as did the New England theocrats, they were descendants of the same Dissenting tradition which rooted itself much deeper than Puritanism proper into our culture. It was this petty bourgeoisie, and not the Cavaliers, who shaped seventeenth-century Southern culture. As Professor Wertenbaker has incontestably shown, the Cavaliers constituted an inconspicuously small percentage of the population, and exerted little influence over Southern culture. A survey of the laws and statutes of early Virginia, for example, will reveal the same spirit as that which pervaded New England. Blue laws were enacted in Virginia which were just as severe as those passed in Massachusetts. The grand juries and vestries were as vigilant in reporting the offenses as the courts were in executing the punishments that were to be meted out to those guilty of inebriety, defamation, sexual immorality, or profaning the Sabbath. In 1649 a law was passed in Virginia forcing every person to attend church. Floggings, exposure in the stocks, and heavy fines were very much in vogue. Laws concerned with limitations of dress were also common. Bishop Bayly's "Practise of Piety, Directing a Christian how to Work that he may Please God," which was popular in Virginia as late as the eighteenth century, was scarcely less gravely admonitory in its tone than the sermons of the New England theocrats. Indeed, so saturated were the early Virginians with this ascetic religiosity that when the Indian Massacre of 1622 occurred the Virginia company attributed it to the "sins of drunkenness and excess of apparell" which prevailed in the colonies. Virginians who went into battle with the Indians did so with prayers not less devout than those of the New Englanders, with strict prohibitions against profanity as part of their martial procedure. Even the witch-hunting craze found almost as secure a foothold there as in the North. Indeed, a record of the trial of a witch, a certain Grace Sherwood, in the county of Princess Anne has been preserved. The inlet in which she was submerged—unfortunately she was able to swim and was transported to jail for more dire punishment—is still known as Witch Duck. In addition to persecuting witches we find that the ecclesiastics forced through the Assembly laws that were in every way as strict as those in New England. Certainly the following laws, which were passed in Virginia in 1662, were not more lenient than those enacted in Massachusetts:

"Every person who refuses to have his child Baptized by a lawful Minister, shall be amerced 2000 pounds of Tobacco; half to the parish, half to the informer."

"The Man and Woman committing fornication shall pay each 500 pounds of Tobacco and to be bound to their good behaviors."

Even in artistic matters their original attitude was not very different from that found in the colonies along the New England coast. While the coming of the Cavaliers during the first half of the seventeenth century had unquestionably tempered somewhat the petty-bourgeois attitude toward art and thus provided leeway for a degree of art appreciation if not art expression which did not exist in New England, the vast majority of the population was unaffected by this influence. Although Governor Berkeley may have approved of the theater and even written plays himself, the populace with its petty-bourgeois antipathy for art refused to be converted to his aesthetic philosophy. Long before Berkeley ever appeared on the American scene, actors were considered in Virginia as part of "the scum and dregs of the earth." In fact as late as 1665 three men from Accomac County were arrested for staging a play known as "Ye Bare and Ye Cubb." Previous to 1665 it is doubtful if any Virginians would have hazarded such a violation of the petty-bourgeois ethic. Even under the protection of Governor Berkeley play-acting was only attempted as an amateur amusement in drawing-room and parlor. Literature itself was looked down upon with scathing contempt. Even in the eighteenth century, when the structure of Southern society had already begun to alter, we frequently find references in *The Virginia Gazette* which testify to the persistence of contempt for *belles lettres*.

The gay South of the plantation aristocracy, therefore, marked not the first but the second stage in the evolution of Southern psychology. The first stage was dominated by the same religious-minded, petty-bourgeois outlook which dominated in New England—and which dominates in the South today. It was only toward the end of the seventeenth century, as the plantation system spread, and a plantation aristocracy came into power, that the second stage began. Nevertheless, even in the second stage, these petty-bourgeois elements were not crushed. These descendants of the Dissenting tradition, many of whom eventually made up the vast yeoman class which developed with plantation economics, clung tenaciously to their creeds despite the lax attitudes of the ruling class in religious matters. They continued to be as self-denying and pious as the ruling class was pleasure-loving and wanton. It was the women of this class who lived through what Corra Harris so well described as "the candle-lit drama of salvation." To them religion was a conviction; to the ruling class it was only a form. In general the Established Church was anathema to them; it was to the evangelical faiths, the Baptists, the Presbyterians, and the Methodists, that they flocked. Their religiosity, accentuated in places by climate and isolation, became more maniacal than anywhere else in America. The grandmother, in Mary Johnston's novel *Hagar,* evinces the effect of this religiosity, when she avows with pride that she doesn't "pretend to be 'literary' or to understand literary talk. What Moses and Saint Paul said and the way we've always done in Virginia is good enough for me."

A POOR WHITE CIVILIZATION

In the light of these facts we can now see what has happened in the South since the Civil War. The Civil War ended plantation rule. The same rural and urban petty bourgeoisie, who had dominated in the seventeenth century, rapidly superseded the plantation aristocracy in power. Southern life began to center itself gradually about cities instead of plantations, until today the plantation has practically disappeared as a force in Southern affairs. The petty bourgeoisie, adapting itself to the new way of life, soon seized control of the reins of government, and, aided by the new economic forces at its command, superimposed its ideology upon the changing environment. In every field this poor-white civilization extended its tentacles of control. Abetted by the alliance with Northern capitalism, it lent its new-found energies to the scrapping of everything old, the worn-out agricultural régime, the hopeless, broken-backed, agrarian tradition, and bent the rest of its energies to the construction of a South that was to be entirely new. Before the end of the nineteenth century the outline of this new South had become very clear and the effects of its new tradition had already revealed themselves in Southern culture. In politics the change was catastrophically precipitate. The Calhouns and Randolphs, political representatives of the old order, the plantation aristocracy, were supplanted by the Heflins and Hoke Smiths, Bilbos, Huey Longs, and Talmadges, the political spokesmen of the new order. With this change in economic life, which chalked off the passing of political power on the part of the plantation aristocracy, the whole plantation ideology collapsed like a mountain of sand before the advance of a typhoon. Ellen Glasgow, in her novel *The Battle-ground,* traced something of the conditions of decay which led to this melodramatic collapse.

But do Southern writers anxious to save the South from its present cultural desolation attack the petty bourgeoisie and ally themselves with forces which oppose its power? The answer is unfortunately negative. What Southern writers have done, as I suggested in an earlier paragraph, is simply to adopt the device of escape. Instead of fighting the evil which confronts them, they either retreat to imaginary towers of their own construction or to a romantic past which is equally remote from reality. The few individuals and forces which have striven to oppose these conditions in a more realistic way have been lost in the shuffle, as it were, and forced to operate in isolation. Individual writers, such as L. P. Wilson, who has carefully studied and criticised the library situation in the South, Edward Mims, who has challenged Southern educators to free themselves from the religious yoke, Julian Harris, who made the bravest fight of all in his struggle against the Ku Klux Klan, religious intolerance, and lynching, and Elmer Scott and Gaynell Hawkins, who with their *Civic Federation* of Dallas and its various extensions have done more than any others to awaken Texas from its intellectual lethargy—these men and a few others have carried on a vigorous struggle against the cultural backwardness of the South of today. That their struggle has not been a more successful one is not due to lack of courage on their part, but to the forces in the environment which have thwarted their efforts and resisted their influence.

With scant exceptions Southern intellectuals view the coming of industry with fear rather than with favor, and therein lies their error. Now that the plantation aristocracy is dead and plantation life has been invested with the glamour of the remote, many Southern writers, depressed at the scene which faces them, have turned to the plantation past for renewed inspiration. Seeking the color of cultural life which once prevailed in Charleston, "the gayest in America," as Crèvecoeur one time described it, preferring the owner who could gamble away his plantations without losing his poise to the petty bourgeois who counts his every cent, these writers have turned to the dead plantation world for escape. The choice that confronted them was crucial. Either they had to turn back to that romantic feudal world, rose-rimmed in recollection, with its "rose order of Southern women," as James Lane Allen phrased it, its gay gentlemen brave to the point of duel, "its singing niggers"—the world which stirred Stephen C. Foster, even though

not a part of it, to immortalize it in his popular melodies, "My Old
Kentucky Home," "Old Folks at Home," and "Old Black Joe"—or like
James Branch Cabell invent a new world of their own, a Poictesme of
intellectual refuge.

RETREAT TO THE NEGRO

No greater proof of this fact is to be found than in the nature of the
work of those contemporary Southern writers who have neither succumbed to the plantation dream nor invented a new world of their
own. Desiring to write about the world in which they live rather than
escape to mythical worlds of the past or future, and yet realizing the
barrenness of the civilization which surrounds them, they have—with
the exception of William Faulkner, Thomas Wolfe, Paul Green, T. S.
Stribling, Fielding Burke, and Grace Lumpkin—turned to the Negro
with an almost inevitable unanimity for their materials. In a word,
it is only the Negro in the South today who can provide them with artistic inspiration. Like Joel Chandler Harris in the previous century,
they have turned to the Negro for those rich human possibilities which
are latent in his forthright, dynamic reaction to life. Harris, in his
"Uncle Remus" sketches, returned to the old days for his facts and
fables. Harris, however, belonged to the romantic plantation tradition
and to the lineage of Thomas Nelson Page rather than to that of the
moderns. These new Southern writers want to deal with the facts and
fables of the Negro which have been carried down into the present.
Paul Green's plays, particularly "In Abraham's Bosom," which won
the Pulitzer prize several years ago (his more recent play, "The House
of Connelly," it is good to note, as well as his novel *Laughing Pioneer* are challenging and significant exceptions); Julia Peterkin's novels,
Black April, and *Scarlet Sister Mary,* which also won the Pulitzer prize
not long ago; DuBose Heyward's "Porgy," which was one of the great
theatric successes in the late twenties, and his novel, *Mamba's Daughters,* which was very popular shortly thereafter—all these products
of this new group of Southern writers have revolved about Negro life
and character. The Negro alone, living in a different world of motiva-
tion, has retained enough of his simplicity and charm and irresponsible gaiety to attract writers of the new generation. While the white
man's world, spiked in on every side by religious ramparts, has become
desolate of cultural stimulus, the black man's world has taken on fresh
meaning. Yet it is not the new black man's world where the new Negro
is the protagonist which appeals to them, but the old black man's
world in which the new Negro has little part. The new Negro is part

of the new South, the South which has grown up since the Civil War and which in this century has opened wide its doors to the coming of industry. This new Negro, represented at one extreme by the Negro bourgeoisie and the Negro intellectual who is largely a product of that bourgeoisie, and at the other by the new proletarian-minded Negro, already turning left, does not interest the Peterkins and the Heywards. This new Negro has already become too much like the rest of the South in his desires and ambitions. It is only the old Negro or the struggling but defeated Negro, who, as in "In Abraham's Bosom," meets frustration at every turn, that arouses the interest and sympathy of this new school of authors. In this sense, however successfully they have managed to avoid the sentimentalities of the old plantation school, these writers are much closer to the plantation tradition than they suspect.

FASCISM REARS ITS HEAD

Another group of Southern writers who have succumbed to the spell of the plantation tradition is the group led by Donald Davidson. In the symposium, *I'll Take My Stand,* these writers have declaimed against the petty-bourgeois South which has grown up since the Civil War, and in verbiage charged with indignation announced their stand in favor of a pre-Civil-War Dixie. Donald Davidson, who edited the symposium, challenged his fellow Southerners to act before action is too late. This whole group is anxious to restore the old South with its plantation ideology and its agrarian economics. Only such a restoration, these writers are convinced, can release the South of tomorrow from the death hand of the petty bourgeoisie. Hopeless as is their hostility to what is already an ineradicable tendency, they have not allowed themselves to be discouraged as yet by the fast army of opposition which surrounds them. In fact, the very intensity of their challenge has a kind of corner-driven desperation about it. Full of intellectual TNT as their words are, they voice nothing more than the expiring spirit of a dead cause. At best, the plantation ideology having lost its economic *raison-d'être*, this group can do nothing more than stand apart, without the support of their environment, fighting a futile battle, modern Don Quixotes stabbing at steel windmills, hoping to destroy them by the gesture.

Since the publication of *I'll Take My Stand,* the same group of writers have crystallized their philosophy into a movement which has adopted *The American Review* as its organ of literary expression. The editor of *The American Review,* Mr. Seward Collins, has definitely described this movement, which is familiarly known as *the new agrar-*

ianism, "as fascist." Underlying this movement, as Mr. Collins pointed out in a debate with me on the issue, is the international fascist appeal to the farmers to fight the industrialists and financiers in an attempt to replace the power of Wall Street by that of Main Street. Mr. Collins even goes so far as to advocate a return to monarchy as the best means of achieving that transformation. What the *new agrarians* aim to do, as their articles in *The American Review* attest, and as Mr. Collins has made most explicit, is to return to a form of pre-capitalist economy, in which horse and buggy transportation will supplant that of the automobile and the steam locomotive, and handicraft production will replace that of machine production, all of which is not only most reprehensively naïve and fantastic but most dangerously reactionary.

Nowhere, then, is there a forward-looking tendency in Southern life. Everywhere the logic of escape prevails. Nowhere is there a single important Southern writer—with the exception of Fielding Burke and Grace Lumpkin who have just arrived, as it were—who has a plan or a program which has any pertinence to what is happening in Southern life today—to what happened in Dayton, Gastonia, Scottsboro, Marion, and Harlan. Nowhere is there a Southern group of intellectuals whose approach is realistic intead of romantic. And therein lies part of the reason for the bankruptcy of the present-day Southern mind. Like the old Confederate veteran, Southern intellectuals still prefer to talk about the conditions before the Civil War, instead of trying to change the conditions which confront them today. Only when they reverse that procedure, forget the old conditions and face the new, work out a program of construction instead of escape, will they be able to come into grips with their environment—and influence it. But that will mean that they will become realists instead of romanticists, radicals instead of reactionaries, for it will only be when they desert the stand of the romanticist and the reactionary that they will succeed in transforming the Southern scene.

The South Is a Bulwark

BY JOHN CROWE RANSOM

I

HERODOTUS, the father of history, told wonderful stories about such things as the search of the one-eyed Arimaspians for gold, and the manners of the rude Scythians. He had a good chance to spread himself because in those days the Greek cities had no sort of contact with the remote barbarian nations. Mr. Calverton, though a modern historian, is ingenious too. His imagination is all the more remarkable since he lives in the age of communication, and at the trade center of the world's largest free trade area, and writes what is technically domestic history, and still is not inhibited.

It would be an error of literary judgment to argue with Mr. Calverton's pretty fancies. He is a serious and sincere thinker, but not I believe with respect to Southern culture in the ordinary sense of the word.

I must construe Mr. Calverton from a distance, for my acquaintance with him is as documentary or theoretical as is his acquaintance with the South; so I may be wrong. His real cultural interest, I gather, is precisely what Karl Marx's was: limited to a very special interest in the political economy of the region. The South is too "petty bourgeois" for him; that emerges as his real concern; which means that the South has not yet gone in wholeheartedly for giant business organizations in the place of small ones, and therefore is not yet ready to be propositioned by the Marxians. The thesis of the Marxians is that the rich must become richer and the poor poorer before the class struggle can attain violence enough to accomplish anything. For that reason they approve of plutocracy if it is nicely "bloated," of high finance, mass production, and technology if they produce depression and unemployment, and of bankers, landlords, and employers if they are so strong and greedy as to arouse the hatred of a multitude of victims. These if's they think will be sufficiently realized under any high-powered version of the modern industrial society. Big business is the stage precedent to revolution. The South's backwardness slows up the program and postpones the millennium.

Mr. Calverton's enthusiasm for the old plantation aristocracy is rather more uncritical than my own, and also, I believe, than that of Mr. Donald Davidson. It is charming, almost disarming. But I reflect that Mr. Calverton is deep, and I remember that any great gulf between the classes is good from a Marxian view because it sets the stage of the revolution, and that a privileged aristocracy, if fat and "gay" enough, would serve the purpose as well as a plutocracy. Unfortunately the gay planters did not wait until the Marxians could appear upon the scene, they went down with the rest of the economic establishment of the region, and were superseded by a society of small owners; a nut that Marxianism cannot crack. So was the French Revolution of 1789 premature too, in that there was no Marxian leadership to direct its outcome. The French aristocracy gave way to a petty bourgeoisie, and there it is today.

So there is an issue between Mr. Calverton and the South, and it is worth discussing. But many other Americans besides Southerners are on one side of it, just as many others besides Mr. Calverton are on the other side of it, and the future of the country depends on which side is going to have its way. Mr. Calverton is the spokesman for certain "forces of progress," the nature of which we can read between the lines. He senses the Southern opposition infallibly. There is plenty of it elsewhere, but it is peculiarly stubborn and substantial in the South. I believe it may be said that if the Union has to be defended against the sort of program which Mr. Calverton would put forward, this section is a very bulwark.

II

The merest tourist, at 300 miles per day, can tell you ways in which the South differs from other sections. Perhaps he notices an unusual degree of warmth, or he may call it curiosity and garrulousness, on the part of the leisurely natives with whom he trades for a sandwich, or a fill of gasoline, or a lodging. They seem determined to import personal relations into business transactions, a habit which is clearly the enemy of maximum efficiency.

Another observation, more to the point, may not be unrelated to this one: the smallness of scale in the objectified economy of the region. The cities are not imposing, the skyscrapers are not high. The biggest residences are not so big, indicating that the richest Southerners are not so rich. The railroads are slow and the automobiles are cheap. The country clubs do not glitter.

Statisticians will confirm his findings, and contribute others which are not so visible. The public schools run on lower per-child expenditures than elsewhere, the public libraries are classified as inadequate, the colleges are below standard in enrollments, libraries, endowments, and other measurable properties. There are no great publishing houses, and no great weekly or monthly journals to act as distinguished organs of public opinion; not money enough for such things.

There may be exceptions to the rule of small effects—a big factory here, a big country estate there. The chances are that the capital or the income which floats the thing is imported Northern money. The South has been discovered in recent years by enterprising capitalists as a good place to plant capital in, and by retired capitalists as a good place to live in. In Virginia, for example, many of these latter have restored the architecture and the superficial form of the old plantations, and are playing at country squire; but the gesture is not significant, since there is no economic reality behind it.

The South simply has less income at its disposal than other sections

have, and it is correspondingly backward in the statistical evidences of
"culture." But there should never be an extended discussion of this
point without some remark about its historical background. Seventy
years ago the South, seeking not aggression but peaceful separation,
was defeated by force of arms, and then by the same force "reconstructed." The two operations were continuous and lasted from ten to
twenty years. The economic result of this disruption was that the South
became a sort of colonial dependency of the East at the time when
the latter entered upon its industrial expansion. The South was fixed in
the rôle of a primary producer. It took its punishment, precisely as a
vegetable economy always does when trading with a mineral economy;
I am borrowing Professor Beard's recent terms.

But a principle of compensation works, though it may be slowly
and darkly, in the interest of the vegetable economy. The profits of the
mineral economy must have somewhere to go and earn, and they are
bound to go eventually back into the vegetable economy, to take the
form of naturalized capital plant, and to initiate industrial processes
there too. So far as the South is concerned, political and sectional attitudes at first stood in the way of this development; but, after all, the
South has more than its share of mineral resources and, a great thing
now, water power. If capitalists are so enterprising and capital is so
mobile as the classical economists have supposed, then the industrial
development of the South is assured; and in fact it is well started. The
financial and industrial domination of the East has seen its best days,
and I suppose even now the financiers and captains of industry in New
York begin to be acquainted in a faint premonitory manner with the
feeling of holding a bag.

I do not know anybody in the South who thinks that industrialization
can be stopped where it is, or wants it stopped there. The Southerners
with whom I am acquainted want economic independence for their
region, and the wish seems modest enough not to rate as treasonable.
To its attainment the planetary influences are now entirely favorable, if
I am an astrologer. Nevertheless, I think that industrialization will be a
little different in the South. The South, as Mr. Calverton says, is rather a
petty bourgeois community.

In the Carolina Piedmont region, and at other places in the South,
industrialization has been taking place very fast and the forces of progress have been jubilant. The North Carolina patriots used to welcome
this development without any qualms. They seemed to go on the theory
which I believe is Mr. Calverton's own, that culture is a function of
income, or of the material advantages which money will buy. The
Carolina thinkers wanted a big income for the South, and could name

very noble reasons: the increase of libraries, publications, schools and colleges, government services; the breeding of big philanthropists. Some liberal-minded Carolinians wanted to see the income widely distributed, too; they were aware as soon as anybody else of the now well-published necessity of distributing the purchasing fund. But they did not want to see it come to the workingman in the form of richer crumbs from the employer's table, but in the form of obligations acknowledged and written into the contracts. To that end they were ready even to stand for militant unionism, and their courage and realism must be honored.

But income is not enough, and the distribution of income is not enough. If these blessings sufficed, we might as well come to collectivism at once; for that is probably the quickest way to get them. In Russia they are building up almost over night a productive plant like that which it took America many years to secure, and they are distributing its benefits more widely than has ever been known in an industrial society. Mr. Calverton, the realist, might not at all object to our taking the Russians for our guides. I think the liberal Carolinians would come to it eventually too; some of them have been coming very rapidly to it. The subtle Marxians see exactly what can happen very easily to a big business economy, even to our own. Thus: the system collapses in labor violence, or perhaps it collapses in depression; yet the productive plant is there still, and the population is there still, already trained and drilled in obedience to orders, already regimented. So the state takes over the plant and assigns the personnel to its posts; the revolution has been accomplished. In the degree that the business organization has done a good job already in enforcing the habit of subordination, the revolution may even be a tolerably bloodless affair.

Another group of Southern minds, if Mr. Calverton will allow the term, has for its locus Tennessee rather than Carolina. They believe that freedom and human rights are as important for happiness as money and goods, and that the advocates of "progress," who applaud the virtues of income and of standards of living as measured statistically, are not the natural interpreters of the section. Considering the genuine public zeal manifested by the Carolinians, they would observe further that big libraries, big educational plants, and unlimited public services all put together do not make a fair price for the loss of private freedom.

There may be an opposition between maximum productivity and private freedom. But there is no fixed opposition between private freedom and a great deal of material welfare, a considerable productivity; these do not exclude one another. The per capita natural wealth of this country is all but beyond comparison greater than that of other nations, and it is astonishing to find economists concluding that its development can proceed only by tactics which are harsh and sacrificial of human rights. I mean this: by the police tactics of the Soviet republics, or even by the impersonal and "strictly business" tactics of our own big corporate businesses.

Nowhere on earth is there a society so well able as ours to afford the luxury of freedom. We are not as Italy, to whom Il Duce, in the name of what we would call the planned society, addressed his famous remark: "Italy cannot afford freedom."

The Nashville Agrarians have been most concerned with the farm economy. They pitched on that as a central problem for the South, which is a rural section, and in which the occupational status is something like 60 per cent agricultural; perhaps also because of their own personal background and taste. But at this moment most of the original writers are making a fresh appearance in a second symposium, *Who Owns America?* (Houghton, Mifflin.) With them are presented a still larger number of other writers, who are not so interested in the agricultural as in the business economy, and correspond to those British economists who call themselves Distributists; they propose "the restoration of private property" in America. Each group, the Agrarian and the Distributist, thinks that it requires the complementary assistance of the other, and that no change in its own principles is involved; for neither the farmers nor the business men can ever flourish in a society in which both these estates are not at once comfortable and secure.

The new book is not written with peculiar reference to the South. If its authors are not mistaken, it advances doctrines 100 per cent pure American; though not exactly the kind of doctrines which seemed to be orthodox in 1929. I shall tell in my own terms the position taken by most of the writers upon the problem of the land, and also upon the problem of industry and business. This position looks almost congenital to Southern habits of mind. But I should describe it also as "early American," and again as "constitutional."

III

As for the land, the Agrarian theory has a fresh statement. It is my impression that it is the only theory that has ever made a realistic approach to the very peculiar problem of American agriculture.

The most obvious thing to say about agriculture in America is that, as a business in the ordinary sense, it can never prosper. Speaking of bankruptcy, there is no bankruptcy like that of Southern cotton planters trying to earn money which is not there to earn; unless it is that of some other group of farmers raising an American staple. Here is a field in which common business principles cannot apply. The common business principles are based on the understanding that each business is a special function in a society of delegated functions, and that those engaged in it make a money income by selling their goods or services to society and then live on the income. Each business tries for maximum efficiency; that is, maximum productivity at minimum cost of labor, material, and capital equipment. But agriculture in America cannot successfully play this part among the other businesses. It has a unique disability.

The disability is this. The volume of productive land is out of proportion to the wants—whether this means the wishes or the needs—of the American community. The land is the fixed capital of agriculture, but it is fixed by nature and not by man, therefore fixed indeed. No European nation in modern times has had to worry with this peculiar condition, and therefore no pattern for handling it is discoverable in European economic, or in any other economic derived from European writings. Technically, the excess of American land is overcapitalization, and an overcapitalized business is always an overproductive one.

The extent of an overcapitalization is not determined by the size of the unmarketable surplus of goods produced. In an old business subject to calculation, production will probably not greatly exceed the demand for any given year, since many producers will gauge the prospect accurately and stay out of production. But until these producers abandon their capital plant, they are waiting their first chance to produce, they are a menace, and they see to it that the ordinary condition of the market shall be one of glut, and the ordinary condition of the business one of insolvency. Most farm economists, however, prefer to measure the overproductiveness of American farmers by the actual surplus, and so they deceive the statesmen legislating for the farmers, and the farmers too, as to the dimensions of the problem. For example, it is suggested that the eating of two extra loaves of bread a year by each American person will cure the plight of the wheat farmers. It is the overcapitalization and not the visible overproduction that counts. The precise excess of American land will never be known; so long as the population stays under a hundred and sixty millions, as it is calculated to do, we can only say of it that it is indefinitely great. The land might easily support several times that population, but naturally it will never set in to prove this for the benefit of doubting economists. It is perfectly natural that American land should be farmed extensively and inefficiently, rather than intensively and according to the principles of agronomy; that is the easiest way to farm it, and it is more than efficient enough. There is always a great deal of marginal land waiting to come in as soon as the good land is earning, and by all means there is a higher productive capacity which the good land is waiting to realize as soon as profits begin to show.

The Agrarians have reluctantly come to the conclusion that the foreign markets offer no prospect of employing the unused capacity of American land. They do not endorse the somewhat vindictive program of Mr. Peter Molyneux, of Texas, who seems desirous of breaking down the American tariff walls no matter what it means to American industry, on the ground that it was American industry which ruined the Southern farmers, and that the ruin of industry may now save them. The South once had a strong case in making this argument, but that was definitely yesterday. It was mostly nature which ruined the farmer in the South, and it is certainly nature which keeps him ruined now. Europe is finding elsewhere cheaper farm stuff than we can supply, and that is about all there is to the argument. The time may come when all American farmers, even the cotton ones, will be thankful for a tariff which protects not only the industrialists but themselves. In any case, it is inevitable that a country which does not require imports will finally have to abandon exports, and work out its economy on a domestic basis, farming included.

The late lamented AAA was an ignoble though humanly natural experiment. Southern farmers accepted its benefits as cheerfully as others, and doubtless with fully as much secret consciousness that the arrangement was slightly disreputable. If the Constitution had not intervened, I imagine that one of two things would have happened before long. It would have been established that it was profoundly uneconomic, and too expensive for the government of the United States, to guarantee income on a fixed capital whose excess had never been computed but was close to the fabulous. Or, if the government continued to deal only, and arbitrarily, with that group of farmers who happened to be caught producing in the year that Triple A took effect, the reasonable and constitutional desire of others to enter this privileged business, working fresh land or working the given land much more efficiently, would have raised clamor enough to wreck the scheme.

There is no hope for American agriculture as a business, with its fatal incubus of too much land; governmental action foreign or domestic cannot save it. But observe a paradox. In spite of this fact farming is a fine and tolerably secure occupation for the right sort of farmers. And here is the secret. To compensate for its peculiar disability, farming has the peculiar advantage that it lends itself not to one economy, as other businesses do, but to two economies. The farmer does not have to live entirely in either one. So the farmer is, now, a money-maker, requiring an income, exposed to the hazards of cost and competition like all the others; very much underprivileged in this economy, as we have seen. But, again, he is in a private economy of his own, producing his own subsistence without money transactions. He is an amphibian and cannot be destroyed.

I have given the order wrong, so far as the American farmer is concerned. He should produce his own necessities first, and then consider his money crops. His present misery is mostly due to the fact that he has learned to put his money crops first, and then more often than not forgotten to produce for himself; he has never had pointed instruction to the effect that agriculture in America is not one of the ordinary businesses, and does not permit this. Naturally he is in a desperate situation. This is what the Agrarians recently have been saying with probably wearisome iteration. In their own section the oral tradition which handed down the detail of the dualistic farm economy is not yet quite dead.

Yet the state should delight to honor the farmer, and to assist him so far as it does not involve direct bounties, or privileged treatment, or a burden of expense which the state cannot bear. The farmers are the freest citizens in this country; the most whole, therefore the most wholesome. Nobody bosses their jobs meticulously, even if they are hired men. If they are owners, they are the perfect examples of the propertied man; the man who actually administers as he pleases a property he owns; whose business relations are personal, moral, and neighborly, not impersonal, legalistic, and corporate. They should be regarded as the staple of our citizenship; and if the South has a large proportion of them in its population then the South is a real bulwark against those revolutions under which men surrender their general integrity and become pure functions, or abstractions, or soldiers in an army. The socialists and communists are quite aware they can do little with the farmers, who like too well their status.

But the farmer needs income; he should not be expected to live as a self-subsistent primitive. The state—I do not mean to specify which of the hierarchy of his governments—can do several things. First, it can nearly or wholly cease to tax his land. The tax is payable in money, not in kind, but the land is not productive of much money. Then it might assure him of his right to buy in a really competitive domestic market, so that his limited funds will go as far as possible; now he has to spend them in a market largely determined by monopolies and combinations. Southern farmers applaud Senator Borah's stand on this matter fully as much as Western farmers do; incidentally, they also share his regard for the Constitution.

The farmer cannot expect to have his income enhanced by government dole. But there is good reason for asking the state to provide him with certain services which are practicable, and also essential to his good citizenship. I am thinking of such services as good roads; provision for first-class general education, as good let us say as Denmark gives its rural population; provision for agricultural or technical education under instructors who know more about farming than how to make money crops; and possibly electricity delivered cheap at the front gate. This last may not have to be strictly a governmental service, but the corporate utilities will have to be hustled if they are going to provide it. The first Roosevelt has come down in fame as the President with a big stick; the second may be associated with a yardstick.

IV

Farmers are bad medicine for Marxians. Business men are a little easier; they cannot have quite such a freedom as that of farmers. But those in the South are obstinate small fry, according to Mr. Calverton, which means that a good deal of work will have to be done with them.

Petit bourgeois. The term is literary and slightly ridiculous, especially where the bourgeoisie is unacquainted with it. It may be expelled through the teeth with the sound of hissing and an effect of moral indignation; in Russia, I believe, good comrades take their conditioning exercises every morning when they get up by reciting, "No petit bourgeois business today." But to be one, as I understand it, is simply to be the sole owner of a small business and to operate it accordingly. A petit bourgeois society is one with a wide distribution of tangible capital properties. That is the sort of society which the South understands.

Now the laws of special function and maximum efficiency do operate in the business world; that is, in businesses whose capitalization is the act of man and not God—if Mr. Calverton will overlook my nomenclature. These laws determine the form of our modern societies and produce our quick wealth. In the name of maximum efficiency the original little businesses are steadily replaced by much fewer but much bigger corporate businesses, and often with unquestionable economic advantage.

Not always, of course. Economists increasingly find that we have overestimated the savings of big business. However that may be, we know that big business gives us a very speculative and dangerous economic system; it gives us precisely the system that we have today; the system that leads many admirable persons to lean towards Mr. Calverton's program in preference. If we must have the extreme benefits of large-scale production we shall find ourselves at last in Mr.

Calverton's net; probably before very long. From big business into collectivism: the Marxians know their formula. But if we are willing to enjoy these benefits in moderation, and leave a great deal of business on the small, personal, moral, and manageable basis, Mr. Calverton cannot get us. We shall remain economically free.

The goose-step of collectivism differs only in degree from the progressive disfranchisement of men as economic agents under big business. A big business operates an army of men, and organizes and regiments them like an army. Each rank receives its orders from above; they are explicit and peremptory. The personnel likes the arrangement to the extent that it has the army temperament. Responsibility is limited in the army, except at the top, and there are certainly many men in the world who like to reduce their responsibility; who like to carry out orders if they suppose that the orders are intelligent with respect to promoting efficiency. It seems that in a modern efficient society like America the best brains discoverable are behind the patterns of conduct which are imposed upon business men at all points. But it becomes increasingly hard to find work for all the good brains that apply. A few brains go a long way. It is an ignominious situation for the many men with economic initiative and intelligence who find nothing to do but go into employment and take orders; and it takes a fantastic ingenuity, almost, to found a new business and make a place of power.

There is no less property to own in the age of big business, but it is owned in a new and peculiar manner. Its ownership for the most part does not carry any responsibility; it is paper ownership. A business may be owned, conceivably, by a hundred thousand admirable widows and orphans, and yet its operation need not reflect either the moral scruple or the business judgment of its tender proprietors; for it may be run by executives who have only a salaried interest. Usually, of course, a business has a few owners with large holdings and a multitude of owners with tiny holdings; the big owners pick the right executives, the little owners concur cheerfully, and are much pleased if the earnings are high.

It is painful to think of adding to the difficulties of widows and orphans, and also to those of the administrators of colleges, insurance companies, and organized charities, whose income is derived from paper property. But it is all but terrifying to reflect upon the extent to which the capital owners in America have delegated their economic agency. Ownership used to be a much sterner affair. Usury was in low repute, though it meant no more than the lending out of money for hire to enterprises in which the lenders did not participate.

In the new group-book I find an agrarian sort of term used to describe those gentry who may well be distinguished in birth, fortune, and education, but whose whole economic vocation consists in watching their "investments." They are called the geldings of the economic society. They exist in great numbers, and the implication is that the economic society could not afford to employ them in their natural potency. But the modern breed of American citizen submits very pleasantly to being gelded. The citizen with large investments is quite an imposing figure. When something happens to the value of some bloc of his shares, he makes a Napoleonic decision, but it is not by way of pitching in to see what is wrong with the business, and then doing something about it; it consists in ordering his broker to sell.

Non-responsibility attaches to the small owners, irresponsibility to the big owners. Determined by these qualities, American business cannot be saved by all the technical efficiency in the world. It will be economically unstable. Morally it will have no status at all beyond that of keeping free of the toils of the law; and the surplus of brains in American corporate business devoted to outwitting the law is larger than the supply of professional legislative and judicial brains engaged in making it stick.

V

It is not likely that the small Distributist-Agrarian group will cause a vast reversal in American economic practice. Mr. Calverton informs me that Agrarianism is dead, and I think he would have said the same for Distributism, except for the fact that there is a stubborn petty-bourgeois survival which he notes in the South. He may be perfectly right. I can easily suppose, as he supposes, that we will put up with big business until the time when it fails too flagrantly to promote, not health and happiness, but life; and that we will then turn the thing disgustedly over to his well-organized group.

But I must suggest to Mr. Calverton what is a very distinct possibility. A great spontaneous political movement may form now, or at any moment, which will press for Agrarian and Distributist reforms without using these terms or even knowing them. Recently we have seen the re-alignment of the West and the South, so long separated. A few years ago Mr. Roosevelt appealed against the spirit of sectionalism, but what chance has the New Deal unless the West and the South unite against the East? If Mr. Calverton should travel among the inner areas of this country, he would discover a very strong impression that the ills of the present economy are due to the domination of big business, whose center is in the East. The farm populations and the petty bourgeois who are the West and the South have a great deal of force if they will realize it; they have ballots. Suppose the West realizes what the South has painfully known for a long time: that it betrays credulity if it affiliates with a party whose interests are all Eastern?

There is no telling about all this. If I try, I can imagine legislatures and Congresses for years to come whittling away at that special instrument of big business, the corporation; working some destruction inevitably while they are about it; but trying however clumsily to secure America again to its former proprietors. That, I feel, will be going Southern and remaining American.

JAMES T. FARRELL AND THE LITERARY LEFT

The publication of James T. Farrell's *A Note on Literary Criticism* in 1936 brought into the open a feud which had been quietly simmering between *New Masses* and *Partisan Review*. From its inception, *Partisan Review* had been more selective in its choice of literary material than any other left-wing magazine; and from its inception, James Farrell was one of the magazine's mainstays. Not only did Farrell regularly contribute stories and essays to the fledgling magazine, but he also became its drama critic. When he reviewed—and dismissed —Clifford Odets' *Paradise Lost* as a pompous play filled with "dull speeches and swaggering platitudes," the split between the two left-wing organs was apparent in Mike Gold's outburst that "That kind of mutual slaughter died long ago, with all other sectarianism, and I for one am sore that it should be revived." Shortly after, *A Note on Literary Criticism* was published and the split was widened. In his own review of Odets' play, Gold had critized the forces of *Partisan Review* for carrying "their Marxian scholarship as though it were a heavy cross." Now, Farrell was contending that most Marxist critics, including those of *New Masses*, did not understand dialectic materialism. In rebuttal, Isidor Schneider, representing *New Masses*, contended that Farrell's book was "so unsatisfactory" because Farrell did not "use the Marxist method." And V. F. Calverton, who had also come under Farrell's scrutiny, claimed that Farrell suffered from "the well-known disease of educating himself in public." "After reading *A Note on Literary Criticism*," Calverton wrote, "it is . . . obvious that Mr. Farrell should have stuck to the novel instead of venturing into criticism." To Farrell's defense came Alan Calmer of *Partisan Review* and Edmund Wilson. A leftist such as Granville Hicks, following Schneider's lead, might wonder "if there is any point at which *A Note on Literary Criticism* is genuinely valuable," but to the independent-minded Edmund Wilson there was no such doubt. Farrell's book was a "remarkable event," Wilson wrote in *The Nation*, which contained one of the "few intelligent discussions of literature from the Marxist point of view which has yet been written by Americans." As for Farrell, Wilson concluded his review, "The effort to examine and to understand is what he has been able to bring to literature as well as to life." And that, Wilson added, "is what is most needed if the writing of the left is to perform any really serious function." The selection from *A Note on Literary Criticism* is from the concluding chapter, while "Sectarianism on the Right," "In Defense of James Farrell," and Farrell's rebuttal, were printed in *New Masses* on June 23, July 14, and August 18, 1936 respectively.

From **A Note on Literary Criticism**

BY JAMES T. FARRELL

CRITICISM, in the literary process, should become the agent that makes for the understanding and evaluation of works of literature. It should create the atmosphere through which a maximum of value and effect, rather than a minimum, is produced by our living literature. It should strive to make the meanings of books clear, to draw out these essential meanings and refer and assimilate them in a wider social area. In performing these functions, criticism will evidently be making judgments, and on the basis of analysis; the criteria for these judgments being not alone internal to the literary process, and not alone external. Like the books to which they are applied they have both a subjective or aesthetic side and an objective or functional side. These criteria must be rationally established, tested by reference to experience, and used flexibly. In other words, they cannot be absolutized and fixed; they cannot be invented. They must have applicability to the literary work that is being judged. This is my conception of ideal criticism; and what I have tried to do in this book is to show the grounds on which it can be justified.

When literary criticism fails to play such a rôle as this, it is failing to function as it should. It is reneging on its duties and thereby sowing the seeds of confusion; for it is making no contribution toward that clarity, that lucidity, that understanding, which is rightfully asked of the critic. The critic must, as I have said, refer the book to life in an *essential* way: He must understand the book as a work of literature, reproducing elements from life, re-creating a sense of them. He must also understand the author's terms, the premises explicitly or implicitly established by the author. And this understanding cannot be merely in terms of formal ideology; it must also relate to the internal structure of events in the book. These tell the critic what the author is trying to say; they provide the clue to estimating how well, and how truthfully, the author has rendered life. The critic is thus enabled to judge the meaning of the work, both in terms of its inherent worth, and in terms of its reference to other but related meanings.

It is to be assumed, of course, that the critic has some original equipment. If he lacks original equipment in sensory capacities, in imagination, in powers of reasoning, then not all the formulae in the world, not all the external categories he may devise, not all his academic learning, will help him. Technique without the ability to apply it is futile. It results in formalism.

This equipment, however, can be assumed in most persons who undertake criticism. A fairly adequate power of thinking, understanding, and feeling is presumably common among them. What I challenge is the way they make use of what equipment they have—their view of the functions of literature and their procedure in measuring and legislating rather than judging it. And I am convinced that if a critic follows such a procedure—unless he seeks to judge, evaluate, relate, understand, feel, and enjoy works of living literature—his critical efforts are vain. He falls into functional extremism. He adds to the number of tasks left for others to perform in the future. He fails to advance lucidity of thinking and thus turns criticism into an instrument for confusion. Or else he sinks into impressionism, his criticism becoming totally subjective. And subjectivism leads him finally—whether he is gifted or not —into sensationalism.

We have had enough of aberrations in criticism. We have had enough extra-literary critical legislation. We have had enough blindness and sentimentalism. The health of both living literature and the revolutionary movement to which it is more and more attaching itself demands that these aberrations be exposed and liquidated. It is because of this present need that I agree with Maxim Gorky, who writes: "I do not want to give our enemies the opportunity to laugh at us by emphasizing the coarseness, the lack of culture and, very often, even the ignorance of our critics. Perhaps our critics are very well equipped ideologically, but something seems to deter them from stating with the utmost clarity and simplicity the science of dialectic materialism as applied to questions of art."

It is time, I think, that revolutionary criticism should concern itself with its proper tasks, and in a thorough and adequate way. The pious expression of generalized conclusions is insufficient. The harping cry that criticism must be raised above the level of personalities, the search for personal motives rather than for ideas and criteria of judgment behind critical evaluations—such serve only to advertise a paucity and degradation of ideas. Critics who have ideas to express need not indulge in pious assent to "Marxian" generalizations which should be assimilated before one calls oneself a "Marxist." And the factors that have militated against our revolutionary criticism thus far have been mechanical legislation leading to these pieties; and sentimentalism leading to equally empty pities. And in each case, these different tendencies either begin or end in mechanism crudity. They absolutize standards, and they absolutize Marx. For several years this process has gone on; its nature and contents have been suggested in my analysis. Its fruits in misunderstanding are incalculable. Again to quote Maxim

Gorky: "For many years a certain professor, writer and critic exalted mediocre writers to the height of classic authors. Serious critics paid no attention to his activities, which were hardly beneficial to the young people who heard him lecture. Now he admits that 'in the last few months he recognized some of his mistakes'! . . . A Russian proverb says: 'Words once uttered cannot be revoked'; consequently the mistakes of the professor remain."

The mistakes of our critics remain, too, and they harm the revolutionary cultural movement, which has much to assimilate, much to understand, much to produce. If it is going to assimilate what is alive from the traditions it has inherited, fight what is dead within them, and carry forward to the future, enlarging and expanding these traditions and creating new ones, it must now stop cooking up recipes for culture. It must understand, must produce culture. And to do that, it must liquidate its sins; it must pay now, with understanding, for the forged checks it has issued during the last few years. For it has been perpetuating old errors, and the point has now been reached where it is inexcusable to keep on doing this. For these are errors that Engels recognized years ago. I conclude with a statement from one of his letters:

"Marx and I are partly to blame for the fact that younger writers sometimes lay more stress on the economic side than is due to it. We had to emphasize this main principle in opposition to our adversaries, who denied it, and we had not always the time, the place or the opportunity to allow the other elements involved in the interaction to come into their rights. But when it was a case of presenting a section of history, that is, of a practical application, the thing was different and there no error was possible. Unfortunately, however, it happens only too often that people think they have fully understood a theory and can apply it without more ado from the moment they have mastered its main principles, and those even not always correctly. And I cannot exempt many of the more recent 'Marxists' from this reproach, for the most wonderful rubbish has been produced from this quarter too."

Sectarianism on the Right

BY ISIDOR SCHNEIDER

FARRELL is among the writers—Robert Cantwell, Josephine Herbst, Albert Halper, John Steinbeck, Leane Zugsmith are others—whose work has been noticeably quickened and invigorated by contact with the revolutionary movement.

Many artists have testified to the refreshment and freedom gained from association, whatever the degree of closeness, with the revolutionary movement, but have expressed it more often in the narration of personal experience than in the formulation of critical attitudes. So far Farrell has refrained from giving us any personal experience story. In his *A Note on Literary Criticism,* on the contrary, he subjects the literary critics in the revolutionary movement to a drastic critical analysis.

Now a creative writer does not interrupt his work for several months to write criticism for any light reason. It means that no critic was doing what the writer felt there was an urgent necessity to do. And it can be taken for granted that Farrell does not speak merely for himself, that his book expresses reservations held by other writers and dissatisfactions and disappointments felt by other writers, but, for one reason or another, never expressed by them. Nor is it likely that Farrell would have written the book had he felt that he would be a lone voice, had he no assurance of the agreement of other writers and critics with his viewpoint. The book, therefore, apart from its own intrinsic character, is important as an indication of a new crisis in revolutionary literature.

First, however, let us consider its purely critical function. It performs some valuable services by making a detailed and documented analysis of vitiating and constricting elements in our Marxist literary criticism. It is true that his is not the first voice raised against them, that some of the very critics whom he attacks have anticipated him; Farrell's book, however, is the first fully elaborated critical attack. No previous statements are of the same order.

Though Farrell's survey of the current literary scene is incomplete, distorted, lacking in perspective and in some ways has the curious abnormality of something held too close to the eyes for focussing, nevertheless, in details, it gives us strongly accented truths.

I enumerate here some of the services Farrell's book performs—all, it will be noticed, in terms of negative criticism:

Its arraignment of anti-intellectualism on the part of some Marxist critics, a diminishing but still existing tendency, and its analysis of some of the false positions it has led to.

Its descriptions of some of the sentimentalities and pieties which have no function as literary criticism but which have taken the place of criticism with spokesmen of an extreme and evangelical form of Marxism—for example, moral exhortations whose effect would be to lead writers to consider writing inferior to organizing and other forms of action.

Its attack upon the use of the categories "bourgeois" and "proletarian," not as descriptive terms, but as standards of judgment.

Its analyses of some of the rootless outgrowths of revolutionary romanticism.

Its exposure of the uselessness of advance formulas for unwritten literature.

Its scoring of infertile speculations such as the wished-for superiority of the "collective" over the "individual" novel.

But most especially its arraignment of the too-frequently mechanical application in Marxist criticism of the materialist interpretation.

Why, then, is Farrell's book so unsatisfactory? Chiefly because, in spite of an imposing array of Marxist citations he does not use the Marxist method. He picks Marxist criticism out of its historical setting out of its social context; he examines it in a virtual vacuum where its life processes are suspended. He does not understand, or at least gives no evidence that he understands, why, at any particular time, Marxist criticism was extreme.

Yet it is necessary to do precisely this, to set Marxist criticism in its historical setting. For Marxist criticism arose to fill a historical need; its functions changed through the changes Marxist criticism itself set in motion. What was useful at one point became obstructive at another; what was faith later became fanaticism; what was a powerful principle at one stage became sectarianism in the next. It is the task of the critic to show when and why a certain approach becomes invalid, where its character changes. To describe the course of Marxist criticism as if it, and the field in which it operated, were static is to be undialectical. But that is how Farrell presents it, as if it arose now out of an interplay of social forces affecting literature but in the fancies of a few writers who, having become interested in politics, made a clumsy attempt to squeeze literature into the Marxist mold. To record what, looked at out of their setting, seems excesses and absurdities, has a very limited value. The thorough critic will examine it, in its time and its place and in all its relationships.

Men resort to extreme action not out of choice but necessity, though they may continue to do so beyond the occasion. Sectarianism and excess were necessary and inevitable at one stage of the revolutionary movement on the literary front. I remember that only a few years ago the presentation of the life of workers in any straightforward and un-condescending fashion, was dismissed as propaganda, and propaganda then was the literary mortal sin. Consider this significant fact: Farrell's own first book had to be issued not in its own character as fiction but in a pretentious disguise as social science! There was no preparation at the time for so objective a presentation of the life of a section of the working class. Only belligerent and sectarian advocacy of the use of such literary material could astound people into considering it at all. I have no doubt that in individual cases this did some harm; but if it did not answer historic necessity, would literature today have such a general Left direction?

If we see so-called sectarianism in its historic context, we see that if performed essential services, in the light of which its shortcomings are insignificant. First, it called attention to the class basis of literature. This may now seem a platitude, but only in the sense in which every revolutionary idea becomes a platitude after its triumph. We do not minimize Columbus because anybody who can pay the fare can now get to America. Secondly, the so-called "sectarians" fought for the right of the working class to appear in literature in its true terms, rejecting the then established notion that working-class experience was not in its own terms a fit subject for literature. Thirdly, it was because the vast majority of American writers ignored the capitalist nature of contemporary society and its class basis, that these prejudices existed.

The fact is that revolutionary criticism in this country first came, long ago, with the humble petition that literature about the working class be accorded a status of equality with literature about other classes— that the proletarian be given the mere status of citizenship in the republic of letters. This was the whole tenor of Michael Gold's "Toward a Proletarian Literature," which was published in 1921.

There were then achievements to put to the credit of so-called "sectarianism." Now let us try to understand why sectarianism developed.

We must bear in mind that the American post-war intelligentsia, disillusioned and disheartened by the Versailles Treaty and subsequently by a misunderstanding of the N.E.P. in Russia, lost interest in social questions, and actually turned upon proletarian literature and Marxist criticism, attacking it as crude propaganda. As a consequence the remaining handful of writers who survived the cynicism and pessimism of the twenties, cast out from the main stream of American letters, concentrated upon propagating the Marxist viewpoint. They and those who subsequently joined them, were as much aware of "literary and human" values as anybody.

It must be remembered that both Joseph Freeman and Michael Gold entered the revolutionary movement as lyric poets and Granville Hicks first won his reputation as an esthetic critic. If men of this type emphasized the class basis of literature it was because that crucial factor was ignored or denied. Another important factor is that, until very recently, the Marxist classics were not available in translation. The American left-wing writer who saw the world from the revolutionary viewpoint had none of the benefits of Marx's, Engels' and Lenin's comments on culture. They had to work out everything for themselves and had to do it in a hostile environment. Historically considered, therefore, the wonder is not over errors committed but the truths arrived at under such conditions.

These are the main reasons why sectarianism developed if by sectarianism we mean an over-emphasis upon social as against the "literary and human" aspects of literature. However, if Farrell had analyzed as a Marxist, instead of merely making points in a supposed debate, he would have taken more care to point out that in the most sectarian days of the sectarian period there was never lacking a corrective tendency.

Farrell ignores other contributions of Marxist criticism in America, its studies of the subtler social interrelations of culture, of the factors making for degeneration of taste in the capitalist apparatus for the production and distribution of cultural commodities. These are not extrinsic to literature; they determine, in the long run, the psychology of the artist and the audience. And while they might be of merely academic interest in a static period, in a period of crisis and rapid change, like our own, they are of vital importance. The failure to give them adequate consideration makes James T. Farrell's book thin.

Throughout the book one looks in vain for those qualities which would give the treatment some proportion and substance. Farrell rarely uses the term *Marxist criticism* without a spoiling adjective. *Mechanical* appears most frequently; the phrase *empty of content* also is frequently used, along with *banal* and *platitudinous*. Although he does not say it outright one can only conclude that he rejects Marxist criticism. It is significant that the title of his book omits the word *Marxist* though the whole of the book is an attack on Marxist criticism; that in his attempts to set down what he *approves* of in criticism he carefully *leaves out the word Marxism*. The one conclusion we can come to, therefore, is that this Marxist rejects Marxism in literary criticism, that he denies it any validity, that he is, in effect, fighting to keep literature safe from Marxism.

The bias disclosed by Farrell's use of adjectives is paralleled by his casuistically adroit misunderstanding. For example, among other things, he elaborates upon a phrase of Malcolm Cowley's that art makes life "more than life." It is not hard to understand what Cowley meant. In the sense that Othello exceeds the normal, tragic figure of a man haunted by jealously and King Lear exceeds the normal figure of a betrayed father, we have life magnified with deliberate intent. But Farrell carefully misunderstands this meaning. That the misunderstanding is deliberate is confessed in a later paragraph. "Mr. Cowley might contend that he does not mean these precise interpretations of his statements.

All that I can reply is that, as has often been said, the road to hell is paved with good intentions." Mr. Farrell, we can see, is determinedly innocent of good intentions.

Furthermore he dismisses obviously useful Marxist forms of analysis as platitudinous, as something generally agreed upon. To assume such an agreement is absurd. The Marxist viewpoint has not won such a sweeping victory. In one instance that he selects, the Marxist review was the only one, in several hundred, to show how social circumstance was reflected in the book and how it determined the author's description of workers. No other approach would have made it clear. Far from being platitudinous, it is an example of how Marxist criticism serves as a new tool which enlarges the area of critical observation.

The real issue Farrell raises is whether there is any function for Marxist criticism. As he presents it in this book, it has presumably an almost complete record of failure. It intrudes extra-literary values into literary criticism; its explanations of the effects of social organization and disorganization upon literature are platitudinous, maladroit or irrelevant; it has formulated no principles valid as literary judgments; those that it has formulated are crude and do more to confuse than to enlighten the reader; it misinterprets the classics by assessing them in terms that do not apply to them; it does not allow for the continuity of tradition and the persistence of certain values unaffected by social changes; it oversimplifies criticism by reducing it to virtually automatic responses to slogans; it makes individualism a crime and discourages individuality; it would subordinate literature as a category of human activity and value it, not for itself, but as a propaganda tool; it throws the stigma of decay upon that literature, however powerful it may be, that deals with the life of a civilization in decay. This is Farrell's presentation, in outline, of Marxist criticism. What else can be concluded from it but that Marxist criticism in America has failed, and should quickly be put away and forgotten?

However, by the terms of his opening definition, Farrell lays the basis for the Marxist criticism that he rejects. He writes: "I think that literature must be viewed both as a branch of the fine arts and as *an instrument of social influence.*" Marxist criticism specifically deals with literature as an instrument of social influence as well as with other social relationships of literature. And before the general advocacy of Marxist criticism we had *sociological criticism* which, however, lacked the sharpness and scientific decision of Marxist criticism because it ignored the class basis of literature.

Farrell reiterates that Marxist criticism denies and imperils the values of individuality. Into this unjustified assumption creep other equally unjustified assumptions. One is that group responses cannot be as subtle, or do not require as subtle an understanding or are not as interesting as individual responses. Again, speaking of the "collective" novel, he writes: "Also I think that this type of novel is frequently written because novelists cannot sustain the development of an individual character and hold the reader's interest over a span of three, four or five hundred pages." It might, with equal fairness, be said that the writer of a novel centered around a main character, chooses this form because he is incapable of managing more than one character.

In every section of Farrell's book such extremism appears and invalidates the services which it could have performed. Despite his apparatus of quotations from Marxist classics, all in one tone, and obviously chosen for his purposes like the citations in a lawyer's brief, Farrell forgets that Marxism is not solely scorn of sectarianism; scorn of sectarianism is only an incidental of Marxism.

Farrell's book of course has its own historical context as I have intimated in previous paragraphs. The general adoption in the revolutionary movement of a united-front program has led to reconsiderations of literary policy and revisions and revaluations of critical attitudes. There has been a recoil from narrow and sectarian applications of Marxist theory in literature. There will be, inevitably, extremism in this direction as there was in the other; Farrell's book is an example of it. To accept his analysis would be to abandon Marxism altogether, to deny the achievements of Marxist literature and criticism, to lay aside good new instruments for extending the range of critical analysis, and to fail in our function of influencing our contemporaries. Dimitrov, in his analysis of the general program for the united front, warned against the political dangers of the swing to the right, of the dissolution of revolutionary principles. The appearance of Farrell's book indicates that the danger also exists in the literary field. Certainly, the fact that the Catholic Book Club recommends *A Note On Literary Criticism* illuminates the nature of its Marxism.

In Defense of James Farrell

BY GRANVILLE HICKS

ISIDOR SCHNEIDER'S recent review of James T. Farrell's *A Note on Literary Criticism* points out that Mr. Farrell seems to be at some pains to dissociate his critical theories from the body of ideas known as Marxism. This is true, and yet perhaps it ought not to be said without qualification. Unqualified, the statement contributes to a danger that is already real enough, the danger that Mr. Farrell's theories may be discredited just because he holds them.

This is a danger for which Farrell is himself in no small measure responsible. In the course of his book he misrepresents the opinions of half a dozen revolutionary critics. Not only does he, as Schneider points out, ignore the historical context of the articles and books he quotes; not only does he wrench his quotations from the surroundings that explain them; he performs obvious feats of distortion in the face and eyes of his readers.

It is, therefore, easy to conclude that Mr. Farrell's theories are as untenable as his polemics are unscrupulous. But we must not be too hasty. We must not be deceived, either by Mr. Farrell's methods of literary warfare or by the praise the book has had in antirevolutionary quarters. The anti-Marxists are applauding Mr. Farrell, not for his ideas, which very possibly they do not understand, but for his attacks on specific Marxist critics. Even the editors of the Catholic Book Club, though they too have had the advantage of a parochial-school education, are taken in by Mr. Farrell's abuse of his comrades in the revolutionary movement. But revolutionaries must keep their thinking straight.

There are not many ideas in the book, and it will not take us long to run through them. Mr. Farrell begins by saying, "I think that literature must be viewed both as a branch of the fine arts and as an instrument of social influence." He goes on to explain that, "for purposes of intellectual convenience" we "may divide human experience into two generalized categories: the esthetic and the functional, the subjective and the objective." The former "deals with the pleasure, value, and elations which we derive from things, from qualities, and from intellectual, emotional, and physiological states as ends in themselves"; the latter "with objects and actions in terms of their use-value."

This means that literature is both pleasurable and useful. The statement cannot be questioned if the adjectives are satisfactorily defined. Does Mr. Farrell, one has to ask, conceive of usefulness in too narrow terms? The answer is no. He says, for example, that "living literature . . . cuts beneath stereotyped feelings and crystallized thoughts, furnishing the material from which extended feelings and added thought are developed. It is one of the agents serving to work out within the individual consciousness the twin processes of growth and decay in a way corresponding to the objective working-out of these processes in society." And so the passage goes on, quite an eloquent passage, not altogether precise, perhaps, but on the right track.

And what of pleasure? Mr. Farrell introduces this aspect of literary experience so portentously that at first one fears he is going to exaggerate its importance. But not at all. When he speaks of the Humanists, he says they were guilty of functional dualism, which means that they ignored the pleasure element in literature. He does not, however, rest there; he goes on, like any sensible person, to show that their philosophical and sociological ideas were reactionary and untenable. More than that, he quotes approvingly from Chernishevski: "Only subject matter worthy of the attention of thoughtful man can save art from the reproach that it is the empty amusement which it all too frequently is." If literature that gives pleasure but has no use is to be condemned in this way, then we need have no fear that Mr. Farrell is exaggerating the importance of the pleasurable element. Rather he is in danger of becoming a Puritan.

He does not even maintain that the amount of pleasure one gets from a book can be regarded as a standard of judgment. He tells us that he likes both *Alice in Wonderland* and *The Remembrance of Things Past,* and goes on: "I should not be able to present any measurement or standard of feeling and experience to prove that Proust affords me a more enjoyable experience than *Alice in Wonderland* does. All he asks is "at least passing acknowledgment" of the "refreshment-value" of literature. This is certainly not an exorbitant demand, and, though it may be questioned whether Mr. Farrell does justice to the pleasurable element in literature, he cannot be accused of overrating it.

His second contention is that some literature of the past has value in the present, both esthetic value—as he, for some strange reason, calls the pleasurable aspect of the literary experience—and use value. Here, if anywhere, one would expect an un-Marxian concept, the concept of absolute, universal human values. But Mr. Farrell is no believer in the absolute. He contents himself with saying what dozens of Marxists have said before him, namely, that "there is a relative objective validity to some works of formal art." Any two Marxists might disagree forever as to what is valid, and why, in some particular piece of literature, but they would never think of denying that its value can survive the period and the class for which it was written.

His third counterclaim is a quotation from Marx: "It is well known that certain periods of highest development in art stand in no direct connection with the general development of society, nor with its material basis and the material structure of its organization." This quotation has proven a stumbling-block to certain critics who have overlooked its too obvious implications: first, that in certain periods art *does* stand in direct connection with the general development of society; second, that it always stands in an indirect connection. Mr. Farrell does not clearly recognize the first of these implications, but he does not deny the possibility of a direct relationship, and he is well aware of the indirect connection. His understanding of these relationships might not always be dependable, but in theory he recognizes them.

We must hurry on. Mr. Farrell says that a book is not necessarily altogether bad because it was written by a bourgeois, and that a good revolutionary novel can be written about an individual. If there is anything un-Marxist about these two statements, he deviates in the best of company. He does not like the slogan, "All art is propaganda," but all he asks is to be allowed to substitute the phrase, "Literature is an instrument of social influence." Permission to do this will, I am sure, be granted by unanimous consent. He says that a novel of decay —such, I presume as *Studs Lonigan*—may be revolutionary. His reasoning will, I think, convince anyone who was not previously convinced.

And that is all. Observe that I do not say Mr. Farrell's discussion of literary criticism is clear, comprehensive, or original. These adjectives do not apply. The discussion is so beclouded by Farrell's personal grudges and his elementary confusions that, as has been noted, it has been loudly welcomed by anti-Marxists. It fails, moreover, to deal incisively with a single one of the problems it raises. In its treatment of the connection between literature and social development it largely disregards the knowledge of social forces that has been given by the Marxian analysis of class alignments. Its examination of the qualities that give literature "relative objective validity" is superficial and unrevealing. Even the distinction between pleasure-value and use-value is no contribution to criticism because Mr. Farrell does not treat the close relationship between pleasure and use. It may be doubted, indeed, if there is any point at which *A Note on Literary Criticism* is genuinely valuable. But we must be careful not to assume that, because the book is an inadequate statement of Marxism, its central ideas are anti-Marxist. Mr. Farrell has built badly, but it is on a Marxist foundation. This we must recognize, for the sake not of the book, but of Marxism.

Rebuttal

BY JAMES T. FARRELL

I consider Isidor Schneider's review of my book, *A Note on Literary Criticism* (printed in the *New Masses,* June 23, 1936) to be such a gross misrepresentation of my views that a reply is demanded.

First of all, Isidor Schneider seems to permit himself the same type of luxury of illogic as that in which Mr. Peter Monro Jack indulged in his review of my book in the Sunday literary section of the New York *Times*. Both Isidor Schneider and Mr. Jack conceded the validity of many of my criticisms of specific revolutionary critics, and of certain tendencies noticeable in revolutionary criticism. Mr. Jack, for instance, agreed with my criticism of the anti-intellectualism and sentimentality of Michael Gold. And Isidor Schneider, in listing seven "services" which my book performed, stated that one of these was "its arraignment of anti-intellectualism on the part of some Marxist critics . . . and its analysis of some of the false positions it has led to." Similarly, Mr. Jack praised my criticism of the mechanical position of Granville Hicks, and on this point, Isidor Schneider wrote that "most especially" my book had performed a service in "its arraignment of the too-frequently mechanical application in Marxist criticism of the materialist interpretation."

While both of them granted specific criticisms of this order, they both set out to destroy my own position. Neither of them offered reasons to show why my specific criticisms were sound, when the position from which I made these criticisms was unsound. The best which Mr. Jack offered was that I ignored morals, that, in fact, I was afraid of the word moral. The best which Schneider offered was that these criticisms were "negative," and that despite them, I was against Marx. These criticisms were not made in a vacuum. They were made from a definite point of view. My method of procedure in this book was to state a number of propositions, to quote statements of critics in disagreement with these propositions, to analyze these statements in terms of my proposition, and then to reassert my proposition. Often, in addition, I offered quotations from Marx and Engels, and presented my interpretation of these statements. If both Isidor Schneider and Mr. Jack are correct in their reviews, it remains that my criticisms are accidents popping up from an utterly unsound and untenable position. Here, we have some interesting demonstrations of logic, both from the Right and from the Left.

I think that the basic reasons for Schneider's misrepresentation is that he suffers from a primary confusion. It is a failure to distinguish between fundamental relationships in society on the one hand, and between tactics on the other. In other words, he does not understand that I was talking about fundamental relationships and general functions, instead of tactics in various immediate situations. The functions which I was discussing were the functions of literature and of literary criticism. The general relationships which I was analyzing were those between the superstructure and the social base, the connections between literature, politics, and economics. Failing to understand what I was talking about, it is, hence, only natural that Isidor Schneider should be guilty of misrepresentation. And it is this failure which leads him to claim that my method is static, undialectical.

He offers a pseudo-historical analysis of revolutionary criticism in America to support the contention that various extreme statements concerning literature and criticism were necessary at one stage of development, and that they are now no longer necessary. He justified his analysis with the argument that, "Men resort to extreme action not out of choice but necessity." In other words, sectarianism was necessary at one time. This argument is an opportunistic one, attempting to justify misconceptions. I criticized two tendencies in revolutionary criticism, revolutionary sentimentalism, as represented by Michael Gold, and mechanically applied materialism as represented by Granville Hicks. My principal objection to these tendencies was that they have misconceived the functions that literature can and does play in society. My analysis attempted to demonstrate that these tendencies misconceived the functions of literature because (a) they were based on a false estimation of the relationship between literature and economics, (b) because of a false estimation of the ideas which Marx and Engels held concerning the relationship between the superstructure (of which literature is one part) and the social base. My contention is that fundamental relationships, such as those between the superstructure and the base, do not change every time there is a new change in tactics, and a revision of the formulations, which express such shifts in tactics. In other words, my argument is that if literature does not obediently follow economics in 1936, it does not obediently follow economics in 1935, 1930, 1920, or even in the year 1848.

For instance, I criticized Michael Gold for his article on "The Gilbert-Sullivan Cult," printed in the *New Masses,* April 24, 1934. Part of my quotation from that article was the following: "When a Nazi with hands dripping with the blood of workers begins to sentimentalize over Wagner, or an ex-Czarist officer who has hung and flogged peasants tells us that Dostoevsky shakes him to the very soul, one is perhaps justified in suspecting both Wagner and Dostoevsky." My contention is that at no time is such a type of "criticism" necessary or useful. Isidor Schneider's point would evidently be that at one time, such criticism was necessary. Similarly, I criticized Granville Hick's book, *The Great Tradition,* because it was based on the false premise that literature obediently follows economics. I quoted Hicks, in criticism of the writers of Theodore Dreiser's generation: "As we shall see, there is not a single writer of the middle generation whose work is not vitiated by faults that may be more or less directly traced to the instability of the basic economic situation." This statement implicitly treats the relationship between literature and economics in the way that I consider untrue. I do not feel that necessity ever forces us to state fundamental relationships falsely. Such a view, according to Schneider, is undialectical.

Isidor Schneider further considers that I am undialectical because of the fact that when sectarianism developed in America, many Marxist classics were unavailable in translation. I do not know what this has to do with my book, or with my argument. I was not writing a definitive history of American criticism. I was presenting a theoretical position on the question of literature, of literary criticism, and of their relationships within society. Similarly, he offers the even more picayune criticism that I do not put the word Marxist in my title. I think that Marx was too great a thinker to be turned into a source of Pharisaical discussion. If Isidor Schneider wants to prove me un-Marxist by such means, I shall not argue. I think that the way we pay tribute to Marx is by applying his ideas, extending them, testing and retesting them in experience, not by using the word Marxist and the word Marxism forty-seven times in a book review in order to prove ourselves more Marxian than the author we are reviewing.

Also, Isidor Schneider takes the liberty of defending my criticisms of his article, "By Way of Review," (printed in the *New Masses,* January 14, 1936). However, he fails to state that he is defending himself. Forgetting thus to mention himself, he defends himself in these words: "Furthermore he [Farrell] dismisses obviously useful Marxist forms of analysis as platitudinous, as something generally agreed upon. . . . In one instance that he selects, the Marxist review was the only one, in several hundred, to show how social circumstance was reflected in the book and how it determined the author's description of workers. No other approach would have made it clear. Far from being platitudinous, it is an example of how Marxist criticism serves as a new tool which enlarges the area of critical observation." Since Isidor Schneider insists that I have not paid tribute where tribute is due, and since he feels that this is the high value of his article, why must he be so modest as to withhold from the reader the fact that he is here talking about himself and his own Marxism?

He writes that the real issue of my book is whether or not "there is any function for Marxist criticism." Here he misstates. One of the issues which may be implied is the following: is there any function for certain tendencies in revolutionary criticism, specifically, the tendencies which I describe as revolutionary sentimentality, and as mechanical materialism? In other words, I did not ask whether or not there is any function for Marxist criticism. But I did question the validity of self-confessed "Marxist" critics of the type of, say, Granville Hicks.

Isidor Schneider also charges me with quoting Marx and Engels to suit my own purposes. That is a statement which he should prove before making. For instance, what interpretation will he offer to the following statement from Marx's *A Contribution to the Critique of Political Economy?* "It is well known that certain periods of highest development of art stand in no direct connection with the general development of society, nor with the material basis and the skeleton structure of its organization." This was one of the quotations which I supposedly used to suit my own purposes. I used it, specifically, to suggest that my contentions on the carry-over value of literature is one which squared with Marx and Marxism. Similarly what interpretation will he offer for the following quotation from Engels, taken from *The Correspondence of Marx and Engels?* "According to the materialist conception of history the determining element is *ultimately* (italics mine) the production and reproduction in real life." More than this neither Marx nor I have ever asserted. If therefore somebody twists this into the statement that the economic element is the *only* determining one, he transforms it into a meaningless, abstract and absurd phrase." I used it in additional emphasis of the point that "the relationship between economics and ideology cannot be graphed as a straight line between two points, nor expressed in a simple equation showing direct relationships, one leading head-on into the other." Additionally, I also used, apparently to suit my own purposes, and in support of the same point, the following statement, taken from Engels's *Ludwig Feuerbach:* "Every ideology, however, once it has arisen, develops in connection with the given concept material, and develops this material further; otherwise it would cease to be ideology, that is, occupation with thoughts as with independent entities, developing independently and subject only to their own laws." Etc.

Isidor Schneider further writes that "Farrell reiterates that Marxist criticism denies and imperils the values of individuality. Into this unjustified assumption creep other equally unjustified assumptions. One is that group responses cannot be as subtle, or do not require as subtle an understanding or are not as interesting as individual responses." I assume that Mr. Schneider is here referring to such paragraphs of mine as the following: "But how does the class struggle make its impact upon the life of the individual? It comes into his consciousness by dictating his relations to other men. It delimits the kind of life that he may or may not live. It builds up habits of response and thinking, of which he may or may not be aware. It sees within him many potentialities of action which will be realized and expressed internally or overtly in terms of objective situations. The class struggle, however, does not in any sense produce so complete a differentiation of human beings that there are no similarities between men who objectively belong to different social classes. Nor does it mean that the class struggle is a direct, potent, conscious factor at every moment in a man's life; it does not cause him to act in every detail of every situation in a preconditioned way that makes him indistinguishable from other members of his class. The class struggle is not something that the worker breathes, so that he goes about breathing two parts of ozone to one part of class struggle. It is an objective set of relationships, fundamental in a society, and it has devious, shifting, differentiating influence (sometimes direct, sometimes indirect) on individuals and on classes. We cannot, then, treat the class struggle as if it were just some lumpy force pushing men in an equal and coordinate way toward two sides of a barricade where they will proceed to fire guns and throw bricks at each other. I repeat, therefore, that the class struggle, as I understand it, is a fundamental set of relationships, and that out of this fundamental set there grow many potentialities of conduct, of thought, feeling, dream, fantasy, as well as of overt action. And I say that the class struggle is not, for the Marxist, simply an article of faith. It is something that he examines, traces, correlates, understands."

Finally, Isidor Schneider suggests that the fact that one Catholic reviewer recommended my book indicates its anti-Marxian character. He has referred to this recommendation twice. Since he has done that, why doesn't he read the particular review and see precisely what was said? Additionally, isn't it time that some of our revolutionary critics quit judging books in such a manner? It seems that if they like a book and someone in the bourgeois press praises it, that proves that revolutionary literature is gaining ground. If they dislike a book, and someone in the bourgeois press likes it, that proves that it is not good. Such practices are almost the ultimate word in critical degradation.

WAS "PARTISAN" TOO PARTISAN?

At the center of many of the most heated controversies in the 1930's was *Partisan Review*. First published in 1934 as an organ of the John Reed Club of New York, *Partisan Review's* specific function was to publish "the best creative work of its members as well as of non-members who share the literary aims of the John Reed Club." Through the literary medium the editors were prepared to participate "in the struggle of the workers and sincere intellectuals against imperialist war, fascism, national and racial oppression"; the defense of the Soviet Union was to be one of their principal tasks.

In the summer of the following year, when Party policy called for the dissolution of the John Reed Clubs, the editors of *Partisan Review* announced that the magazine would no longer be published as an organ of the club; henceforth, it would be "a revolutionary literary magazine edited by a group of young Communist writers, whose purpose will be to print the best revolutionary literature and Marxist criticism in the country and abroad." In February of 1936, *Partisan* once again underwent a change, this time combining with Jack Conroy's magazine, *Anvil*. But in the fall of the same year, the slackness of mood of the editors (caused by the political disillusionment arising from the Moscow trials), coupled with the financial predicament of the magazine, resulted in the suspension of publication of the magazine then called *Partisan Review & Anvil*. It was not until December of 1937 that *Partisan Review* resumed publication, and this time it was the voice of opposition: "*Partisan Review* is aware of its responsibility to the revolutionary movement in general," the editors wrote, "but we disclaim obligation to any of its organized political expressions. Indeed we think that the cause of revolutionary literature is best served by a policy of no commitments to any political party." The reappearance of *Partisan Review* on an independent basis thus signified the editors' conviction that "the totalitarian trend is inherent in [the Communist] movement and that it can no longer be combatted from within."

The break between *Partisan Review* and the Communist Party was not sudden. Indeed, almost from its inception, *Partisan* was at odds with certain phases of the Party's program; most particularly, as William Phillips and Philip Rahv commented in the first *Partisan Reader* (1946), their differences with the Party may be said to have originated "in a protest against the official idea of art as an instrument of political propaganda." Although the editors of *Partisan* paid homage to *New Masses* in their first editorial, it was not long before their relatively high artistic standards resulted in a quiet feud between the two left-wing organs. By the time *Partisan* merged with *Anvil* early in 1936, the feud was no longer quiet; and, as previously mentioned, with the publication of *A Note on Literary Criticism* the two journals became openly hostile toward one another. The exchange between William Carlos Williams and the editors of *Partisan Review*, which appeared in the January 1938 issue of *Partisan*, offers an interesting (Katherine Anne Porter called it "hair-raising") aspect of the controversy.

The feud between the forces of *Partisan Review* and those of *New Masses* gave Malcolm Cowley a chance to express his displeasure with the anti-Stalinist editors of *Partisan Review*. Cowley had helped save *Partisan* in 1935 when the Party wanted to stop publication of all literary organs of the John Redd Clubs; but by 1938 he felt compelled to take it to task. In his article entitled "Partisan Review", which appeared in *The New Republic* on October 19, 1938, Cowley accused the editors of letting their politics interfere with their duties to literature (the very reason, he pointed out, that they had criticized *New Masses*). Cowley disapproved of Trotsky and those Marxists who had repudiated Lenin and Stalin, and when Edmund Wilson criticized him for talking "about the value of a non-partisan literary review after the way you've been plugging the damned old Stalinist line,"

Cowley replied that the editors of *Partisan* had become "such extreme and un-compromising revolutionaries that they don't have to work with other people, and in fact don't have to work at all, except just enough to prove their moral superiority."

Cowley's article of October 19 was answered by the editors of *Partisan Review* in a letter published in *The New Republic* on November 9, 1938; but because the letter was cut to 1,000 words, the Fall 1938 issue of *Partisan Review* reprinted the full text of the original letter, and it is this letter which has been reprinted here. In the November 9 issue, *The New Republic* also printed Cowley's answer to *Partisan's* rebuttal, in which Cowley suggests that a truce be called while there was still time: "Let's forget these quarrels about the international communist movement which are so convenient for the international fascist movement," he wrote. "Why not leave the metaphysics of politics to the political metaphysicians and work together for the human aims that most of us share?" It is with this article, "Red Ivory Tower," that the section concludes.

The Temptation of Dr. Williams

As our readers know, the Communist Party seems to consider the destruction of *Partisan Review* as important an effort as the destruction of Franco—perhaps a bit more important. The campaign seems to have two aspects: (1) open denunciations in the Party press; (2) a whispering campaign of slander supplemented by backstairs intrigue. Last month we gave some examples of the press attacks. And now we are able to present amateurs of literary politics with the interesting case of Dr. William Carlos Williams.

Partisan Review regards Dr. Williams as an extremely accomplished poet. Consequently, when we set about reviving the magazine, we asked him to contribute. He replied:

> Sept. 8.
>
> Your note of Aug. 20 rec'd. I shall have a poem for the *Partisan Review* in a week or ten days. Thank you for asking me to contribute. . . . Sincerely yours, W. C. Williams.

A few days later we received a poem from him. We kept it in our files, but wrote him again asking to see others. "O.K.," he wrote back, "Try this on your victrola!" and he enclosed a poem called "The Defective Record." On the strength of all this, we announced Dr. Williams as a future contributor. After consideration, we decided that neither of the poems in our possession represented his work at its best, and so we returned them, explaining our reasons and asking him to submit others. In reply he sent a postcard: "Your patience will make the flowers bloom." This was cryptic but seemed friendly enough.

We were, therefore, astonished to read in the *New Masses* of November 16 last:

> Watch for these articles next week or later: . . . (2) a study of the writings of contributor H. H. Lewis, by William Carlos Williams, author of *In the American Grain* and other works. Incidentally, some of our readers may have seen an advance notice of the Trotskyist *Partisan Review* announcing the anti-Soviet, anti-Communist contents of the first issue. William Carlos Williams is listed as a contributor, but he writes to the *New Masses* that "the *Partisan Review* has no contribution of mine nor will I send them any."

So it appeared that *Partisan Review* was using Dr. Williams' name without any license! And the *New Masses* liked this idea so well that they repeated it in their next number. Now it happened that at this time *Partisan Review* had not appeared; we knew of nothing that might have prompted Dr. Williams to make such a statement. So we wrote him asking for confirmation. He replied:

> Your letter of yesterday calling attention to a quotation from a letter of mine which appeared in the current issue of *New Masses* reached me this morning. I hasten to reply—not that there is any need for haste but out of courtesy to all concerned.
>
> You know, of course, that I have no reason for liking the *Partisan Review*. I have, at the same time, no partisan interest in the *New Masses*. I had occasion to appear as a writer, for a special reason, in the *New Masses* and it looked as though I might appear also in the *Partisan Review*. As my contribution to the *New Masses* was of longer standing and of more importance to me than the other and since I found the *New Masses* violently opposed to you on political grounds, so much so that they refused to print me if I remained a contributor to *Partisan Review*, I made my choice in their favor.
>
> Their quotation from my letter was correct.
>
> If this letter is to be quoted will you please quote it entire.

This is plain enough. Seldom, in fact, has a transaction of this nature been avowed more frankly. The *New Masses* refused to print him unless he boycotted *Partisan Review*—a condition in itself humiliating enough for a writer of Dr. Williams' standing. Apparently it was further stipulated—it is hard to believe that Dr. Williams volunteered for the job—that he also allow his relations with us to be publicly misrepresented. (It is, of course, literally true that we have no contribution of his—since we sent both poems back to him. But the implication is, to say the least, misleading.) We are distressed that Dr. Williams should lend himself to such shennanigans. And we are puzzled when he writes, "You know, of course, that I have no reason for liking the *Par-*

tisan Review." All we know is that he thought well enough of our venture to send us two poems and to promise others.

In its efforts to stifle independent left-wing expression, the *New Masses* has so far been signally unsuccessful. The Williams episode is its first triumph, so far as *Partisan Review* is concerned. But what a victory! Conditions! Threats! Pressures! These are the tactics of the underworld. And it is now clear from which quarter factionalism in the left-wing literary movement issues. When Dr. Williams was invited to contribute to *Partisan Review* he was not asked to boycott any other publication; nor would we for a moment presume to put any such conditions on our writers. When the real situation becomes clear to Dr. Williams, as in time it must, we hope he will send us some more poems.

The Editors of *Partisan Review*

Partisan Review

DURING the last few months I have been growing more and more impatient with *Partisan Review*. The friends of that magazine will say that my irritation is purely the result of political differences, and notably of a confirmed bias on my part against Trotsky and his admirers. The answer is that if *Partisan Review* had followed the policy announced in December, 1937, the political differences could have been overlooked. But perhaps the editors have forgotten what they said in the first issue printed after they had broken away from the Communist Party:

Partisan Review is aware of its responsibility to the revolutionary movement in general, but we disclaim obligation to any of its organized political expressions. Indeed we think that the cause of revolutionary literature is best served by a policy of no commitments to any political party. Thus our underscoring of the factor of independence is based, not primarily on our differences with any one group, but on the conviction that literature in our period should be free of all factional dependence . . .

Partisan Review aspires to represent a new and dissident generation in American letters; it will not be dislodged from an independent position by any political campaign against it . . . Our editorial accent falls chiefly on culture and its broader social determinants. Conformity to a given social ideology or to a prescribed attitude or technique will not be asked of our writers. On the contrary, our pages will be open to any tendency which is relevant to literature in our time.

The same ideas were restated elsewhere in the magazine, and reëmphasized in the issues that followed. "In this period, when the blight of political meddling in behalf of narrow party interests makes so much thinking about literature insincere and superficial, it is good to see vital *literary* differences again coming into the open."—"The *Partisan Review* has been founded to fight the tendency to confuse literature and party politics." At this point, however, there are signs of ambiguity. Was *Partisan Review* being "founded" or was it merely being revived? And in either case, why did it insist on using the same name as a magazine founded three years before by Communist sympathizers? Two of the former editors had been retained, but that was hardly a sufficient answer. The whole point of the new magazine seemed to be that it was trying to avoid partisanship. It wanted to be judged as a nonpartisan literary monthly.

For such a monthly there was and is a real need. Almost all the little magazines have disappeared, and there has been nothing to take their place as an organ for young or unpopular writers. Not a single literary magazine is now being published by the Communist Party or its fellow travelers. From time to time *The New Masses* prints a literary supplement, with a great air of being kind to culture, but *The New Masses* is really interested in politics; nobody reads it for astute technical criticism or to learn what the youngest poets are doing. Moreover, the effort to unite all liberal and democratic tendencies into a People's Front has made *The New Masses* more timid and conventional in literary matters than it used to be. It cultivates established writers—including the second and third-raters—and hesitates to print anything that will hurt its friends or comfort its enemies. *Partisan Review* could be more carefree and irresponsible; and it could give their day in print to the unruly kids who may or may not become the established writers of tomorrow.

Yet the best of the writing in *Partisan Review* has been critical—the long essays by Edmund Wilson, Lionel Trilling and William Troy (who would be marvelous if only he wrote in English instead of schoolmen's Latin); and perhaps even better the shorter analytical pieces by Philip Horton, R. P. Blackmur and F. O. Matthiessen. I can remember two fine American poems and two only: "The Dwarf," by Wallace Stevens, in December, and in February "Those Autobiographical Blues," by Winfield Townley Scott, a picture of a New England mill town spoiled only by the self-conscious title. "Ballad," by D. S. Savage, is a fresh and effective piece that had already been printed in England. Most of the other verse in *Partisan Review* has been bad in a bumbling, uncertain fashion—written, you would say, by belated Symbolists lost in their own vague symbols and lacking the keen eye, the sure ear and the hidden depth of feeling that justify Symbolism at its best. As for its fiction, it resembles the poetry, with less influence of Mallarmé at second hand and more of Kafka; the one really successful story is Eleanor Clark's "Hurry, Hurry."

The first issue of the new *Partisan Review* contained no purely political article (though Sidney Hook's long review of "Attitudes Toward History" was party politics in a thin disguise). In the next issue, however, there was an extract from André Gide's second attack on the Soviet Union; and in the third issue Philip Rahv abused the American Writers' Congress. Since then, the space devoted to political writing has increased from month to month, and it is all of the same type—attacks on the Soviet Union, on literature and art in the Soviet Union, on politics in the Soviet Union, on American friends of the Soviet Union, a grand anti-Russian campaign under the infra-red banner of the Fourth International. In the latest issue, for August-September, a climax is reached with five anti-Soviet articles out of eight contributions—with Trotsky sounding off in an article on "Art and Politics" that has little to say about art and a great deal to say about Stalin, and with F. W. Dupee, Victor Serge, Dwight Macdonald and James Burnham all writing as if to illuminate a text from Trotsky. There are, as I said, three literary contributions to the issue, but they look as scared and subdued and neglected as three doves in a cage of screaming parrots.

But the worst of it is that factional politics has got into the book reviews and critical articles and has made them, in many cases, sneering and superficial. There was an example of that in the very first issue, where Sidney Hook reviewed Burke's "Attitudes Toward History" and, as the author complained in a letter published the following month, made the "whole book appear like a mere offshoot of the Stalin-Trotsky controversy, an issue to which he devotes more space in his five pages than I do in my 480 pages." But the tendency was carried to an extreme in the March number by F. W. Dupee, when he wrote a long essay on André Malraux and ended by dismissing him as "the type of liberal Comintern lobbyist thrown up by the stooge politics of people's-frontism." One reads a phrase like that with real dismay. Dupee in the past has written reviews in which he showed a sense of literary values. What blind rage has so obsessed him that he can no longer read or understand what an author is saying? And what sort of tone-deafness permits him to talk about a serious novel in terms of political platitudes pinned on like price tags in a chain grocery store?

Just what has happened to the magazine? People of a suspicious nature might interpret its history as a plot to capture the younger literary rebels—the idealists, the formalists, the symbolists, the libertarians—and enroll them in an anti-Soviet crusade, not under the direct leadership of Leon Trotsky, but still with Trotsky as guide and political director. For my part I prefer to believe that the editors were absolutely sincere, last December, when they made their original statement of aims. But slowly, in the midst of their battles against the Communist Party press, their opinions solidified into hatreds, fixing their minds into one frozen mold, so that they scarcely realized they were committing all the literary crimes they charged against their opponents. "The blight of political meddling in behalf of narrow party interests makes so much thinking about literature insincere and artificial." Could there be any better proof of that than *Partisan Review?*

Meanwhile, there is still a need for a magazine devoted primarily to literature, one that can publish long poems and leisurely essays and long stories of literary merit that wouldn't have a chance in the commercial weeklies or monthlies—a magazine, in short, that would carry on the traditions of *The Dial,* dead in 1929, and *The Hound and Horn,* dead in 1934. I saw both of them go without much sorrow, but I miss them more as time goes on, and I think they are missed by every serious writer. Today there is *The Criterion,* edited by an Anglo-Catholic in London, and there is *The Southern Review,* edited in Baton Rouge by a group of de-reconstructed rebels; both these magazines are tolerant of revolutionary opinion so long as they are expressed with force and scholarship. Here is a place that *Partisan Review* might have filled in New York; but it chose to move in another direction. Put a green cover on it and today you could hardly tell it from *The American Mercury.*

MALCOLM COWLEY

Letter to The New Republic

IN the October 19 issue of the *New Republic,* Malcolm Cowley published a lengthy article abusing *Partisan Review* as 'factional', 'anti-Soviet', a perpetrator of 'literary crimes', and 'hardly' distinguishable from the *American Mercury.* As we go to press, the *New Republic* has promised to print our reply in an early issue. Pleading limitations of space, however, the *New Republic* insisted that we cut down our original letter to 1,000 words—although Mr. Cowley's attack ran over 1,700 words. (The only specific omission they stipulated was the sentence: "Isn't this the same Malcolm Cowley whose use of his position on the *New Republic* to play Communist Party politics has long been a literary scandal?" This, Bruce Bliven wrote us, "obviously transcends the legitimate boundaries of public controversy"—though Mr. Cowley was apparently within those bounds when he implied that *Partisan Review* is a quasi-fascist organ. For the interest of our readers, we print below the full text of our original letter. It may be regarded as a restatement of our political position as well as an answer to Mr. Cowley.

Editor, The New Republic,
Sir:

We sympathize with Malcolm Cowley's growing impatience with *Partisan Review*, whose literary and political values are at drastic variance with his own. But we must point out that his article on our magazine is a malicious and politically motivated attack masquerading as a matter of literary differences. These are strong words. We think we can show they are justified.

Mr. Cowley makes two main charges against *Partisan Review*. (1) We have proclaimed that literature should not be degraded to an instrument of political factionalism, and yet we devote much space to what Mr. Cowley calls "anti-Soviet articles." (2) This secret addiction to politics has reduced *Partisan Review* to the literary level of the *New Masses*.

To support his first charge, Mr. Cowley quotes from our opening Editorial Statement, which announced a policy of "no commitments to any political party." This he interprets to mean that *Partisan Review* had foresworn politics and was going to devote itself to an above-the-battle kind of pure Literature, such as the *Dial* once stood for. And so he points triumphantly to the fact that we have actually paid a good deal of attention to politics. But we have never aspired to stand for Pure Literature. We have always agreed with Mr. Cowley that the contemporary writer must concern himself with politics if his work is to have any deep meaning for our time. Mr. Cowley's quotations from our editorial were, to say the least, very selective. One sentence he did *not* quote was: "Any magazine, we believe, that aspires to a place in the vanguard of literature today, will be revolutionary in tendency." That is clear enough, surely.

But Mr. Cowley also objects to the *kind* of political approach we have had, insisting that to attack the Communist Party's cultural line is to play factional politics. This we deny. The struggle between Stalinism and revolutionary Marxism seems to us to go far beyond party or factional issues. By this time, Stalinism has ceased to be a revolutionary tendency, and in fact is rapidly turning into the opposite.

We do not consider our struggle against it as committing us to any party line, any more than we consider our constant criticism of capitalist values—whether 'democratic' or fascist—a matter of factional politics. Many radical groups, from the Fourth International to the Social Democratic Federation, oppose Stalinism for much the same reasons we do. We have never endorsed the political line of any of these groups—which obviously on other subjects have deep-rooted differences among themselves—nor have we excluded any contributor from our pages because he belonged to or didn't belong to any of these groups. And if the literary sympathizers of the Communist Party have not appeared in our pages, it is because they have yielded to a well-organized boycott campaign.

Mr. Cowley quotes extensively from two paragraphs of our six-paragraph Editorial Statement. But he neither quotes from nor mentions the three central paragraphs, and for the very good reason that to do so would explode his main charge: that we are running under false colors. These paragraphs were devoted to a single theme: our reasons for considering the influence of the Communist Party a major threat to both literature and revolution in our time, and our determination to fight against this influence. Mr. Cowley is simply misrepresenting when he implies we have made any secret of our position on this issue. We must also object, in passing, to his expression, "anti-Soviet articles." He may identify the Kremlin with the Soviet Union. We don't, any more than we identify any particular administration with the United States of America.

Mr. Cowley's other charge—of inferior literary quality—he is careful to make almost wholly in the form of innuendo. Thus he implies but does not state that *Partisan Review* is on the same cultural level as the *New Masses*. (Our lawyers assure us that, although calculated to injure our business, this is an expression of opinion and so not libelous.) He implies but does not state that, for political reasons, we have shut the door on talented young unknowns. (We might note that our $100 short story prize was divided between two young writers whose prose we were the first to print, and that we have printed work by James Agee, Delmore Schwartz, Mary King, E. S. Bley, Jackson Matthews, Parker Tyler, Elizabeth Bishop and many other young and comparatively unknown writers.) Mr. Cowley accuses us of substituting political for esthetic criteria—and also objects to our poetry and stories as "second-hand" Kafka and Mallarmé. Does this imply that Kafka and Mallarmé followed a Trotskyist-Bukharinist line? He also charges that "factional politics has got into the book review." To date, we have printed 31 reviews, in only one of which—Sidney

Hook's review of Kenneth Burke's book—is the Stalinist issue raised explicitly. At least two books by writers close to the Communist Party —Richard Wright and Ernest Hemingway—were praised.

Mr. Cowley states: "F. W. Dupee . . . wrote a long essay on André Malraux and ended up by dismissing him as 'the type of liberal Comintern lobbyist thrown up by the stooge politics of people's frontism'." This is a flat misquotation: Mr. Dupee applied these words not to Malraux, but to Garcia, the central character in *L'Espoir*. His article on Malraux, furthermore, is not a simple-minded political diatribe against a writer with whom he is in political disagreement, but a precise and painstaking analysis which attempts to correlate the literary and political qualities of Malraux' work. Mr. Cowley may or may not agree with Mr. Dupee's conclusions, but he had no right to imply the article is a mere piece of abuse such as—shall we say?—Mike Gold might have written.

It seems odd to us that Mr. Cowley, whose passion for Pure Literature burns in every line of his article, has never criticised the *New Masses*—which, with a great show of being fair-minded, he admits is "more timid and conventional in literary matters than it used to be" —as he now attacks *Partisan Review*. It also seems odd that Mr. Cowley should find our literary standards so low when such non-political and exclusively literary magazines as *Poetry, New Directions*, and *The Criterion* have printed flattering notices of *Partisan Review*.

Who is this Galahad of Pure Literature who is demanding that *Partisan Review* emasculate itself politically and who can say a kind word for neo-Catholic literary magazines and Southern Agrarian literary magazines but not for anti-Stalinist literary magazines? (His position amounts to this: if you're going to touch on politics, be Stalinist: if you can't be Stalinist, then back to the Ivory Tower with you!) Who is this belated mourner at the bier of the *Dial* and the *Hound & Horn*. (According to those who followed his writing when those magazines were still alive, Mr. Cowley's admission that he "saw both of them go without much sorrow" is a masterpiece of understatement.) Isn't this the Mr. Cowley who not so long ago wrote an article defending the political censorship of literature? Isn't this the same Mr. Cowley we remember exhorting us at Writers' Congresses to climb up on the bandwagon of revolution? Isn't this the same Malcolm Cowley whose use of his position on the *New Republic* to play Communist Party politics has long been a literary scandal? And could we have mistaken the name signed to a review in the *New Republic* a few weeks ago which argued that Yeats was saved from "a broken career and an early death" by his political interests, even though he had "in many cases the wrong opinions"? "Some other week," concluded Mr. Cowley, "I should like to talk about Yeats and political criticism, as it is represented in this country by magazines like *Partisan Review*." But when he came to writing the article, he said nothing about Yeats. Perhaps he realized the cases were hardly parallel. Yeats was "wrong" on Irish political issues which have only an academic interest here today, and so his political interests enriched his poetry. But Partisan Review is "wrong" on issues which very intimately and tenderly concern Mr. Cowley, and so *our* political interests have destroyed and corrupted our literary perceptions.

Mr. Cowley concludes his high-minded defense of literary values by remarking of *Partisan Review:* "Put a green cover on it, and today you could hardly tell it from the *American Mercury*." This is Red-baiting, C. P. style, no more and no less.

The Editors of *Partisan Review*

October 17, 1938.

Red Ivory Tower

I WAS less surprised than bewildered by the letter from the editors of *Partisan Review* that is printed on page 19 of this issue. Of course they would disagree with what I said three weeks ago about their magazine. But the letter is a vehement answer to no article that was ever written by me or printed in *The New Republic*. To list a few of the misapprehensions:

I did not make the "two main charges against *Partisan Review*" that the editors represent me as making. My point was simply that it started out as one sort of magazine—a sort for which there is a great need— and seems to be ending as another. It started out as a literary monthly opposed to "political meddling in behalf of narrow party interests"; it seems to be ending as a narrow party organ.

I did not interpret the policy of "no commitments to any political party" as meaning that *Partisan Review* had forsworn political discussion. The statement was taken absolutely at its face value.

I do not believe that attacking the cultural line of the Communist Party is the same as playing partisan politics; that was made clear in my review of "The Seven Soviet Arts." But such attacks become partisan politics when there is practically nothing else in a magazine. It was after reading the August-September issue of *Partisan Review* that I wrote my article. The issue contained, exclusive of correspondence and editorial comment, fifty-eight pages of anti-Soviet or anti-Communist polemics, as against eight pages of literary material.

I did not imply that the editors made any secret of their opposition to the Communists. My complaint was that they let it become a fixation, a mania that ended by driving almost everything else out of their minds and magazine.

I did not state or imply that *Partisan Review* was on the same cultural level as *The New Masses*. That might have laid me open to libel suits from both magazines. What I did imply was that they shouldn't be compared or put themselves in a place to be compared, since *The New Masses* set out to be and has remained a journal of political comment whereas *Partisan Review*, to quote its cover, is "a literary monthly."

I did not state or imply that, for political reasons, it has "shut the door on talented young unknowns." It deserves credit for printing several, especially in the first few issues, though I think it often failed to find their best work. Later, of course, they were crowded out by articles like Dwight Macdonald's relentless and apparently endless feud with the Soviet cinema.

Did I misquote F. W. Dupee's essay on Malraux? The last few lines of it read as follows: "Garcia thus achieves the dignity of a social type, short-lived, no doubt, but authentic enough while it lasts—the type of liberal Comintern lobbyist thrown up by the stooge politics of people's-frontism. 'L'Espoir,' too, comes under that head." Since "L'Espoir" is a novel and therefore could not be a lobbyist, I assumed that Mr. Dupee was referring to the author of the novel. Of course my point was that phrases like "liberal Comintern lobbyist" or "stooge politics of people's-frontism" have no place in a serious literary discussion, whether they are applied to Malraux or his novel or his created characters.

There are other mistakes or misreadings that ought to be corrected, but enough samples have been given already. The editors of *Partisan Review* didn't read what I wrote, or read it through a distorting lens. I could answer them best by referring them back to my original article.

Near the end of their letter, the editors introduce a topic that ought to be discussed quite apart from the present controversy. It is the old topic of the interrelation between art and politics. I am said to be demanding "that *Partisan Review* emasculate itself politically" and become a magazine of pure art; those are harsh words but let them pass. On the other hand, I argued a few weeks ago that the political life of

William Butler Yeats helped to save him from a broken career like those of his friends. Why should politics have a good effect in Dublin and a bad one among the New York intellectuals?

The obvious answer is that the word "politics" and its derivatives are being used in two different senses.

In the case of Yeats, they refer to his temporary but direct and vigorous participation in the struggles of his people. He was not saved —no poet can be saved—by adopting the right political opinions. I was much more interested in his political *actions*. There was a time, I said, "when he worked and fought among the Irish masses, shared their hopes and hatreds, learned to speak their language and transformed it into a medium for great poetry. He had broken his isolation, stepped out of his private world; he had found a subject and an audience." And Yeats's experience is by no means unique in literary history. Every writer starts out with a store of material accumulated in childhood and youth—starts out, as the critics used to say, "with at least one good novel in a pack on his back." Almost every writer lives to see that pack emptied. It must be filled again, from the outside world, but it cannot be filled by a cold and deliberate accumulation of facts. A writer has to live and work with people and share their inmost feelings before he can make their experiences part of his own store. That helps to explain why revolutionary movements and periods have re-awakened many talents.

In the case of *Partisan Review* and several other magazines, the word "politics" takes on a different meaning. This time there is no question of sharing in popular struggles, of fighting or marching or even raising money. Instead there is a great interest in the ethics and esthetics and metaphysics of politics, an interest in opinions as divorced from action, in theology as divorced from religion, leading to a doctrine of salvation by revolutionary faith alone. The result is a retreat from practical life into something that I heard described three years ago as the red ivory tower. It is a place beyond the world, as lonely and as lacking in human warmth as the white ivory tower of the Symbolists.

But the mention of Yeats brings up still another topic that needs discussion. One of the reasons why he withdrew from the Irish national movement was his disgust with the endless quarrels between factions. He found that they led to blindly fixed opinions and sterile hatreds. "Most of us were prosecuting heretics," he says. "Our conventions . . . were dominated by little groups . . . which had the intensity and narrowness of theological sects." He reflected that much of the bitterness was due to what was really loathing for oneself or one's world. "If that loathing . . . remains but loathing, world or self consumes itself away, and we turn to its mechanical opposite. Popular Nationalism and Unionism so changed into one another, being each but the other's headache." For Popular Nationalism and Unionism we can substitute any two sects of the 1930's. The forms of political opposition remain the same, even though the substance changes.

Today in the progressive movement we have the same theological quarrels that helped to discourage Yeats. They exist on a larger scale and are likely to have a more disastrous effect. Already I notice that many writers are drawing back—either into an ultra-radical idleness or else into an assortment of mysticisms, cynicisms and revolutions of the pure world. If the process is carried farther, it will be a bad thing for the American progressive movement, which can use talent or enthusiasm from any source. It will be still worse for the writers who retreat.

I suggest that we call a truce while there is still time. Let's forget these quarrels about the international communist movement which are so convenient for the international fascist movement. Let's write books for a change, and argue about them, and praise the books by other people that are being neglected. Writers are specialists in words, feelings, sensations, and not in abstract theories. Why not leave the metaphysics of politics to the political metaphysicians and work together for the human aims that most of us share?

MALCOLM COWLEY

Caricatures made at the First American Writers Conference by William Gropper, Phil Wolfe and Russell T. Limbach. (New Masses, May 7, 1935)

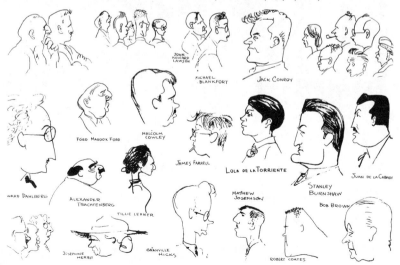

IF WE WOULD GUIDE BY THE LIGHT OF REASON WE MUST LET OUR MINDS BE BOLD

Fresco mural by George Biddle, Department of Justice Building, Washington, D.C., 1932-34.

A World to Win

The proletarians have nothing to lose but their
chains. They have a world to win.

—THE COMMUNIST MANIFESTO

RESPONDING to a letter from Alan Calmer, one of the editors of *Partisan Review,* Sherwood Anderson wrote rather testily on January 2, 1936: "I really do not know what is meant by 'proletarian writers.' If it means that blacksmiths and railroad mail clerks suddenly begin to write, all I can say is that the same thing has always happened. If, on the other hand, it means writing with understanding about workers, farm hands, etc., what in hell has Dreiser been doing all his life? What have I been doing all my life? What did Turgenev do when he wrote *Annals of a Sportsman?*" The point was well taken. Proletarian literature was undoubtedly the most distinctive literary form of the thirties; but, paradoxically, no one seemed to know exactly what it was.

Most obviously, the term proletarian literature suggested a literature produced by a member of the working class about the working class. To Michael Gold, for example, it was only when "there is singing and music rising in every American street, when in every American factory there is a drama-group of workers, when mechanics paint in their leisure, and farmers write sonnets," that "the greater art" would grow. The worker-artist had only to tell of the proletariat's struggles and eventual triumphs; his sweat was technique enough. " 'Technique has made cowards of us all,' " Gold proclaimed. "There is no 'style' " —only clarity, force, and truth: "If a man has something new to say, as all proletarian writers have, he will learn to say it clearly in time: if he writes long enough." But to write long enough one must have the time to write. And to have the time, one cannot be a member of the working class.

Although an author's subject matter and background were all-important to Michael Gold and the followers of the *New Masses,* to others it was a writer's ideology that mattered most. Edward Seaver, writing in *Partisan Review,* maintained that the proletarian novel was not necessarily "a novel written by a worker, about workers or for workers." It could only be defined, Seaver insisted, in terms "of history and of political philosophy: the materialistic dialectic, recognition of the class struggle, acceptance of the historic role of the proletariat in the formation of a new and socialistic society." A writer's vision—not his subject matter—formed the basis of a revolutionary art. A story of middle-class or intellectual life, "if it is alight with revolutionary vision," Waldo Frank told the American Writers' Congress, was more effective proletarian art "than a shelf-full of dull novels about stereotyped workers."

But the revolutionary vision, when applied to art, as James Farrell made clear, was often confused and self-destructive. Proletarian literature was a critical term, and Farrell felt that one trouble was that most "Marxist" critics had little understanding of dialectical materialism. Moreover, unlike Marx and Engels, the revolutionary critic did not seem to understand that "certain works of literature possess a human worth and a carry-over power which endow them with a relatively inherent persistence-value after they have been divorced from the material conditions and the society out of which they have been created." Marxism was helpful in understanding the social significance of a work of art, but it offered no criteria for determining whether a book was good or bad. By coming to a work of literature with inflexible principles and standards, Farrell insisted, the Marxist critic failed in his role. Because revolutionary criticism made no attempt to interpret and evaluate art as art—because it made no attempt to understand what an author was trying to do, and how well he did it—it could only breed sterility.

For many, proletarian literature, as well as revolutionary criticism, is indeed sterile. It is no accident that the growth of proletarian literature in this country between 1930 and 1935 coincided with the growth of the Communist Party. Nor is it a coincidence that some of the worst writing in the thirties was done under the aegis of the *New Masses*. What the *New Masses* wanted was a literary monster like Clara Weatherwax's *Marching! Marching!,* to which it gave a prize as the best new proletarian novel of 1935. Art was a weapon; art was propaganda. Art was not art. Only with the publication of *A Note on Literary Criticism,* the formation of *Partisan Review* (which argued that the Left could learn from bourgeois writers), and the Moscow Trials was this dictum seriously questioned among the leftist writers—and only then did proletarian literature begin to die.

Of course, not all proletarian literature was lifeless and without artistic value. As the following selections will show, many of the proletarian authors wrote with a power and sensitivity that is still impressive. Whether all the selections are examples of proletarian literature —as distinguished from revolutionary or radical literature, for example—is open to question. And perhaps, ultimately, the distinction is not very important. The tone of the selections may vary, but the purpose is the same: it is a literature of social protest, a cry for equality and justice. The writers are not of the working class, but they have allied themselves with the struggle of the proletariat. They are angry and hopeful, and they sing equally of bedbugs and martyrs. If there is little gaiety and romance, one need only recall the words of Alfred Kreymborg to realize why: "It's pretty hard to sing of moonlight now,/ Of benches in the park and lovers' lanes/ . . . What shall a lover sing when half the land/ Is driven cold and lives on dank despair?"

Cow

BY BEN FIELD

THE first summer I worked for Dan Smith we got stuck in the middle of our haying because two of the hired men went off on a drunk and remembered in that happy state not to come back.

Gnat, the shrivelled little foreman, seemed glad at first, but the boss looked more worried than ever. And his fat wife said, "Drunken bums like that hates hard work like poison. We got to git some strong farm boys now."

Gnat ogled her and whined, "Me and Mose kin finish all the haying."

She snorted when he mentioned me.

The boss picked at the broken horn of his nose and scribbled a letter to the agency in New York.

A couple of days later as the foreman and I were clearing a meadow along the road, we heard the old worm fence creaking behind us. Up rolled a tremendous Jew with a battered suitcase and stuck a slab of a hand under our noses.

"So you're the feller from the agency?" Gnat cracked a sour smile at the card. "We'll be gitting back soon and you kin hop up and ride along."

"O. K., Captain."

While he lumbered back to drop his suitcase near the fence, Gnat whined, "Nothing more'n a cow. He won't last long."

The big Jew heaved up to us and pointed to a fork. "Boys, I'll start now." He must have heard Gnat, for he grinned. "My nickname's Cow. What's yours?"

I threw him a fork, and he went at the hay in his shirt sleeves and city clothes. He grinned when we roared at his antics.

He held his pitchfork as if there were a poison adder in front of him, and when he did get it into the hay, he tried to lift the whole earth with it like a cock of hay. The sweat streamed down his face, but he stopped for a moment only to watch how we handled our forks, and then he went on again digging up sod.

"Cow" originally appeared in the non-proletarian magazine, *Hound and Horn*, in 1931. Almost four years later, James Farrell told the American Writers' Congress that because of Ben Field's use of overtone and apt metaphors, and "because of the author's feat in characterization, *Cow* can well be a lesson in writing for all of us. And it is . . . one of the few short stories treating revolutionary characters which does not fit into Michael Gold's apt description —'stooge fiction.' "

When the wagon was loaded, he refused to climb up. "It's good discipline to walk when you don't want to." He lumbered behind the wagon, chewing on a spear of grass.

When he saw the boss, he burst out laughing, "My name's Cow." The boss seemed satisfied at the first shot and ordered that the other bed be made in the room where I slept.

Disappointed that no handsome stripling stood before her, the fat missus grumbled that he could make the bed himself if he was in that hurry. But when she heard the new man's hearty laugh and felt his eyes on her, she shuffled upstairs.

Cow showed up in some faded khaki for evening chores. Clumsy at first with the cows, he showed infinite patience fiddling with their teats. He'd get up with a sort of bow and pat a kicking heifer. As it was flytime and unbearably hot, the rest of us clubbed the brutes until their muzzles ran red snot. "That ain't discipline being so nervous with your dumb sisters," he boomed across the barn at us.

Smelling of milk, he sat beside the boss's two kids at supper and patted them. "I got to get a pair, too."

"So you're married, Cow, and run away from your wife." Gnat winked at the fat missus.

Cow laughed. "Young feller, it takes more than you to get my goat. I had a grandfather in Russia, who used to call my grandma Cow, too, but hell! she was sharp as the old knives she'd sharpen on the edge of her pots. Afraid of nothing and always on the go. I come out here to be like a cow and get rid of some itches that ain't good for discipline and study farm conditions. I'm a carpenter by trade, but it's slack now. And anyway there can't be much of a revolution without the farmer horning in."

He guffawed to see the expressions on our faces.

The first night he was with us we had the regular bottling to do in the milk shed. Dead-tired, we crept down the red clay road, stable lamps swinging, while he rolled behind whistling. Gnat seemed more peevish than ever probably because the missus had looked at the big fellow two or three times across the table. As Cow leaned against the shed and admired the sky pulsing with stars, he said something about most Jews being heavy blabbers and light workers.

Cow just smiled and picked up an old bottle. He grunted a little and the bottle cracked in his hand, and then, as he shouted a shout that rolled over the hills, he shivered the bottle in his awful paw. "Only a little trick, Captain."

Gnat seemed to shrivel up more and didn't give another peep in the milk shed.

The boss sighed, "You're a pretty good man. Jesus, I was hefty my-self once but never like that . . . a goddamn bull trampling a feller don't do him much good. . . ."

"So farming ain't a joke," Cow said, dusting his hands.

"It's a hell of a one. I got ruptured monkeying with a stuck wagon and then the lousy bull." He crept out into the night. "See you git every-thing to rights."

When the three of us were done, we waded through the wet grass up to the farmhouse.

Gnat tried to get friendly. He sniggered, "After the boss, he found he weren't going to be good for much, he crawls downstairs and gits his rifle. He used to be a feller with a terrible temper, but now he ain't got the guts of chawed sparrow grass. He begins peppering that there bull from his bedroom. He carried it on slow till the bull stood on his head and then was astraddle the fence and over in the road. Then he shoots him right through the ear fine's silk."

Cow looked at me and said nothing.

Up in our hot bedroom he undressed and stood naked, his chest slashed in places and tattooed with a splendid woman with a hammer in one hand and a sickle in the other. He said something about her being without either and without clothes, but for the sake of somebody who liked him, as he had been unable to get her off, he had had all added. Grinning, he began writing a letter on some old-fashioned pa-per with a mark like a sealed fountain in the corner. As he wrote he fired questions at me, and I explained I was working on the farm to get some material for some farm stories.

He grunted and little by little threw some of the clothes off his life.

When he was five, his family came to America and settled in Passaic where his father managed to make some money in the handkerchief business. He went to the public schools for about ten years and then, after he became too big to keep away from the shopgirls and took to reading Jack London, he ran away to sea. He'd been everything but a farmer. During the war he worked in South America in a quartz mine where he lost all his hair inside of a few weeks because of the heat and sweat. He spent almost one year tramping the Andes backbone, and there were days when he was without water and had to soften his grub with his own urine. Back in the states he joined a circus as strong man, finally drifting east. Here he got married last year, still had fits of rest-lessness; every other day suffering hell to remember himself playing with holystones like dice on the decks of rat-infested tubs.

"Lousy system that makes a feller with guts something like an outcast. I'm a carpenter by trade and I won't quit till I help make a coffin for it." He laughed and finished his letter.

As he tried to put his part of the room into shipshape, he rumbled, "Now supposing you bowl over some pin-head publisher and get your stuff popular and get rich, won't everything be hell yet for most everybody in the same rotten system? You writers only worrying about yourselves and sticking out all your nice parts like a whore before a looking glass or a customer. Even London was like the rest sometimes. Have you read this?"

He chucked *The Iron Heel* at me and then jumped into bed, where he began reading a pamphlet. I soon fell asleep and when I woke after midnight he was still up, examining with care a little buffalo-chested moth he had caught.

I thought I'd have a hell of a job getting him up at about four o'clock for milking. He was up, however, even before the hollow-eyed boss and sniffling Gnat.

He began to get the hang of milking, and the swollen bags seemed no more than toys in his immense paws. During meals he ate more than all of us put together and between them outworked us all. The knack of pitching came to him the second day, and he had the sore Gnat buried underneath his cocks of hay more than once in the meadow next the farmhouse, to the great amusement of the fat missus.

He radiated so much energy that even the ailing boss took on another hay wagon, and in about two weeks we were far ahead of our haying schedule. Then we turned to weeding the truck on our fours, and Cow took to it like a duck to water, his shirt bellying out in the terrific heat like an immense bladder full of quarts of sweat.

Though we were on our feet from four every morning until about nine at night, he would wash his clothes before going to bed (of the hired men only Gnat had his washed) and then walk two miles to the post office to mail his letters. Back from his hike he would gab until past midnight with anyone he could keep from hitting the hay. And in spite of such prodigious tirelessness, he sighed to me once, "Nothing helps much. Now I'll roll around in bed, the flesh like a jib-boom."

Whenever he could he dragged me Sundays to town, where he got into baseball games with some of the farm boys behind the feed store or horseplayed with them and told them about señoritas sweet and bitter as Canton ginger. After such stories he'd invariably grow sarcastic about their being so dumb about a system that worked them like oxen and had some of them hopping as though they were having shotguns of rock salt spraying their hindquarters. One morning as we passed the church, he burst into gargantuan laughter and pulled me in after him.

After the sermon, he talked to the minister and left him startled with, "My dear feller, you need a buglight working in such darkness." Out in the road he said, "You got to give that Jesus Christ credit. He didn't give a pinch of guano for his family or the women and just sailed without tacking for his idea with good discipline. Ever read that French feller Barbusse?"

The fat missus thought he was showing some interest in her because he washed and dried dishes for her a couple of times, and once, when she wasn't well, even kneaded dough and baked a half dozen loaves. But he explained to me that he was making a thorough study of farm conditions and added that it was good discipline for a man of his type to hang around such a splendid field of flesh.

One hot morning after the boss had driven the milk truck to the dairy, Cow and I went to the orchard for some spicy apples which he could eat by the peck. We heard some whispering in the fencerow of the lot adjoining the orchard. We sneaked up. There lay the fat woman all spread out like a field with her two cocks of breasts and Gnat fussing around her.

Cow tightened up and stared at me.

"That's an old story," I whispered.

"And he—he lets her get away with it?"

"Can't help himself. The farm's hers. There's his condition."

"Leading a lie of a life. Hell! and they call me a cow. Why, they're the ones being jumped—all of them and you, too."

In the barn during evening chores when Gnat shrilled his favorite song about his wanting to be like boar hogs because of their tirelessness to please sows, Cow burst into a roar of bitter laughter. "Every little bug worried about its own appetite and the whole world go hang—no trying to wrestle it down even for a good cause." He spat into the drop and yanked so hard at her teats that the heifer kicked. He got up and knocked her down with a blow of his fist.

At the supper table he couldn't sit still for a moment, but pitched in with his first bite about the working conditions on farms and how everybody didn't worry a goddamn so long as he filled his bellies and women.

The boss turned brick-red. "If you don't like it, you kin go back to Russia you're always batting so much about."

Cow only let out his rumbling laugh while the fat woman smiled at him as though she were drunk.

A couple of days later as I was sharpening some mowing machine knives in the tool house, I heard the boss and him yelling at each other as they were slopping the pigs.

"You got to have guts. She ain't bad looking and you can't blame her much. You don't even know if those kids are yours. Chuck the lie of a life you're leading and—"

There was the sound of a smack.

I looked out and saw the boss held up in those big paws like a trussed capon.

"But you're living a lie—a goddamn lie, fool you."

The boss flapped his hands helplessly and began sobbing like a kid. "What the hell diff-diffrince makes to you?"

Cow dropped him in a heap in a pig's wallow. "I'm stronger and I'm responsible for you. You're living a lie and making things rottener, little stinkbug, you."

His thumb hung down like a teat. He tugged at it and it snapped back into place while the sweat beaded up all over him and stood in wreaths on his bald head.

The boss sat in the wallow and just simply cried not only from sheer humiliation but also, probably, from remembering his helplessness and the long barren field of life still before him. After a while he got up and blinked around, but nobody was in sight.

I thought that after this scrap, Cow would be surely fired. Nothing came of it. And still, hammer and tongs, he went at the three of us. The missus, her skirts yanked up to her knees, listened with her oxlike eyes on him. The jealous Gnat tried to show his sting several times.

"They're slackers—always talking about the rich that worked for it."

The boss said huskily, "Some wants to, and they can't."

"You got the ticket now," Cow cried.

A sick grin tugged at the boss's face, the first I had seen in a long time. He spoke out and didn't mind his wife. "It ain't every day they kills a bull and throws the ballocks to the poor. Don't that show something's out of gear? Who gits the ballocks all the time?" He couldn't keep his face from creasing and stumped out into the night.

When we were up in our room, Cow smacked the slabs of his hands together. "He'll wake up yet."

I said, "You'd better hold your horses or something'll happen around here. You're so fanatic about—"

He laughed and sat down to write another letter on the paper with the mark like a sealed fountain. "My dear feller, when a man's right, he's always what you call fanatic."

"But life's too complicated to butt into other people's affairs. One should be an indifferentist like Chekhov and at the same time liberal and open and—"

"Open like a whore. Chuck your Chekhov into a cow drop. A feller's got responsibilities. Read this." He fired a pamphlet at me and went downstairs to get a drink.

He came up laughing. "Sh, sh . . . She ambushed me in the kitchen and said she'd do my washing for me. And I shouldn't be worried about the boss, he couldn't fire me no matter what I did."

He was a little restless, however, and went to bed instead of finishing his letter. He kept sighing, "Nothing helps much. I wonder how poor redhead looks away from me so long."

The next few days he worked around with less pep and was glad to get away to build a chicken coop for the leghorn pullets. Gnat and I finished up the last of the hay that season, some redtop in the poorest meadow, by the time he was through with his carpentering.

Our next big job was to cut the oats which we were going to use for hay. We got it down and then began filling the barn near the farmhouse with it. Gnat stayed on the wagon unloading, while I drove the team which pulled the grapnel fork full of oats up to the rail on the rooftree and then dumped it in the mow when the trip rope was jerked. Cow was up in the mow and did the work of at least two good men.

The first day we carted the oats, his spirits seemed to have jumped over the moon. He told me that the boss had taken one of his pamphlets and had spent one of his sleepless nights trying to dope it out. Also the night before when he had come back from his hike to town, he had found the missus puttering around the kitchen in her nightgown.

"My discipline was O. K. I just patted her on her moon and sent her back to bed." Then he looked at me. "Do you believe me?"

"Sure I do."

He shrugged his shoulders and climbed up to the mow where Gnat, who was getting more jealous of him day by day, tried to swamp him under huge dumps of oats. It couldn't be done so easily to a man who could handle two full milk cans as though they were Indian Clubs. Cow began to tease him by pulling the horses back on their haunches by tugging on the rope.

Gnat started snarling at him until even the boss, who sat among the pecking chickens in the barnyard watching us, asked him in a wheedling tone to stop.

"Like hell I will. Who the hell are you?"

The boss turned red and looked down at his hands.

Cow yelled, "You little bug, shut up or I'll come down and squash you." Then, stripped to the waist, his back to the wagon, he went on with his work up in the mow.

One had to be careful how one handled the trip rope, and now

Gnat, mad as the devil, jerked it so the grapnel fork slipped from its car and shot like a huge spider down on the broad back. Light as a cocksparrow on his feet when he had to be, Cow jumped and flew from under it. One of its teeth struck him and bowled him over. Gnat hurled his pitchfork into the hay on the barn floor and backed his horses until they crashed into the silo in the yard. He swung his fist and shrilled, "I seen you in the kitchen with her, I seen you last night."

With a bellow Cow picked himself up and jumped from the mow— a distance of about thirty feet. The barn floor was packed with hay; he had dived down a number of times. I expected him to bound up like a rubber ball and get Gnat with one bounce and knock hell out of him.

Something awful, however, seemed to happen. When the dust cleared, he was astraddle the pitchfork Gnat had hurled handle up into the hay. It must have gone quite a distance into him, for as he crashed to the floor he jerked his hands and feet like one of those wooden toy men with strings pulled in back.

How we managed to get that limp bulk to the bedroom is still a miracle to me. Each of us was bathed in blood. The boss, almost out of his mind, called up the veterinary first. Gnat kept on snivelling, "Lousy fork."

When the doctor came, that awful tail of wood had to be pulled out. Neither the boss nor I could stand it, and we left the room. Gnat helped and showed he had guts, and so did the missus after she had quieted the scared kids.

"It was long's a bull's rod," Gnat told us later. "And that feller wouldn't take nothing but yell 'Pull,' and then he went off."

He was the nurse that night and helped the doctor, who stayed on and gave Cow needles. The boss and I sat under a sky with a moon like a broken thumbnail and shivered. Just before milking at dawn I plucked up enough courage and climbed the spotted stairs.

He was lying still and at last opened chewed lips. "No discipline," he mumbled, "I'm a bug, too . . ." His face twisted as he whispered something about poor redhead, and then his muscles knotted and a great red bubble broke from his mouth.

I blundered downstairs.

Towards evening he died.

We went through his papers with the marks like sealed fountains and found his city address. In answer to our telegram the phone rang that midnight and the missus blurted out the whole story. Next morning with the first train, there appeared a tall pregnant woman, head red and cut so close that it resembled a daisy that had lost its petals; with

her was an old Jew with a beard like a nose bag who kept oying continually after the first glimpse at the corpse.

They stayed up in his room all day without eating a bite while the
body was in the hands of the undertaker. The wife wept only once and
that was at night when we overheard her father say, "I told you not to
let him go, him with strange ideas and no feelings to be a family man."

Next morning the feedman, who was also the undertaker, came in
his big car, loaded on the tremendous coffin and the two mourners,
and lumbered towards the city.

The whole nasty business seemed to take the starch out of us. We
didn't do anything but our chores that whole day. After supper the
missus and Gnat stole away into the warm evening to solace themselves.

The boss, who was trying to play with the kids on the lawn, quivered.
"Now they ain't even hiding about it."

I walked over to him wearily. "Dan, I'm leaving tomorrow."

He jerked back in a scared fashion. "Going!"

"No use, I've got to go."

"You been here so long and winter we give you some time for that
there writing of yourn." He blinked down at his hands. "You're part
of the family."

Always suspicious of me, Gnat was glad to see me go, and the missus
scratched herself and said, "We'll git from now on only real farmboys."

The boss drove me over to the station next morning with the milk.
I lugged along an old suitcase, my Chekhov to read on the train, and a
heavy heart. It was raining and the red clay roads and the wet grass
looked as though a huge cow had been disembowelled and bled over
the broad countryside.

At the station we shook hands, and he held on for a moment. "I'm
sorry, Dan, but something's got a hellhold on me. I feel I need guts
and I owed somebody more than money. I got to get back to the city."

We looked at each other and he probably like me saw again our fellow worker of the summer, who had come in our midst like a bomb
and, bursting himself, planted his fragments in some of us, perhaps,
forever.

He let go and made two fists that looked like ballocks. "I—I feel like
I owe somebody something, something like a shotgun." His face broke.
He ran to the truck and it bucked down the road.

I climbed into the train and tried to read some Chekhov, but I felt
too miserable. I imagined hearing strange sounds. I took out my pipe
and went into the smoker where I sat among mill workers on their
way to the mills.

Did God Make Bedbugs?

BY MICHAEL GOLD

I

IT rained, we squatted dull as frogs on the steps of the rear tenement. What boredom in the backyard, we kids didn't know what to do. Life seemed to flicker out on a rainy day.

The rain was warm and sticky; it spattered on the tin roofs like a gangster's blood. It filled our backyard with a smell of decay, as if some one had dumped a ton of rotten apples.

Rain, rain! The sky was a strip of gray tin above the terraced clotheslines, on which flowery shirts and underwear flapped in the rain. I looked up at them.

I heard the hum of sewing machines, surf on a desolate island. A baby wept feebly. Its hoarse mother answered. The swollen upper half of a fat woman hung from a window, her elbows like hams. She stared with dull eyes at the rain.

A wooden shack occupied a portion of the yard; it was the toilet. A bearded man in suspenders went in.

Masha sang from the next tenement. The deep Russian songs helped her pain, the blind girl was homesick. Other girls sang with her often, many nights I fell asleep to that lullaby. Now she sang alone.

Because there was nothing to do. Rain, rain, we had tired of our marbles, our dice and our playing store games.

The backyard was a curious spot. It had once been a graveyard. Some of the old American headstones had been used to pave our Jewish yard. The inscriptions were dated a hundred years ago. But we had read them all, we were tired of weaving romances around these ruins of America.

Once we had torn up a white gravestone. What an adventure. We scratched like ghouls with our hands deep into the earth until we found

---

Michael Gold's *Jews Without Money* was published in February, 1930, and by October had gone into its eleventh printing. Despite objections by the leftist reviewers to Gold's "nationalistic vehemence" and relative lack of interest in the unionization of the garment industry, and despite objections by the conservative press to the revolutionary ending, *Jews Without Money* remains the best-known of all proletarian novels. "Did God Make Bedbugs" is the fifth chapter of Gold's autobiographical novel.

moldy dirty human bones. What a thrill that was. I owned chunks of knee bone, and yellow forearms, and parts of a worm-eaten skull. I had them cached in a secret corner of my home, wrapped in burlap with other treasured playthings.

But it would be boring to dig for bones now. And we were sick of trying to sail paper boats in the standing pool above the drain pipe. It was choked with muck, too sluggish for real boat races.

Then a cat appeared in the rain and macabre gloom of the yard. We were suddenly alert as flies.

It was an East Side gutter cat, its head was gaunt, its bones jutted sharply like parts of a strange machine. It was sick. Its belly dragged the ground, it was sick with a new litter. It paused before a garbage can, sniffing out food.

We yelled. In slow agony, its eyes cast about, as if searching for a friend. The starved mother-cat suspected our whoops of joy. It leaped on a garbage can and waited. It did not hump its back, it was too weary to show anger or fear. It waited.

And we pursued it like fiends, pelting it with offal. It scrambled hysterically up the fence. We heard it drop on heavy feet into the next yard. There other bored children sat in the rain.

II

There is nothing in this incident that ought to be recorded. There were thousands of cats on the East Side; one of the commonplace joys of childhood was to torture cats, chase them, drop them from steep roofs to see whether cats had nine lives.

It was a world of violence and stone, there were too many cats, there were too many children.

The stink of cats filled the tenement halls. Cats fought around each garbage can in the East Side struggle for life. These cats were not the smug purring pets of the rich, but outcasts, criminals and fiends. They were hideous with scars and wounds, their fur was torn, they were smeared with unimaginable sores and filth, their eyes glared dangerously. They were so desperate they would sometimes fight a man. At night they alarmed the tenement with their weird cries like a congress of crazy witches. The obscene heartbreak of their amours ruined our sleep, made us cry and toss in cat nightmares. We tortured them, they tortured us. It was poverty.

When you opened the door of your home there was always a crazy cat or two trying to claw its way inside. They would lie for days outside the door, brooding on the smell of cooking until they went insane.

Kittens died quietly in every corner, rheumy-eyed, feeble and old before they had even begun to learn to play.

Sometimes momma let you pity a kitten, give it a saucer of milk which it lapped madly with its tiny tongue.

But later you had to drive it out again into the cruel street. There were too many kittens. The sorrow of kittens was too gigantic for one child's pity.

I chased and persecuted cats with the other children; I never had much pity; but on this rainy afternoon I pitied the poor mother-cat.

I found myself thinking: Did God make cats?

III

I was oppressed with thoughts of God because my parents had put me in a *Chaider*. I went to this Jewish religious school every afternoon when the American public school let out.

There is no hell fire in the orthodox Jewish religion. Children are not taught to harrow themselves searching for sin; nor to fear the hereafter. But they must memorize a long rigmarole of Hebrew prayers.

Reb Moisha was my teacher. This man was a walking, belching symbol of the decay of orthodox Judaism. What could such as he teach any one? He was ignorant as a rat. He was a foul smelling, emaciated beggar who had never read anything, or seen anything, who knew absolutely nothing but this sterile memory course in dead Hebrew which he whipped into the heads and backsides of little boys.

He dressed always in the same long black alpaca coat, green and disgusting with its pattern of grease, snuff, old food stains and something worse; for this religious teacher had nothing but contempt for the modern device of the handkerchief. He blew his nose on the floor, then wiped it on his horrible sleeve. Pickled herring and onions were his standard food. The sirocco blast of a thousand onions poured from his beard when he bent over the *Aleph-Beth* with you, his face close and hot to yours.

He was cruel as a jailer. He had a sadist's delight in pinching boys with his long pincer fingers; he was always whipping special offenders with his cat-o'-nine-tails; yet he maintained no real discipline in his hell-hole of Jewish piety.

I was appalled when my parents brought me there, and after paying Reb Moisha his first weekly fee of fifty cents, left me with him.

In the ratty old loft, lit by a gas jet that cast a charnelhouse flare on the strange scene, I beheld thirty boys leaping and rioting like so many tigers pent in the one cage.

Some were spinning tops; others played tag, or wrestled; a group kneeled in a corner, staring at the ground as though a corpse lay there, and screaming passionately. They were shooting craps.

One of these boys saw me. He came over, and without a word, tore the picture of W. J. Bryan from my lapel. The boys gambled in buttons. He wanted my valuable button, so he took it.

At a long table, hacked by many knives, Reb Moisha sat with ten surly boys, the beginners' class. Soon I was howling with them. Over and over again we howled the ancient Hebrew prayers for thunder and lightning and bread and death; meaningless sounds to us. And Reb Moisha would pinch a boy, and scream above the bedlam, "Louder, little thieves! Louder!" He forced us to howl.

There was a smell like dead-dog from the broken toilet in the hall. A burlap curtain hung at one end of the hall to disguise the master's home, for he was the unlucky father of five children. His wife's harpy voice nagged them; we could smell onions frying; always onions for the master.

His face was white and sharp like a corpse's; it was framed in an inkblack beard; he wore a skullcap. His eyes glittered, and roved restlessly like an ogre's hungry for blood of little boys.

I hated this place. Once he tried to whip me, and instead of the usual submission, I ran home. My mother was angry.

"You must go back," she said. "Do you want to grow up into an ignorant *goy?*"

"But why do I have to learn all those Hebrew words? They don't mean anything, momma!"

"They mean a lot," said she severely. "Those are God's words, the way He wants us to pray to Him!"

"Who is God?" I asked. "Why must we pray to Him?"

"He is the one who made the world," said my mother solemnly. "We must obey Him."

"Did He make *everything?*"

"Yes, everything. God made everything in this world."

This impressed me. I returned to the *Chaider.* In the midst of the riot and screaming I would brood on my mother's God, on the strange man in the sky who must be addressed in Hebrew, that man who had created everything on earth.

IV

My mother was very pious. Her face darkened solemnly and mysteriously when she talked about her God. Every one argued about God.

Mendel Bum, and Fyfka the Miser, and my Aunt Lena, and Jake Wolf, the saloonkeeper, and the fat janitor woman, and Mrs. Ashkenazi, of the umbrella store, and Mottke Blinder, and Harry the Pimp—all were interested in God. It was an important subject. When I discovered this, it became important for me, too.

I couldn't get the thought out of my head; God made everything. A child carries such thoughts about him unconsciously, the way he carries his body. They grow inside him. He sits quietly; no one knows why; he himself doesn't know. He is thinking. Then one day he will speak.

V

In the livery stable on our street there was an old truck horse I loved. Every night he came home weary from work, but they did not unhitch him at once. He was made to wait for hours in the street by Vassa.

The horse was hungry. That's why he'd steal apples or bananas from the pushcarts if the peddler was napping. He was kicked and beaten for this, but it did not break him of his bad habit. They should have fed him sooner after a hard day's work. He was always neglected, and dirty, fly-bitten, gall-ridden. He was nicknamed the Ganuf—the old Thief on our street.

I stole sugar from home and gave it to him. I stroked his damp nose, gray flanks, and gray tangled mane. He shook his head, and stared at me with his large gentle eyes. He never shook his head for the other boys; they marveled at my power over Ganuf.

He was a kind, good horse, and wise in many ways. For instance: Jim Bush abused him. Jim Bush was a fiery little Irish cripple who lived by doing odd jobs for the prostitute girls. Jim Bush was a tough guy only from the waist up. His blue fireman's shirt covered massive shoulders and arms. His face was red and leathery like a middle-aged cop's. But his legs were shriveled like a baby's.

He cracked dirty jokes with the girls, he was genial when sober. When he was drunk he wanted to fight every one. He would leap from his crutches at a man's throat and hang there like a bulldog, squeezing for death with his powerful hands, until beaten into unconsciousness. He always began his pugnacious debauches by abusing Ganuf the Horse.

He seemed to hate Ganuf. Why, I don't know. Maybe to show his power. Jim was the height of a boy of seven. He stood there, eyes bloodshot with liquor, mouth foaming, and shouted curses at the horse. Ganuf moved; Jim struck him over the nose with a crutch. Jim grabbed the bridle. "Back up!" he yelled, then he sawed the bit on poor Ganuf's tongue. Then he clutched the horse's nostrils and tried to tear them off.

The poor horse was patient. He looked down from his great height at the screaming little cripple, and seemed to understand. He would have kicked any one else, but I think he knew Jim Bush was a cripple.

People always marveled at this scene. I used to feel sorry for my poor horse, and imagine there were tears in his eyes.

This horse dropped at work one summer day. They loosened his harness, and slopped buckets of water over him. He managed to stand up, but was weak. He dragged the truck back to the stable. Waiting there as usual to be unhitched for his supper, he fell gasping; he died on our street.

His body bloated like a balloon. He was left for a day until the wagon came to haul him to the boneyard.

When a horse lay dead in the street that way, he was seized upon to become another plaything in the queer and terrible treasury of East Side childhood.

Children gathered around Ganuf. They leaped on his swollen body, poled sticks in the vents. They pried open the eyelids, and speculated on those sad, glazed big eyes. They plucked hair from the tail with which to weave good-luck rings.

The fat blue and golden flies swarmed, too, around the body of my kind old friend. They buzzed and sang with furious joy as they attacked this tremendous meal sent them by the God of Flies.

I stood there helplessly. I wanted to cry for my poor old Ganuf. Had God made Ganuf? Then why had He let Ganuf die? And had God made flies?

The millions of East Side flies, that drove us crazy in summer, and sucked at our eyelids, while we slept, drowned in our glass of milk? Why?

VI

Did God make bedbugs? One steaming hot night I couldn't sleep for the bedbugs. They have a peculiar nauseating smell of their own; it is the smell of poverty. They crawl slowly and pompously, bloated with blood, and the touch and smell of these parasites wakens every nerve to disgust.

(Bedbugs are what people mean when they say: Poverty. There are enough pleasant superficial liars writing in America. I will write a truthful book of Poverty; I will mention bedbugs.)

It wasn't a lack of cleanliness in our home. My mother was as clean as any German housewife; she slaved, she worked herself to the bone keeping us fresh and neat. The bedbugs were a torment to her. She doused the beds with kerosene, changed the sheets, sprayed the mattresses in an endless frantic war with the bedbugs. What was the use; nothing could help; it was Poverty; it was the Tenement.

The bedbugs lived and bred in the rotten walls of the tenement, with the rats, fleas, roaches; the whole rotten structure needed to be torn down; a kerosene bottle would not help.

It had been a frightful week of summer heat. I was sick and feverish with heat, and pitched and tossed, while the cats sobbed in the yard. The bugs finally woke me. They were everywhere. I cannot tell the despair, loathing and rage of the child in the dark tenement room, as they crawled on me, and stank.

I cried softly. My mother woke and lit the gas. She renewed her futile battle with the bedbugs. The kerosene smell choked me. My mother tried to soothe me back to sleep. But my brain raced like a sewing machine.

"Momma," I asked, "why did God make bedbugs?"

She laughed at her little boy's quaint question. I was often jollied about it later, but who has answered this question? Did the God of Love create bedbugs, did He also put pain and poverty into the world? Why, a kind horse like my Ganuf would never have done such a thing.

Woodcut by Howard Simon
for the original edition
of Jews Without Money.

Can You Hear Their Voices?

BY WHITTAKER CHAMBERS

THE ARKANSAS FARMERS' FIGHT FOR FOOD

IT's like a fire," said the young dirt farmer, Frank Frances, who had been on the prairie only a year. "Everything burns up. Now my cow's sick, and if *she* dies! Why is it? Why is it?"

"Oh, it's—on account of the sun," said the dirt farmer, Davis, whose smile seemed a part of his drawl. "Ever notice it up there, Frances? Warms the earth, makes the farmer's crops grow, ripens the apple on the bough! Just now it looks like a red hot silver cartwheel. Better take a long look at it, it's about the only 'cartwheel' you'll see this year. The drought won't stop with your cow, Frances. First *all* the water'll go then the corn and the alfalfa. If there's anything left, that'll go, too. Then winter'll come—"

"And then?"

"Then," with a mock in his drawl as he looked the younger man over, "well, then—I don't know about you—but some folks ain't going to starve. Not so long as they have guns."

"Oh, you mean hunting."

"Yeah—I mean hunting all right."

David was right: the water went first in the shallow holes in the range-lot. The bottoms blistered in blunt diamond shapes of dry mud, peeled, and the edges rolled up till they met in the middle.

The grass dried, the alfalfa burnt to stalks. The corn was stunted and never developed ears. What wheat there was never developed in the heads. The vegetables in the kitchen-garden died.

You could see the bottom of the wind-mill shaft, though it stood surrounded by aspens at the back of the farm-house: the leaves were

---

Can You Hear Their Voices? was published in the March 1931 issue of *New Masses* as "You Can Make Out Their Voices," and was immediately regarded as a classic of revolutionary literature. Based on the storming of the business section of England, Arkansas on January 3, 1931, by 500 farmers demanding food for their starving families, Whittaker Chambers' story was reprinted in 1932 as a pamphlet and was also produced as a play at Vassar College. Edwin Rolfe, reviewing the story for *New Masses* in September, 1932, wrote: "The story itself, written directly, straightforwardly, eclipses anything that can be written about it. It is the sort of fiction which will take its place as a valuable experience for every worker and farmer (and, it might be added, every writer in the field of revolutionary fiction) who reads it."

thinned out as if it were autumn. And as less and less water was pumped up, it was cloudier and cloudier and tasted sickeningly of alkali. The poor farmer, Wardell, his wife and two boys, began to envy the aspen roots that went down and sucked up whatever water there was: they ended by hating them.

Animals overcame their fear to seek water near the houses. The Wardell boys found a gopher, a pair of jack-rabbits, dead. A red-headed woodpecker lay on the front path, its wings spread out. The boys took it into the house. In the shade it revived. They gave it a drop of their water; it uttered its single sharp scream; batting itself against the windows that were always shut now, to keep out the hot wind that blew the length of the prarie, and dried the saliva out of your mouth.

In front of the house the eldest boy killed a four foot rattler that put up no fight. The boys wanted to see if it would die before sundown; it hardly twitched after its skull was crushed.

Hearing the blows and the boys' shouts, their father came out. "The drought killed it, like everything else," he said, "no insult to your courage, John."

The two boys stood at either side of their father, looking at the snake. In their overalls both were lean, bony and tall, but shorter than the man. Like his, their hair was burned white by the sun and wind, but his had turned sandy. Their faces were tanned, but smooth and unwrinkled. His had three deep lines on either side. One where the ends of his mouth went down. Two, curving parallel, on either side, ran to his smooth, long jaw-bone whose end was part of the rough angle of his chin. His long curved nose ended almost on a line with his mouth, the nostrils running back sharply, almost parallel with the bridge, and lying close to his face.

His brown eyes had seldom been afraid. They had never been dismayed except by death. Both boys' eyes were blue.

"That shows what the drought has done," he said. "They never come out of the hills. I remember when Purcell started his mines there, the men drove the snakes down, but when he closed the mines, they went back again. There hasn't been one killed around here since I was your age. It's dead all right. If the drought hadn't weakened it, it'd twitch. Of course, it's all superstition that they don't die till after sundown. It's their nerves keep them twitching. They die hard, but this one's too weak."

By afternoon a crowd in dungarees had collected to see the snake. It was a pretext. There was no work for the men to do in the heat, with the crops burnt. They wanted to talk in a body.

They stood around the dead snake in a rough circle, mostly keeping their eyes on the ground.

The sun blazed just as mercilessly in the sky, going west, as it had at noon.

They talked about the dry spell.

"How long will it last?"

"Do you think there's any chance of rain?"

"The papers don't tell you, they say there's *hope.*"

"They've been saying that a long time," said Wardell. "Besides, it don't make any difference if it does rain. The corn's done for."

"My cow died this morning," said the young farmer, Frances. He was considered a newcomer in the district, having been there only a year. They thought him a bad farmer, and unsteady, and they didn't like his whine.

So Davis turned and said drily, over his shoulder, "Mine died a month ago."

"Your wife hasn't got a baby," said Frances.

They ignored it. "What do you think, Wardell?" they said partly to shut off the young man's personal plaint—(Hell, you're no worse off than us!)—"will the government help us?"

Wardell smiled. it was the first time any of them had ever asked *his* advice.

"What do you think the government'll do for you? Think you're the only poor farmer in the country?"

"They'll have to make the banks give us some kind of loans," said glum Davis.

"They'll have to give us some kind of credit to live."

"If the cows keep on dying, they'll have to do something about milk."

"They'll have to make banks give us some kind of loans, but before they do that it'll have to be worse! Much worse!" A Bohemian named Drdla spoke. Round, smooth face, and full lips smiling while he added his drop of gloom.

"What about winter coming? What are we going to do if there ain't any food? How are we going to feed the babies?" asked Frances, panicky.

"Anyway, *you've* got one less mouth to feed," said Davis, again over his shoulder.

Everybody laughed.

"A dead cow ain't no joke," said Frances.

Everybody laughed again.

"Well, the government ain't going to do anything, if you want to know," said Wardell. "At least, I'm not counting on it handing me anything. Of course you can look at things like Mort Davis: we don't have to feed the cows that die. On the other hand, they might feed the babies."

"They're stopping credit at the stores in Paris."

"Think they'd give it through the winter? To all of us? They've got to make a living, too."

"You mean there ain't going to be nothing to eat?"

"There's plenty to eat in the stores in Paris. All you've got to have is the money to buy it. In fact, you can eat like a hog—if you're a store-keeper," said Wardell. "We only *grow* the food—when we can: they *sell* it. But as I haven't got the money to buy and neither have you, I guess we'll take it or starve."

They understood only slowly.

"You mean you'd steal it?" asked an alarmed voice.

"I mean that when I'm hungry I like to eat. And when my wife and children are hungry, I'm likely to take food where I can get it. If that's stealing, then you can say I like to steal. Does that hurt your feelings?"

Most of the men had driven over in flivvers. A heavier car drew up. A heavier man got out and came over.

Purcell had been a colonel in the war. "Talking about the drought?" he asked, eyeing each face in turn.

"Wardell's John killed a rattler in front of the house," said Davis. "The folks came over to find out just what a dead snake looks like. Would *you* like to see?"

A voice as vibrant and deep as Purcell's was a surprise, issuing from the small slit of his lips, while his full angular jaws worked up and down. He spoke deliberately, with his own emphasis.

"This 'drowt,' or 'drooth' as Wardell calls it, has been a lucky break for you, Wardell. You were running pretty low in your line of knocks when this bad luck came along." Little gray eyes glared gleefully on either side of his small, fighty wedge of turned-up nose.

"The 'general' 's got his chip on his shoulder," one of the Wardell boys whispered to the other.

"On his face, you mean, to keep his eyes from running together," John Wardell said aloud, staring at Purcell's nose.

"Some of us call it 'drowt' and some of us call it 'drooth'," said Wardell, "but they both mean that the crops are done for, water and forage are dried up, the cattle are dying, and we'll be needing food when our credit gives out at the stores in town. Unless, of course, the banks want to make us long term loans."

Purcell, the richest farmer in the district, had a finger in the Bank of Paris, of which his son-in-law was cashier.

"The trouble with Wardell is," Purcell said, preserving his good temper, but talking rather to the gathering than to Wardell, "the trouble with him is that he spends too much time nights reading those books he has in the house, and looking up the long words in the dictionary. So he gets sleepy and sore at the world, don't you, Jim?" The men smiled, being let in on the joke by the big boss. "What was that book, in that package of yours that came undone in the post office that time?" Purcell was also post-master. " 'Socialism Yewtopian and Scientific'!" He laughed. "Well, every man's got a right to read what he wants to in his own house, I guess, if he don't try to force others to think his crazy ways, too. But I went to school with Jim Wardell, didn't we, Jim, and I know he's still the same wild Jim, wild ideas, but a heart of gold. So if you get hungry, and he tries to feed you Socialism Yewtopian and Scientific, if you don't feel full, and I guess you won't, I think the Red Cross will do more for you all. I got to go. So long, Jim. So long, boys."

"The Red Cross!"

"The Red Cross!"

"They did fine work in the Mississippi flood!"

"The Red Cross!"

They began to drift away from Wardell's to town or home.

"So it's the Red Cross next," thought Wardell. "I know you dirt farmers! You've got to find out for yourselves. So it's the Red Cross you'll find out about now! And when you have, and I guess you'll get your chance this time, you'll be ready to show them a few things—"

"Say, Frances," he said when they were the last two left, "we can spare some of our milk for a baby, I guess. While the cow's still giving any. Drop in after milking. Throw that snake off the path, boys," he called from the porch, not to hear the young man's thanks.

Two days later the snake was a length of shrivelled skin and spinal bones. The sun had dried it up.

It dried up the last "pot-hole" in that stretch of prairie, too, and the alkali sparkled thick on the bared bottom, with a likeness to snow strange under the red hot sun.

The "yellow-heads" from the "pot-hole" gathered in great flocks, and the farm people would stop to watch them escaping through the sky, deserting the country, as in the fall when they feel the cold coming.

"Say, Lil," said Purcell to his daughter at supper one night, "I thought Frances' cow died. I thought he'd be buying milk from us now. He's got a baby, ain't he?"

Purcell had been one of the first farmers to turn to dairying when the borers gnawed away the margin of profit the banks and railroads left on corn in that section. He had a fine herd of Holsteins and, as he could afford to ship in ensilage and water by the tank, had preserved them through the drought, leaving it to the dry spell to carry off the few heads owned by his small competitors.

"See, you don't know everything down at the bank," said his daughter, a fair, fat girl with big breasts, glasses and a gold incisor. "I happen to know that Jim Wardell is *giving* Frances milk."

"*Giving* it to him? I wonder if Frances has ever seen the way Wardell keeps his cow? I wouldn't give any baby of mine that milk. I guess Jim's got to give it away. He couldn't sell it. Well, it's only a few cents anyway."

Frances used to come a little early and sit in the kitchen a few minutes in the evening while Wardell was milking the cow.

"And how's the baby and how is Hilda today?" Mrs. Wardell would ask.

"It's very bad up there. Since she lost her milk, it's terrible. And then the cow dying. Yours is the only cow left around here, except Purcell's."

"Take this home to them," she would say when he went, his milk-can full. Wardell never asked her what was in the nameless parcels. But even the boys were going oftener to bed hungry, after eating everything there was. Sometimes there was no milk on the Wardells' table.

"The cow won't last much longer at this rate," said Wardell to his wife one night. Such a ridiculous sentence to make her heart almost stop beating!

One evening Ann Wardell thought Frances looked as if he hadn't eaten for two days, so she set some boiled dried beans, part of supper's only dish, before him. Wardell came in without the dribble of milk, and sat down. "Don't you think the time is coming, Frank," he said, "when the poor farmers, people like you and me and the Davises and Wiggens and Drdla, will have to go and take the food out of the store-windows in Paris? There's always plenty of it there."

"You're a Socialist, ain't you?" Frank asked, ever so slyly, over his spoonful of beans.

("The branding reproach of Communism!")

"I'm a Communist, Frank."

"What does that mean?"—the beans suspended midway to the mouth.

"In this case, it means that I'm for unlimited free groceries and meat to all poor farmers. No rent for two years. Free seed. Free milk for babies."

"I guess you Reds want everything free," said Frank.

"I guess you will, too, before the baby's dead." Hard and bitter to hammer it home.

"Jim!"

"I know what I'm telling him, Ann. We're both dirt farmers, poor men, both come from the same class, so there's no reproach in your taking something from me when you need it, Frances. And there's no reproach meant, in my telling you that your kid would be dead but for your getting the milk from my cow. You couldn't buy it. Not from me, I wouldn't sell it to you. And you couldn't buy it from Purcell because he *would* sell it to you, and you haven't got the money to buy it. Well, my cow's dying. Now what do you think about having milk *free?*"

"Dying? Your cow's dying?" Frances was the color of milk himself.

"She'll be dead by morning. Now I'm going out to see what I can do for her. There won't be any milk tonight or from now on. But don't forget that it was the dirty Communist, the Red, the Bolshevik who wants everything free for every poor farmer, who kept the kid alive till now."

Frances stumbled, with the empty milk-can, out the door Wardell had left open, past the barn where he saw a light, and the cow lying on her side, and Wardell bending over her.

"Jim's cruel, but Jim's right," said Mrs. Wardell. Her husband did not come back into the house, and she waited half an hour before she slipped out and across the field paths, with another milk-can.

Lily Purcell came to the door. "Oh, hello, Mrs. Wardell." The gold tooth haloed in a golden smile.

"Our cow's died," said Ann, holding out the can.

"Oh, she died, huh? Mr. Frances said she was going to."

"Did Frank get some milk?"

"Well, we milked early, Mrs. Wardell, and we had only enough for ourselves. Mr. Frances didn't have no money. There's so many like that now."

"I've got some money," Ann said.

"Well, I'll see if mother could spare a little. Give me the can."

Ann walked in the open door where it was plain to see the chickens also walked. They didn't hear her come.

Hilda Frances was not crying. She was walking the bare floor, saying, "Baby, baby, baby, baby!" when she reached the wall she would stop. When she paced back, she would begin again, "Baby, baby, baby!" It was Frank, with his head in his arms, on the table, who was crying.

"We did get some milk, after all," said Ann Wardell.

Hilda stopped. "Milk! God bless you, Mrs. Wardell, God bless you! Oh, God bless you!"

"A funny God that brings babies into the world, and takes away their mother's milk, and kills the cows that feed them, Mrs. Frances. But let me have a look at the baby before I go."

"You got milk for them at Purcell's!" Jim said when she came in. "Yes."

He frowned but said nothing.

"You've got to stop," he told her a week later. "You can't do it. The cold's coming. We've only got so much. You're taking the food from John and Robert."

"You can't let a baby die."

"Worse things will happen before this winter's over. What good does it do? Keep it alive another week. You'll *have* to stop then. And you're only taking it away from the boys. They'll be up against it soon enough. That's the trouble with your charity. You can't keep it up, and it only makes Frank and his wife hope it's forever. It makes them content. And they can't be. When he sees the baby's going to die, he'll cry for milk and food along with the rest of us. He's got to. It's coming. It's coming soon."

"Say, are you really a Socialist?" asked Davis, driving his Ford up to the house.

"What do you want to know for?" asked Wardell with his foot on the running board. "Bunch of the boys want to lynch me?"

"Not yet, Jim," grudging a lop-sided smile since his face was lop-sided. "Hell *is* going to break loose around here soon, if things don't get any better, and they may be wanting you then. But this here I came about, is personal business. There's a family of greasers squatting on my land, and they won't get off. They've got four kids, and the woman just had twins last night. No doctor! They haven't got no food, and the man says they ain't got no gasoline so they can't go on, they've just got to stop on my place. Well, they ain't going to. We can't feed the white men up there now, let alone greasers. Of course, I can have them run in down in Paris. But on account of the woman having those kids last night, I thought maybe—some of your Socialist ideas—you'd let them stay on your place."

"I'm not a Socialist," said Wardell.

"What the hell are you then?"

"I'm a Communist."

"What's that?"

"Well, just now it means I want free food for every farmer that can't pay for it, free milk for the babies, free rent, and if we can't get free food, I'm for going and taking it."

"What did you say you called yourself?"

"A Communist."

"That's like a Red, Russians, huh?"

"No, workingmen and poor farmers, like you and me."

"Do you have a secret society?"

"The Communists are a political party, called the Communist Party of the United States."

"And they believe in free food?"

"Yes."

"I'll be over tonight," said Davis, "I've got to go to Paris now. Goodbye, Jim. I'll tell those Mexicans to come down here."

"If you won't let them on your own place."

That day it began to snow, suddenly, before dark.

"Ann, I think Davis will come over to us," he said as he sat down to the boiled beans.

"Come over?"

"To *us*. He's coming here tonight."

"Jim, be careful."

"I'll be as careful as I can. The time is past when we can afford to be too careful. Stay up tonight, boys, and listen to what Mort Davis and I talk about."

The deep snow separated the farms, but it made starvation general.

At first they burned the fence-posts, those who had them; the others, the floor boards in the barns. Those who had no barns burned their hen-coops. But after charcoal, what?

The men took out their guns, the pretext being to hunt jackrabbits, though most of them had died in the drought. But the women had no pretext and no will to escape the wailing of the babies, for whom there was no milk, and the whimpering and gaunt eyes of the older children.

The men made an honest search for game, but by afternoon most of them drifted into Paris, with their guns under their arms.

Many of them passed the bank windows, never suspecting what was going on within. Purcell saw them as he leaped to his feet in the fury of wrangling with his son-in-law, the cashier, and old Dr. Jesperson, the president, and walked to the front window of the Bank of Paris.

"They're walking around the streets with guns now, and you talk about closing the bank! I knew you'd do this," he screamed, shaking his fist at his son-in-law, the heavy jaws turkey red. "I knew you'd do this, I knew you would! You and your damn fool farm mortgages! And now the bank will crash, and so will you, and so will the Doc! But I won't! I took care of that!"

The main road entered Paris after turning a right angle, around an osage hedge, and crossing a creek, dried up in the drought, on a wooden bridge. It passed the double row of store-fronts, and returned to the prairie on the other side. Two tracks led south and north to scattered farms. The latter had once been busy when Purcell worked his ground-level mines in the hills, twenty miles to the north. They had been closed down for years.

Wardell and Davis found about thirty armed men on the main street.

"I don't know what to do," said a little man named Shays, "my baby's dying. He's dying all right, dying. And we haven't got milk."

"Neither have we!"

"We haven't had any for two days. My baby's dying."

"We got some but my credit's gone. We can't even get any food. But milk comes first."

"There's only one place you can get milk around here," said Wardell.

"Where's that?"

"At Purcell's."

"We know that! Where are we going to get the money? He's not giving it away, and he don't trust now."

"Did you say your kid was dying, Dan?" Wardell asked Shays.

"Yes, he'll die if I don't get him milk."

"I'm glad you got your rifle with you. Will you come with me to Purcell's and make them give you milk?"

The little man blenched. "Take it from Purcell, you mean?"

"That's what I mean. Will anyone else come with us? Will you, Doscher?"

"No, I won't. I know your Socialist ideas! What do you think I am, a thief?"

"Will you lend me your gun, Doscher?" asked Davis. "I'd like to go with Jim and Shays. You know, our farms are too near together, and I can't stand listening to your baby scream itself to death, even if you can."

"I'll go!"

"I'll go!"

"I'll go!"

In the end, Doscher went, too.

They tramped out the western side of the town, fighting their way through the snow, and, in half an hour, were at Purcell's.

Wardell led them to the back door.

"Lilian," he said, "some of these men have babies, and all of us have children. None of us have any money. If those babies don't get their milk tonight, some of them will die. They'll all die in a week or two. Will you give us milk?"

"*Give* it to you? How can I give it to you, Jim Wardell? You're crazy!"

"You've got to give it to us."

"How can I give it to you? To *all* of you?"

"You've got to give it to us. We know how to milk cows just as well as you do. If you don't give it to us, we'll go down to the barn and take it."

She screamed. "I won't."

"In other words, you want us to take it. All right, we'll take it!"

"Wait, wait a minute, wait!" She flew into the house.

All three men sat stiff and terrified as the phone rang in the bank.

"Well, then, I'll answer it," said Purcell.

"They want you to *give* it to them?" he shouted. "*Guns?* Oh, I see," he said, "Wardell! I see. Well, give it to them! Give it to them! *Give it to them!*" He missed the hook as he slammed the receiver against the case.

"There's only enough here to last two days at the most," said Wardell as they broke up.

"We'll make it last five," they said, laughing.

The night the bank failed Frank's baby died.

He had not been out of the house for three days. He knew nothing of the milk seizure at Purcell's. The wailing of the baby and his own hunger kept him awake, but at last exhaustion stretched him out. He awoke with a start to see Hilda bending over the drawer where they kept the child in some dirty blankets. It seemed to him as if someone had screamed.

"What is it, Hil?" She had a blanket in her hand.

"I think baby's dead."

"No." He leaped up. He looked at it and listened for breathing. "I'll get the doctor."

"Oh, what's the use of the doctor, he won't come now."

"He will!"

"You can't get him in time, you know there's no gas in the Ford."

"I'll go. I'll run. I'll get him. I'll get him."

He did not tie his shoes. He stumbled where he broke through the snow. He felt the ice-crust under his hands as he fell, and its edges cut his ankles. But he kept running.

"How can I get two miles through this snow?" asked old Dr. Jesperson, the bank president, who for some reason was up alone at that hour, with a bottle of whiskey on the table.

"You can make it in the car. You must try to save her, Doctor, you must."

"Oh, don't plead, don't plead, I know I've got to go! God damned Hippocratic oath!"

"Of course, it's dead," said the old man, standing well back from the drawer which smelt of wet as he of whiskey. "Been dead a couple of hours! What do you mean bringing a baby into this world when you can't take care of it! What do you get married for? I don't suppose there's a crumb of bread in the house," he said, looking at the walls. "Damndest profession in the world! Damndest profession in the world! Now there'll be an epidemic of dying. There ought to be."

Hilda watched him drive away.

Frank was sobbing with his head on the table. Suddenly he straightened up. "Wardell killed her," he shouted. "He stopped the milk on her, I know he did. The dirty lousy Red. He did it. He killed her, God curse him!"

"Don't be a fool," said Hilda quietly, "I killed her myself. Do you think I wanted to see her tortured to death by inches? I killed her with the blanket.—God?"

He sprang at her, but she ran away from him and out the door, slamming it. She ran farther, thinking he would follow, but he stopped beside the baby.

She saw the big square outlines of Purcell's house and barns against the white snow. Milk! She had barely passed it when it seemed to her as if an army were pursuing her, crunching through the snow, with bells and sounds like faint horns snorting. She was overwrought. Vengeance is mine, saith the Lord. Might He find pleasure in taking vengeance on a mother who has smothered her baby? Was He after her? She ran, wilder and wilder, mad with a desire to scream, but terrified to silence. Finally she just began to laugh. It was much simpler, and it was all funny, and she just laughed and laughed and laughed.

What she had taken for God was Purcell's blooded Holsteins. He was removing the whole herd, in the dead of night, to the livery stable in Paris where there was law and order. There would be no more free milk.

When the snow fell, they moved the Mexicans into the upstairs room. The Wardell boys slept in the remnants of hay in the barn loft. It was bitter cold, and they were grateful for the meetings that postponed till late the necessity of trying to sleep.

Wardell and his wife, Davis, and the two boys would sit around the table, with the five sheets of paper and pens before them, and the bottle of ink in the middle. Carrillo, the Mexican, sat to one side. He spoke only broken English, but his black eyes gazed fixedly from either side of his nose, with its coarse pores, in an undefeated effort to grasp by chance word and gesture what the others were discussing.

There was no hectograph, no mimeograph, no typewriter. Everything had to be written by hand. There were five right hands. At the top of their first handbill they printed:

"YOUR MILK GIVES OUT TODAY! WHAT ARE YOU GOING TO DO NOW?"

The bills were tacked to the front porches of houses on each of the four roads into Paris, east and west, north and south. Drdla had one, and Doscher, Davis and Wardell. One of the boys took one to Ryder's, a farmer who lived ten miles farther to the south where the men seldom came to town.

"Are you going to the meeting at Wardell's?" Doscher asked Shays, who was reading the tacked up bill.

"Of course, I'm going. Who got us the milk?"

"He got it for us all right last time, it might not be so easy now. Jim's a queer bird. He's a Socialist."

"Well, what of it? Anyway, I hear he ain't a Socialist."

"Ain't a Socialist?"

"No, they've got some other name for it. They call it a Commun*eist*."

"What's that make him?"

"It makes him for us, I guess. That's all I know about it. I'll see you at Wardell's."

"Why should I go to Wardell's?" Frances answered Davis. "Don't you think I know what Wardell's up to? He'll be running for something next. Anyway, the Red Cross is going to help us, ain't it? The paper says so."

"You'll find out what a whole lot of good the Red Cross is going to do you, when they get here—if they get here."

"I guess I'll be there," Wiggens, a heavy-set farmer, who had just began to feel the pinch, told Drdla. Drdla objected to tacking up the handbill, so the men simply came to his house and read it. Wiggens stood reading it with his wife, a tall spare woman whose black eyes looked in a perfectly level line out of the bones of her face.

"I'll be there," she said. "Look at them!" The five children sat in the back of the Ford. They made no effort to get out.

"But I see the Red Cross is going to help us," her husband objected. "They won't like this." He rapped the handbill with the back of his hand.

"We may need them both," said his wife.

Purcell's frantic wires to the Governor, and Senator Bagheot in Washington, described the seizure of milk at a local farm by one hundred armed farmers, led by loafers. A supplementary wire described the leader, one Wardell, a chronic trouble-maker.

The Senator was handed both wires at breakfast by his young wife, who continued to act as his secretary.

"I did not want to disturb you with them last night, Senator," she said.

Bagheot read them through with a concentration that was partly the difficulty that he had in seeing; at seventy he would not hear of glasses.

"A cheap demogogue!" the old man exploded when he had finished the characterization of Wardell. "A cheap demagogue! Trading on the sufferings of those poor farmers! They always come to the front in times like these."

He acted with promptness and efficiency. Talking over long distance with the Governor of the State, he made sure that the Red Cross would be operating in Paris the next day.

"Even a very little relief . . ."

"I can't hear you," said the Governor.

"Well, why the Devil can't you hear me! What's the matter with your connection? I said even a very little relief will quiet the mob. Unless you take some such measures, the merchants must either put their stocks in the streets, or machine-guns in their windows."

"Yes, yes. Everything of that sort will be seen to. How is it in Washington, as cold as it is here?"

"Well, we've had a little snow," the voice quavered.

Senator Bagheot then dictated to his wife his statement to the press. "Conditions in my State, brought to my attention today by the newspapers, show extreme suffering in the country districts. I shall move for Federal aid tomorrow. Congress has not treated the suffering resulting from this winter sympathetically, but I believe that when the members of Congress return, after facing their constituents, their action will be a little different."

"That's good, eh, huh?" he chuckled to his wife. "I guess that will show them who lives in a glass house, politically speaking!"

"Remember, Dr. Styres said you were to have no undue excitement."

The State organization of the Red Cross proved itself equal to the situation which it was called upon by the Governor to control. Over night, it completed plans for immediate relief for all who could furnish evidence of bona fide suffering.

In this work it was planned to cooperate with local community leaders, since they were assumed to be better informed as to local persons, cases and needs, rather than to "foist an alien organization on the town from without."

They simply sent a supervisor, who sat beside Lily Purcell, the local head of the Red Cross, in the little relief station they had rented in her brother's empty store.

Back of the counter, at which they sat, were cans of milk, bags of flour, sugar, etc.

"We ought to spread some bags of flour on the counter. There's nothing like it for psychological effect, for raising the spirits of hungry people," said the Red Cross supervisor, who, like Miss Purcell, wore glasses. "It's unfortunate, though, that you had this thaw last night. It's opened the roads, and of course it would have been better if we had had a few days to get things firmly in hand. It will probably let more of them through to that meeting at Wardell's, too. But I calculate that our opening at the same hour as the meeting will also have its psychological effect. I guess they'll here, rather than there."

That morning the Mexicans left Wardell. He heard them talking all night, Carrillo urging, his wife opposing, but at last her opposition growing fainter, perhaps tired out.

In the morning they all came down into the lower room. The children stood in a ragged line, mute, and stared. The wife, looking much like the children, but with a twin on either arm, also stared.

"Companero Ooardell," said Carrillo, "we are going away. You have no food for yourselves. The roads opened last night. Companero Ooardell, you are a good man. Your wife, she is a good woman. Your sons, they are good young men. If I go east or if I go west, if I go north or if I go south, I will always come back here. Sometimes I will come to take, sometimes to bring. But I will always remember that you saved our lives. I thank you, my wife thanks you, and my children thank you. Goodbye, companeros."

His wife smiled and nodded, and they all went away, having somehow gotten their Ford to start.

"So the Carrillos have left you?" said Davis. "I guess that Mex figured there was going to be shooting, and a fight's a poor place for a greaser."

"Think so? I wouldn't be too hopeful about the shooting, Mort. In the first place, what are we going to get by shooting—yet? In the second place, though that crowd learned some kind of a lesson when they took the milk from Purcell, they've had time to think it over. You'll see, those that come here today are a little scared of themselves."

"You forget their kids are still crying."

"I don't forget it at all."

Before noon the little house was so packed with men and women's bodies, you couldn't walk a foot. The heat rose perceptibly and with the smell of cow and horse manure and humans.

"We can't talk in here," Wardell called out. "Everybody outside!"

"Line up those cars in a half dozen rows," he said, "and sit in them." His own car was standing in front of the house. It was open and the top was down. His wife got in, and Davis. Wardell stood on the front seat and talked.

"I'm glad to see that there are so few of us here," he said. "It means that only the most reliable and the most needy are here. It means we can move together easier, and have more confidence in each other. And we need that."

"I'm glad to see, too, that you women have brought your babies with you. It's another sign that you're not afraid, and it means that we'll never lose sight of why we're going to Paris.

"And we're going down to Paris. We're starving, and we're going to Paris to get food. I hear that the Red Cross is going to give it to us. Now I want to tell you *how* they're going to give to us.

"First of all, before they give us anything, we've got to prove that we're not 'imposters.' That's what they're calling some of us now. In other words, we've got to prove that we really are starving to death. Can you prove it?"

Growls.

"Then, when we've proved that we're starving, I want to tell you *what* they'll give us."

"How do you know what they're going to do?" asked a voice. Other voices: "Ssh! Ssh!"

"Never mind, Ar Crocker, just remember that we *did* tell you, when the time comes," Davis bawled back.

"They're going to give us *one* loaf of bread! Not one apiece, but one to each family! One bag of flour—the same! Maybe some bacon!"

"How much milk?" called a woman.

"Enough for two days."

"What good does two days do? We had a day's before, and we made it last three. Now if they give us two day's, and we make it last five, what'll we do when it's gone?"

"It's the same with all the rest of the relief. It will last two days. What are you going to do when it's gone? There's food enough in the stores of Paris to last us for weeks. But they won't give it to us, because the Red Cross will only give a little money for a place like Paris, and most of that went to buying Purcell's milk for today's relief. Never mind how I know!

"The thing for us to do now, is to force them to give some food today. And to do that, we've got to all go down together. If we go in one by one, they'll cheat us, or they'll say we're not starving, and we won't get any relief at all.

"Now before we go, I want to ask you something. How many of you have guns in your cars? Nine, ten, eleven. You, too, Doscher? Good! Every man who brought his gun today, was with us when we forced Purcell to give us milk. Those men learned something. But you've got to be doubly careful today not to use your guns unless somebody starts shooting at you first, I'll tell you why. We're starving. But they don't want to give us food. They give us food only to keep us quiet. You men with guns are the leaders in forcing them to give us food. Because they're afraid of guns. But they'll kill you if some of you keep on fighting. They'll kill you, because you're out-numbered. And when you're dead, Purcell and the rest will be boss here, and your babies will go just as hungry, but there'll be nobody to get them food. The time is not quite ripe for shooting. Do you understand?"

"Yes."

"We can threaten them today, we can force them, we may even *have to* shoot, but don't fire a gun if you can help it. Not today!

"Now, the cars with guns in the lead! Let's go!"

The grating of thirty gears, slipping from first to second, to high.

"I don't see how he can possibly claim to be starving," said Lily Purcell to the Red Cross supervisor: (The milk Frances did not buy!) "His baby died two days ago, and nobody knows where his wife is!"

"Well, at least he can't have any milk. That settles that right off!"

Frank Frances had not gone to the meeting. He was one of the first outside the relief store doors when they opened. For fifteen minutes he had been attempting to establish his status as a starving man. Meanwhile the line grew behind him, at first grumbling, then shouting, "Give him something!"

"This is no way to begin!" The supervisor scanned their heads disapprovingly. "Too many eye sockets!" he thought. He was unwilling to cede ground at once, and would not give Lily Purcell the order, "Let him have some bread."

Suddenly there was a shout from the edge of the crowd. "They're coming! They're coming!"

From the west the line of thirty cars swept into the town, two abreast.

They stopped in the middle of the street. The men and women got out, the men with their guns, the women with their babies.

The crowd opened for thirteen men with guns. "Now we'll get some food!"

Wardell and Davis stopped where Frances stood suspended in an act of appeal. Lily Purcell and her supervisor stared.

Shays, Doscher, Drdla, staring back over the ends of their guns, which they rested on the floor.

Mrs. Wiggens with a baby in her arms had pressed to the front.

"Yes, what are you going to give us?" asked Mrs. Wiggens.

"What are you going to give us?" said Davis.

"I don't know that we're going to give you anything. At least until you put those guns down," he said, tonguing his lips that were like earthworms that have been out too long in the rain.

"Give that man some bread," said Wardell.

"I don't think he deserves any. And I'm not taking orders here, I'm giving them!"

Several men laughed.

"And you, Lily, give Mrs. Wiggens some flour."

"She *certainly* don't need any. I know her well. She's a regular trouble-maker." She appealed to the Red Cross knight.

"Give her some flour!"

"Don't give her flour!" said the supervisor. "These people are not ready for relief. They don't know how to take it. *This place is closed!* Get out!"

"Take it, men," said Wardell. "Don't hurt anybody. See that everybody gets a bag, Mrs. Wiggens."

"Oh! Oh! They're stealing our flour! They're stealing our flour!" Lily continued to scream until the store was stripped and empty. Mrs. Wiggens, who had been passing out the bags, was the last to leave. As she took up her own bag, Lily tried to stop her.

"You can't have that, you *can't* steal it!" She hung on to the bag with the grip of a kind of death she felt freezing her. Finally Mrs. Wiggens wrenched it loose. The girl's nails had torn the bag.

"Sow!" cried Mrs. Wiggens, seeing the waste. She struck Lily Purcell across the lower face with the bag. The flour whited her face like a clown's. Her glasses fell off and smashed. She screamed.

"She's killing me! She's killing me! She's stealing! She's killing me! She's stealing!" She was sobbing, a gulping blubber that shook her breasts.

"Shut up!" Mrs. Wiggens herself screamed. "Shut up! I'm sorry I hurt you!"

Picking up the baby, she ran out of the store.

"Into the stores, men!" cried Davis and Wardell at opposite ends of the street. Some of the storekeepers tried locking up.

"If you don't open that door, we'll come in through the window," shouted Drdla.

The doors opened.

It was dark before all the milk had been taken from Purcell's cows, and the food apportioned and piled in the cars.

They started on a signal from Wardell, moving more consciously together as a mass than ever before. As they left the village, they were grim, still. Once outside it they began to laugh. They felt strong. They also felt afraid.

By then it had begun to snow again, fat, heavy flakes.

"How long do you think this lot will last?" asked Davis in the head car with Wardell.

"The food about two weeks, the milk, of course, only a few days."

"Then?" asked Davis.

"Well, they'll never *let* us do this again."

"You mean—shooting?"

"I suppose so. Everything depends on quick organization now, Mort. Shays and Doscher and Drdla and Mrs. Wiggens, and Frances, and any others we're sure about. You can be sure Purcell sent the SOS over the wires by now. Tomorrow or the day after, they'll have the troops here."

"I've been wondering about Purcell's old mine shafts in the hill."

"Oh, you have?"

Later Davis said, "I think you're wrong about Frances, Jim. I don't trust him."

"Of course, you may be right. It's true he's weak. It takes a lot to bring him over, and a lot to keep him going. But he's been through a lot by now. We've got to make the most of what we've got."

The cars moved slowly, so close together that the lights, many of them dim or missing, cast a blurred glare from the rear-ends on the snow.

A car appeared, moving in the other direction. It stopped. They came abreast and stopped also.

"Mister Ooardel?"

"It's your Mex," said Davis. Wardell got out.

"I hear in the town ten miles away, there is fighting in Paris. Everybody is much excited." He was excited himself. "Everybody says he will take food, too. So I came back, Companero, I thought you need men."

"Them greasers have a long nose for food," said Shays. "They can smell a jumping bean no matter where it hops."

"Go get your own, Mex," said Drdla, "there ain't any here for you."

"He ain't asking you for food!" Drdla's eyes blinked before Davis turned away. "He's asking you if you'll allow him to shoot a gun shoulder to shoulder with you. I suppose you know you may be needing him. You come up to my place, Carrillo. You and your reti*noo*." He looked at the battered Ford.

It stopped the laughter. The cars dropped away one by one.

"I'm sending my boys away tomorrow, Mort," said Wardell.

"Where to?"

"East, to the comrades. I want them to be gone before the troops come. I'm driving them to the main road, at Tyrone, in the morning."

"Yes, I suppose you're right. Though I guess I couldn't do it."

"Anyway, out there they'll be learning something. What is there for them here—shooting, lynching? That's our business yet. Theirs is to learn more about Communism first."

"Tell the comrades what we are doing," Wardell said as he stopped the car at the cross-roads the next morning. "Tell them we're organizing. Tell them that already there are many of us. Tell them we've got the dirt farmers here in motion. And make them understand that what we need above everything else, what we must have, is a hectograph.

"Try to get jobs and stick together.

"Now go along. I think you can hitch; if you can't, be careful on the freights. We've got no use for dead men or cripples. Come back alive in the spring, there's nothing here for you now but hunger."

The snow was fine and dry, and blew in little lifting spirals on the asphalt of the highway, which was comparatively open.

The boys got out and walked off together toward the east. The road followed the roll of the prairie. Coming to the top of the first rise, they turned and, standing together, waved.

They shouted. The cold wind preserved the ring of their voices that the snow might have muffled, blowing their words to the silent man and woman beside the Ford.

"We'll be back in the spring!"

"Could you make out both their voices?" she asked.

A Place to Lie Down

BY NELSON ALGREN

Mopin' down the ties, feelin' mighty low
Got to keep movin', got no place to go
Just one more hungry poor sonofabitch
Wond'rin why he goes hungry in a country so rich

Two hungry bums in Texas, mopin' down the S. P. ties. On either side of the tracks stretched the Texas prairie, half-unseen now under a fog. Within the fog a cowbell tinkled, near at hand and coming nearer. The black 'bo drew a battered pack of cigarettes out of his hip pocket.

"Say," he asked his white companion, "You know why they made Ol' Gol's in the first place?"

The white didn't know.

"To keep niggers an' Jews from smokin' camels is why."

They both laughed, without strength, and moped on.

The Negro paused, stood on one leg like a heron, and slipped off his right shoe. His toes were encrusted with a fish-like scale; he rubbed them with gaunt knuckles until brownish chips brittled off onto the ties.

"It itches," he complained, "It itches like the crabs."

The white offered advice: "Y'all ought to wear a white sock on that. On *anythin'* like that."

When they reached El Paso streets were deserted; but morning was breaking over Juarez, and an empty C.C.C. truck rolled past as though to herald an empty dawn.

Neither boy knew where this city's breadline, if any, was to be found; so they walked on aimlessly. Once they paused in a doorway while the Negro removed his shoe once more, and again scraped his

---

Several proletarian writers—Edward Dahlberg, Martin Delaney, and Albert Maltz, among others—dealt with those people whom Dahlberg called the "bottom dogs" of American society. But only a few writers chose to concern themselves with the very lowest class in the social scale, the *lumpenproletariat*—the "social scum" which *The Communist Manifesto* disapprovingly described as the "passively rotting mass thrown off by the lowest layers of old society." Of these few writers, Nelson Algren was by far the best. This story about the *lumpenproletariat*, "A Place to Lie Down," originally appeared in the January-February issue of *Partisan Review* (1935).

knuckles with his toes. Above them an unshaded night bulb still burned feebly, casting a sickly greenish glow across a staircase leading up to nowhere. A woman passed the doorway, head down and hurrying through the rain along the unlovely southern street.

"I'm tired as a old hound, aint you?" the Negro asked as he scraped.

"Yeah," the other answered, "Bummin' takes all the tallow out o' mah pole. Ah aint been eatin' so reg'lar o' late, neither. What's yore name, nigger?"

"Call me Mack. What's yours?"

"Call me Tex."

"If I jest had a sock like you said, Tex, do y' think it'd keep it from rubbin' some?"

Tex surmised that this must be a northern Negro, to judge by his speech.

The fog lifted a little, and the El Paso sun came through. They came to a park with a picket-fence going around and around; there were teeter-totters for small children and swings for smaller children; and at one end was a net whereon two large men swung and belammed one small red ball. A stretch of grass looked dry for sleep here. The 'boes found a gate, and entered.

The small grass bent itself between Tex McKay's fingers. Long shadows trembled in the light. . . .

"Ah better shake this shine," Tex counseled himself.

Surreptitiously, the Negro began bathing his foot by wriggling his naked toes beneath a dripping bush. He did this for several minutes, covertly, then declared his foot well.

"But a sock. . . . If oney I had a white sock now." His eyes closed even as he muttered, and in a moment he was sleeping soundly, one arm in a ragged sleeve outflung and the other shielding his eyes; as though fearing in sleep to be struck.

"Ah ought to got me a coat fo' the night that's comin'," Tex thought, watching sunshadow between half-closed lids. Sun-shadow made him think of wet lengths of yellow ribbon stretched flat aslant the grass to dry. Some lengths were narrow and some were quite wide, some intertwined and became one, then wriggled away into many, all yellow-wet and delicate across green shadowgrass.

The Negro wriggled his toes, in sleep. Tex's own feet had gone sockless for months, he too was very tired; but even as he felt himself dozing off he became aware of someone coming toward him. Then a silver badge above small boots, a row of brass buttons and a neck on thighs swung up a winding cindered path twirling a club-on-a-cord like a swagger-stick. Tex saw him coming, shoved Mack, and ran. From be-

hind the picket fence, safe outside, Tex watched. Boots budged Mack
until he rolled over, moaning like a sick man. He was sweating in sleep,
his mouth drooled saliva, then he woke with a start, his eyes bulging
out; there was, for one moment, no flicker of understanding in his eyes.

"White-folks' park, nigger. Git a-goin' 'for ah fan yore fanny."

He twirled his club-on-a-cord significantly, boy-fashion, threatening.

Tex waited on the street. He'd like to josh the nigger a little now.
But when the Negro joined him they walked on silently, and Tex said
nothing at all.

On a street lined with radios competitively blasting the air into
splinters, they sat down on a Keep-Our-City-Clean box. Both were
hungry enough to chew their tongues; but they were both too weary to
think consistently even about food. Tex rested his feet on the curbstone
and watched the gutterflow swirl past.

Much was being borne on that gutter-tide: a frayed cigar-butt came
past first; then a red beercork; and then, its pages flung wide in a dis-
graceful death, a copy of *Hollywood Gossip* came floating by. It lay
flat on its back, a whore-like thing. Tex sniped the cigar and the magazine, crushed tobacco onto a dry page, and rolled a rude cigarette.
Smoking, he looked at the magazine's pictures. One page bore a picture of Douglas Fairbanks, Jr., in a stove-pipe hat, hugging two girls
in one-piece bathing suits. Out of Fairbanks' ears Tex fashioned four
long cigarettes, but the figures of the girls in the bathing suits Tex Mc-
Kay preserved, studying them as he smoked.

The cigarettes were strong, hence good; he offered Mack one, but
the boy shook his head as though he were too tired even to smoke. To
make a few more, Tex ripped one of the bathing girls up the middle.
He had an odd feeling when he did that, and looked through the
book for more bathing girls' pictures; but there was no other dry page,
and he began to feel tired again.

As he sat Tex recalled that, the last time food had passed his lips, he
had been in some place where there was snow on the streets. But he
could not remember the name of that place, though his mind sought
sleepily and long. Somehow, much seemed to depend upon the remembering: Chicago, Little Rock, Memphis too. His brain stopped on Railroad street in Baton Rouge, and could go no farther. So he dropped
the magazine in the gutterflow, wiped his nose on the back of his hand,
and poked the Negro. Mack followed Tex mechanically. When Tex
turned, he turned; when Tex paused, he paused; when Tex hurried forward, he hurried forward beside him. Only once as they went did he
speak. "Bummin' takes 'most ever'thin' outen a feller, don't it?" he
asked as they turned a corner.

Tex McKay nodded, "Sho' do. Knocks all the tallow outen' yore pole." And to himself: "Ah better shake this shine, we might get picked up."

When they reached a second Keep-Our-City-Clean box Mack wanted to remove his shoe again; but his fingers slipped around his ankle like a little child's fingers. So McKay took it off for him, kneeling as the other sat; he pulled a wad of paper out of the box and wadded it into the shoe's torn places. Beside him a barefooted Mexican boy holding a small girl by the hand stood and watched with a cynic's air. A woman with furred shoulders went by on high heels, her head in the air and her nose sniffing elegantly at the sun; as though about to snort green phlegm skyward. As Tex struggled to get the shoe back on Mack's foot, someone behind him spat in the gutter across his shoulder; he saw the gob, like a speckled bug, being borne away on the stream. People were gathering behind him; it was time to be getting on.

They had not gone half a block when Mack stopped and complained, half-accusingly, like some petulant little pickaninny: "It hurts. You just made it worse you did. Now it hurts worst." But they could not stop here, there was no place here to stop; and Mack continued to complain with a rising irascibility.

"If oney I had a sock. A *white* sock mind you. Hev *you* got that kind?"

That was the last thing he said to show he knew that Tex was still with him; after that he seemed slowly to lose awareness, he became like a man mildly drunk or doped. Tex had not known what havoc the simple fact of over-tiredness could wreak. Only a few hours before he had picked up with a husky young buck; now there plodded beside him a half-helpless black boy who depended on him to put on his shoes. Tex began to feel a mild responsibility.

Mack stopped dead still and planted himself directly in front of a bespectacled white youth with books in both hands. He looked to be frightened at Mack's glance. When Tex looked at Mack it was not hard to tell why: Mack's eyes now were fever-bright, and burning hollowly. Tex took his arm, but he would not budge one inch.

"*You.* Gimme that sock."

He took the boy by the lapel, and the boy dropped a book.

"Saaaaay—I'll call a cop on you I will." The boy's voice quavered shrilly as a frightened school-girl's; his eyes besought pleadingly those of the crowd.

This time two silver badges; two rows of brass buttons—two pairs of pointed black boots shining in the sun.

"Here, niggers—at it again? All right, Smitty, take 'em both along."

Tex McKay cocked his head, unable, for one moment, to believe what he had heard. Slowly then, he understood: A white man who walked with a 'nigger' was a 'nigger' too. He recognized the park bull as the other took his arm, and he said, "Ah'm no nigger."

Tex was too weary to feel keen fear; and going to jail was all a part of this life anyhow. No one escaped it for very long, and he'd been lucky for a long time now. What he didn't like, what got him by the short hairs, was that crack about a nigger.

He saw the big park bull start reaching for Mack when Mack was still five feet away and Specs stood in between. Specs ducked wildly when the cop's paw came over his shoulder; the paw seized Mack's shirt and pulled him free of the sidewalk with a yank which ripped the sleazy cloth down to the navel. Mack came straight forward, so that his head would have rammed the cop's Sam Browne belt had not the cop stiffarmed him with his open palm.

Tex glanced at the cop who was holding his wrist.

"Ah aint no nigger, mister," he said; but the bull didn't seem to hear.

It was shameful to see the Negro so, his shirt in tatters so that his navel showed thru.

A man in the crowd barked brief hard laughter; a girl fled titillating—"Oooooo—What I *saw!*"

"Ah aint no nigger, mister," Tex repeated; but the bull didn't look like he'd heard.

Mack's voice was a low moan. "You got no right!" he said, and his arms flailed stiffly against the brass buttons. The edge of his sleeve caught in the cop's star; the cop jerked away, and the star was left hanging lop-sidedly.

"You got no right!" Mack's fingers clawed weakly upward again; the club-on-a-cord whizzed in a gleaming circle a foot above his head, Mack reached toward it, and the club came down. It cracked down slantwise across the temple with the hissing sound of a large stone thrown through a thin paper wall—a brief sound, sharp and ripping and cold. Mack stood still for one long moment. He had stopped screaming rather suddenly. A dark star appeared on his temple, and his head began sagging slowly; like a wounded fighting-cock's head. Hands caught him under the arm-pits as he fell. While hands held him tentatively, offering him out to the cop like an unclean dish rag.

"My! Wasn't that *brave!*" a woman called from the crowd.

The big bull turned, for that voice had been mocking; but it was not repeated, so he turned toward his patrol.

"Oh, officer!"

A boy's voice this time.

The cop's eyes were shifting uneasily, for the eyes of the crowd were unfriendly. The cop remembered how, once when he was ten, he had been beaten by a smaller boy while other boys stood in a circle and watched: he remembered, seeing encircling eyes. So without fixing his gaze on any one face, he asked, "Well, who wants to see me?"

No reply, till he turned.

"No one, officer my dear. Who would? You stink most awful vile." The woman's voice.

"Who said 'at to me?" he bluffed loudly, "Who said 'at—huh?" His big face looked ready to burst with its bluff. Then he saw laughter starting, and got inside the patrol just in time. The other officer followed with Tex, in front of a chorus of catcalls that sounded like the mad thousand applauding. But Tex McKay heard only one thing clearly. Just as the door slammed someone shouted in, "Niggerlickers —that's what cops is. That's all they do in this town. Big tough niggerlickers, an' that's all they *do* do."

Mack's eyes opened, he revived slowly. On either side of him sat a bull. Tex wondered whether Mack understood all that had happened. His own hands were free, but Mack's were handcuffed. Tex, watching him revive, was torn between regret for having walked with him, and pity for seeing him in pain. The Negro looked sickly grey.

From where he sat guarding the door, the bigger bull glanced over to Tex and spoke warningly. He was still out of breath, and a bit bewildered at something, it seemed.

"This'll go mighty hard with you two. Mighty hard, I can say that now. Almost a riot call it was, an' a riot call al'ays goes harder"—he gasped for breath—"Oh lots o' trouble you boys made"—gasping— "trouble in the park first—"

His rump-like face was streaked with sweat. As though to reassure himself of the penalty the were certain to have incurred, he questioned the other officer.

"A riot-call al'ays makes it twice as bad, don't it, Arthur—huh?

Arthur nodded. He was thin, and freckled, and looked unhappy.

"See what Arthur says!—ya almost instergated a riot, that's jest what I'm sayin'. Ya'll get ninety days fer this"—gasping—or elts I'm not yer witness."

In spite of exhaustion, Tex McKay went sick with fear.

"He just wanted a sock on account his foot is so sore," he protested, "Honest, mister, that foot looks ready to drop off'n his laig."

The silver badge looked at Tex McKay with a huge and expressionless, a moon-like wonder. The big thick brain behind the eyes be-

gan to move slowly, painfully, like a heavy door opening onto a room
long-closed. Then his face looked somehow cunning-cruel, as understanding at last came into it. And he guffawed. Thwacking his thigh
resoundingly, he yawped his face so near to Tex's that Tex smelled the
foulness of his breath like a breath from a privy.

"He jest wanted a sock! He jest wanted a sock! Hey, Arthur, did
y' get that, Arthur? He jest wanted a sock—an' aint that jest what I
given him?"—He went off into whole gales of laughter, his body shaking to its very fingertips. "Say—Art—D'ya get it?—He jest wanted a
sock—an' that's what I given him." Arthur smiled a bit wanly, a bit
indulgently, and said nothing at all.

"Ho! Ho! He wanted a sock—a *clean* sock! Ho! Ho!"

Outside, the late afternoon sun was waking trembling checkered patterns on low stone buildings rushing past.

They were going to jail; they were going to eat; they are going to
have a place to lie down.

Tex said, "Ah aint no nigger."

Mack looked up. "You'se ridin'—aint yo'?"

"White Justice" by Joe Jones.

Courtesy ACA Gallery; photo by Geoffrey Clements

I Have Seen Black Hands

I

I am black and I have seen black hands, millions and millions of them—
Out of millions of bundles of wool and flannel tiny black fingers have
reached restlessly and hungrily for life.
Reached out for the black nipples at the black breasts of black mothers,
And they've held red, green, blue, yellow, orange, white, and purple
toys in the childish grips of possession,
And chocolate drops, peppermint sticks, lollypops, wineballs, ice cream
cones, and sugared cookies in fingers sticky and gummy,
And they've held balls and bats and gloves and marbles and jack-knives
and sling-shots and spinning tops in the thrill of sport and play
And pennies and nickels and dimes and quarters and sometimes on
New Year's, Easter, Lincoln's Birthday, May Day, a brand new
green dollar bill,
They've held pens and rulers and maps and tablets and books in palms
spotted and smeared with ink,
And they've held dice and cards and half-pint flasks and cue sticks and
cigars and cigarettes in the pride of new maturity . . .

II

I am black and I have seen black hands, millions and millions of them—
They were tired and awkward and calloused and grimy and covered
with hangnails,
And they were caught in the fast-moving belts of machines and snagged
and smashed and crushed,
And they jerked up and down at the throbbing machines massing
taller and taller the heaps of gold in the banks of bosses,

Richard Wright was born on a sharecropper's farm near Natchez, Mississippi on September 4, 1908. After reading H. L. Mencken's *A Book of Prefaces* he decided to become a writer and moved to Chicago and then to New York. He contributed to the *New Masses,* the *Daily Worker,* and a number of small magazines; in 1938 his collection of short stories, *Uncle Tom's Children,* won a $500 prize, and the following year he was awarded a Guggenheim Fellowship. Wright belonged to the Communist Party for a short time and wrote of his experience as a Party member in *The God That Failed.* "I remembered the stories I had written," Wright said when he decided to leave the Party, "the stories in which I assigned a role of honor and glory to the Communist Party, and I was glad that they were down in black and white, were finished. For I know in my heart that I should never be able to write that way again, should never be able to feel with that simple sharpness about life, should never again express such passionate hope, should never again make so total a commitment of faith."

And they piled higher and higher the steel, iron, the lumber, wheat,
   rye, the oats, corn, the cotton, the wool, the oil, the coal, the meat,
   the fruit, the glass, and the stone until there was too much to be
   used,
And they grabbed guns and slung them on their shoulders and marched
   and groped in trenches and fought and killed and conquered
   nations who were customers for the goods black hands had made.
And again black hands stacked goods higher and higher until there was
   too much to be used,
And then the black hands held trembling at the factory gates the
   dreaded lay-off slip,
And the black hands hung idle and swung empty and grew soft and
   got weak and bony from unemployment and starvation,
And they grew nervous and sweaty, and opened and shut in anguish
   and doubt and hesitation and irresolution . . .

III

I am black and I have seen black hands, millions and millions of them—
Reaching hesitantly out of days of slow death for the goods they had
   made, but the bosses warned that the goods were private and did
   not belong to them,
And the black hands struck desperately out in defence of life and there
   was blood, but the enraged bosses decreed that this too was wrong.
And the black hands felt the cold steel bars of the prison they had
   made, in despair tested their strength and found that they could
   neither bend nor break them,
And the black hands fought and scratched and held back but a thousand white hands took them and tied them,
And the black hands lifted palms in mute and futile supplication to the
   sodden faces of mobs wild in the revelries of sadism,
And the black hands strained and clawed and struggled in vain at the
   noose that tightened about the black throat,
And the black hands waved and beat fearfully at the tall flames that
   cooked and charred the black flesh . . .

IV

I am black and I have seen black hands
Raised in fists of revolt, side by side with the white fists of white
   workers,
And some day—and it is only this which sustains me—
Some day there shall be millions and millions of them,
On some red day in a burst of fists on a new horizon!

Four Poems

BY JOSEPH FREEMAN

I

In this black room, midnight and morn are each
Aeons away; the open window brings
The sea's insistent roar against the beach;
Loud in the night the hollow bellbuoy flings
Skyward its melancholy monotones;
Above the clamor of the breaking waves
Far off its lonely clapper moans
Like some despairing idiot who raves
Crawling on hands and knees through empty streets
To doors that seem familiar, there to weep.
While one unconscious twisted knuckle beats
For succor, for compassion and for sleep,
He rends the silence with a final cry
To which the stubborn night makes no reply.

New York, November, 1931

II

Mankind looks forward, but the hurt look back:
Broken of will, distracted and afraid,
They who have had no childhood but the rack
Shall yet be judged for what they've done or said.
And if their feet, once crucified, now drag,
We'll nail them once again upon our scorn:
When mankind marches, let the weak not lag,
Cursing the time and place where they were born.

Joseph Freeman was one of the most influential and respected figures of the literary left. Although his poems were never collected, his importance to many of the young poets was summed up by Edwin Rolfe, who wrote in the *Partisan Review* of April-May 1935: "It was Joseph Freeman who finally showed some of us our real direction, our real goal. 'You are revolutionists,' he told us. 'You need no better start as writers, as poets . . . Stop thinking of yourselves,' he said, 'as poets who are also revolutionists or as revolutionists who are also poets. Remember that you are *revolutionary poets.* Then work hard at your poetry. The rest will follow.'" The four poems reprinted here were originally published as a unit in the February-March 1934 issue of *Partisan Review*.

The past dies, save for those whom it has broken;
They will remember whom the world has maimed.
Let them be silent! Things must not be spoken
Which hide deep in the thought of man, ashamed:
Or, if their lips are bitter and inflamed,
Let them speak all by symbol and by token.

New York, 1925

III

Still young, our faces may deceive
Your eyes, ironic in their gaze:
Since we have learned no more to grieve
We must have entered a maturer phase.

We must be growing old; indeed,
We must, since we accept the fair
And foul, the open heart and greed,
Goodness and malice both without despair.

There was a time we pounded gates,
Called down interminable stairs,
Denounced the treachery of the fates
Who sit in darkness spinning deadly snares.

We knew the iron teeth of guilt,
Were twisted on the rack of shame,
Lived in a night that nightmares built,
Were loth to place and glad to take the blame.

O happy youth, O happy age
To whom these poisons are remote;
Whose voices, ignorant of rage,
Babble forever on an even note.

The world is not to bless or curse;
In rain and wind, in sun and shade
Take it for better or for worse—
While we shall strike the blow that you evade.

New York, November, 1931

IV

Drums of the world, beat!
beat a loud call for war against this madness!

Blue for a billion years, the sky
having seen at the world's dawn
man crawl up from slime,
still beholds the terror,
indolence, stupor, robbery, superstition,
blood and lies from age to age;
bones of butchered men cracking in the fields,
diplomacy's crooked smile,
the oppression of peoples,
cries of the poor in all times and lands,
the hatred of parents and children
(boys and girls twisted at life's gates
by the poison of unconfessed jealousy and revenge)
the struggle of nations, classes, factions, individuals;
hands that come empty into the world and leave empty.

Beat, drums of the world!
let the workers storm from the factories,
the peasants from the farms;
sweep the earth clean of this nightmare,
build new cities, a new world,
ringing with the clear voices of new men!

New York, 1931

What the Thunder Said: A Fire Sermon

BY SOL FUNAROFF

Where are the roots that clutch, what branches grow
Out of this stony rubbish?—T. S. ELIOT

A CINEMATIC POEM

The Communards, they are storming heaven!

A damp gust of March wind
swirls and scatters papers.

And the hot, critical July days!—
tense wireless bristling with flashes,
stammering, stuttering,
awaiting what code,
what code to translate
Capital, Famine, Predatory War,
into what dialectic odyssey
the machine gun's riveting shall inscribe—
the Leatherjacket fatally indite?

In the Smolny:
the decisive delegates,

Sol Funaroff was the editor of the left-wing poetry magazine, *Dynamo*, as well as the editor of the Dynamo Poets series (which published Kenneth Fearing's second volume of poems in 1935). In 1938, he published his own collection of poems, *The Spider and the Clock*, from which "What the Thunder Said: A Fire Sermon" is reprinted. In his notes to the poem, Funaroff wrote in part: " 'What the Thunder Said: A Fire Sermon' is a poem of the Russian Revolution and is based upon Marxian philosophical concepts. As symbol and as history this event challenges the fundamentally political and religious attitudes of negation, frustration, the martyrdom of the individual and the decay of the materialistic world which find their most significant poetic expression in T. S. Eliot's *The Waste Land*."

drawn faces,
burnt cigarettes, telephones,
wires, leaflets,—
telegraphic congresses:
and in the chill streets
armed workers, soldiers,
add fuel to the street fires.
Rifles ready. Waiting. Deciding.
Who are the riders?

When the thunderheads hammer,
the palaces reverberate,
the napoleonic columns fall;
the cracked plaster of paris Narcissus
drowns in his fragments.

The Thorthunder speaks:
Workers! Soldiers! Sailors!
We are the riders of steel storms!
We are the fire-bearers!
Ours the heritage of the first flame-runner
racing up the steep dark slopes,
lightning in the night!
Created and creator of fire!
We are the riders of steel stallions—
we are the fire-bearers,
the kinetic synergy of factories
snorting flambent plumes,
charging,
rushing up the tracks beacon-eyed!

And scarlet ships of space
wing time's fires
cataclysmic bear
earth's heirs
the communists with battle shouts
rumble over the skyways,
scatter cannonades of stars,—
flowers of life and death,
flowers of revolution
rocket amid acrid clouds!
The Thorthunder says:

(rumblin crumblin)
Da!
Da Da!

All Power To The Soviets!

The Spring rain blows over the steppes.

In October
lightning ripples in the windwaved wheat—
great streak of silver whistling scythe!
And tractors bloom in the wheatfields!
They rumble,
they crumble the earth to their powerful wills.
They speak:
Gigant!

Overhead—
soft sunsetwinds blow rosegold odors
twilightly descend with their first young star.
Over the bridge strong hands on wheels and levers skim.
Over the bridge trains bead red stars
weld through fire and iron
five years!—
electric songs of speeding lights!
A blow torch simmers sparkles
and the Leatherjacket welds
stars over the waters below.

Red coals toss in torrents
in waterfalls of the Dnieprostroi,
and the Dnieper sows her banks with rubies.
There spring up socialized cities . . .
Workers of Magnitogorsk, with huge blast furnaces,
write in flame,
through fire and iron,
steel statements of steel deeds:
armored trains of revolution
dynamic steel drilling through black rock
dynamiting tunnels
mining blackgold ores!
Subways without christbeggars

whose blind eyes beseech a penance!
While the bursting sun flings from chaotic flame-pits
the synthesis of new worlds . . .
and the sun like an executed head falls
and the whole sky bleeds
dripping over church and skyscraper
and arms like hammers strike stars
forge new worlds shoot upwards
yes!

Detail from Rockefeller Center mural by Diego Rivera.

photo by Dan Budnik

New York, Cassandra

BY HORACE GREGORY

I

Cassandra, the world's on fire; the harvest's sour:
from Salem into China, an old sailor's song
sung to the yellow sea that pours
oceans of grain over us, fire and flood;
it will be hard to sleep.

Macbeth has murder'd sleep, sleep festering
under his eyelids, Cassandra, like an old wound split wide.
Macbeth shall sleep no more—good night, Macbeth—
wake well tonight:
                                    spring (naked mind)
arms, sheets, window curtains pushed aside
to see the fire, hear the guns.

Breakfast will be delayed beyond Canopus,
lunch clean, untouched by human hands, embalmed in cellophane,
revolving in an automat, will wait . . .

From 1930 to 1935 Horace Gregory published three important volumes of poems: *Chelsea Rooming House* (1930), *No Retreat* (1933), and *Chorus for Survival* (1935). Upon the publication of the last volume, Louis Untermeyer stated that of all the poets "who 'emerged' during the last five or six years, none is more distinctive than Horace Gregory." It was in the same year, 1935, that Gregory, one of the founders of the John Reed Club, aroused the anger of many left-wing writers by trying to make a case for keeping art apolitical. Despite the Marxian influence on his early poems, Gregory summed up his position when he wrote: "No matter what others may think of my work I should like to have said of me what was said of Baudelaire, a far greater poet than I: 'He belonged to no school. . . . He copied no one, but he used everyone that suited him, making what he had taken his own and something new.'" "New York, Cassandra" is reprinted from the 1933 volume of poems, *No Retreat.*

Somebody said that Macbeth went insane,
leaped thirty stories down to Birnam wood

                         (inane,

O Dunsinane, your palaces are empty)
The king bled through the sheets (cock crow) Macbeth
grew sick, cracked the eternal verities
engraved upon his heart in rock:

    Pick me sweet verities,

                    sweet verities;

    where shall we find again such girls as these?
    Nightingale Venus, bright Beatrice shall sing tonight,
    silverlipped requiem Mary shall answer them,
    clothed in the blood of Christ down to her knees.
    Pick me sweet verities,

                    sweet verities.

                             They stand,
a row of broken statues from Alexandria (B.C.)
to Salt Lake City.

II

Give Cerberus a non-employment wage, the dog is hungry.
This head served in the war, Cassandra, it lost an eye;
that head spits fire, for it lost its tongue licking the paws
of lions caged in Wall Street and their claws
were merciless.

    Follow, O follow him, loam-limbed Apollo, crumbling before
    Tiffany's window; he must buy
    himself earrings for he meets his love tonight,
    (Blossoming Juliet
    emptied her love into her true love's lap)
    dies in his arms.

                  He is a poet,
    kiss him, Socrates.

They say the red arm of the Proletariat swings,
Hammer and Sickle, a quarter moon in the sky,
the dogstar comets leap . . .
They say Macbeth embezzled funds, the market

fell too soon, too soon the hands of Christ
withered on the cross.

His wife was barren
(her eyes are flowers
blowing in the field down where the Lackawanna railroad runs:
flow softly rivers of coal and steam)
His life insurance went to the banks.

III

There are five limousines, unbought, rotting behind plate glass,
delicate worms in leather and sharp April grass
piercing steel joints . . .
Talk to the guns, Cassandra, tell them this is peace,
not war, not war,

peace,

PEACE.

We came to you with a city in our hands;
we said:

Destroy this city, by God, we hate this city.

You heard us and your house was a tower of flames . . .
Remember there was once a king, an old king with an iron beard,
whose life was like your house, a floor of ashes.

He put out his eyes, Cassandra.

We shall keep

our eyes though we learn nothing . . .

The night is cold,

Cassandra.

FOUR MARTYRS

Revolutions and protest movements are built and sustained by their martyrs. In the thirties, Joe Hill, Tom Mooney, Sacco and Vanzetti, and the Scottsboro Boys—still foremost symbols of repression and injustice—were a common source of literary inspiration. From the extensive literature which was built up around them, we have selected four representative poems.

Joe Hill, "The Wobblies' Troubadour," was arrested on a murder charge in 1914. Although he claimed that he was framed by state authorities who wanted to run the IWW out of Utah, Hill was convicted and sentenced to death. Despite two appeals by President Wilson to the governor of Utah that the case be reconsidered, Joe Hill was executed by a firing squad on November 19, 1915. His final message to the Wobblies—"Don't mourn for me, organize," became a rallying cry for the labor movement in the United States. Kenneth Patchen's elegy for Joe Hill first appeared in *New Masses*, where it aroused considerable comment; it was later reprinted in *Proletarian Literature in the United States* and in Patchen's 1936 collection of poems, *Before the Brave.*

Tom Mooney was a leader in the labor struggles in California prior to 1916, at which time he was arrested and convicted for the bomb killings at the San Francisco Preparedness Day Parade. His case aroused international interest, and in 1918 Mooney's death sentence was commuted to life imprisonment. But because of the confessions of perjured testimony, as well as the existence of contested evidence, such liberals as Theodore Dreiser and Upton Sinclair sought to obtain a new trial for Mooney. Although they were not successful, Mooney was given an unconditional pardon by Governor Culbert Olson of California in January 1939. Lola Ridge, the author of the poem about the Mooney case reprinted below, was born in Ireland and came to the United States in 1907. In 1929 she published her fourth volume of poetry, *Firehead*, a long poem on Christ's crucifixion, which was inspired by the Sacco-Vanzetti case; and, in 1935, she published her fifth and final volume of poems, *Dance of Fire*, from which "Stone Face" is reprinted.

Sacco and Vanzetti have become the foremost martyrs of the century. They were arrested for killing the paymaster and his guard while robbing the payroll of a Massachusetts shoe company on April 15, 1920. Both men were anarchists, and both had avoided the draft. When they were convicted, there was a widespread feeling that it was their political beliefs, rather than the weight of the evidence, that had condemned them. Both before and after their execution on August 22, 1927, their cause was taken up by intellectuals on both sides of the Atlantic. In Europe, Galsworthy, Wells, and Mann spoke out in defense of Sacco and Vanzetti; while in America, the two anarchists became the sympathetic subject of works by Maxwell Anderson, Lola Ridge, Upton Sinclair, Edna St. Vincent Millay, Malcolm Cowley, and John Dos Passos (who wrote in *U.S.A.*: "If the state of Massachusetts can kill those innocent men in the face of the protests of the whole world, it'll mean that there will never be any justice in America again"). Among those who saw in the execution of Sacco and Vanzetti the corruption of American capitalism was David Wolfe, considered to be one of the leading revolutionary poets of the thirties. His poem, "August 22, 1927," appeared in *Proletarian Literature in the United States.*

The Scottsboro case was the cause célèbre of the thirties. Nine Negro boys were charged with the rape of two white girls on a freight train in Alabama; at the trial held in Scottsboro, Alabama, in 1931, eight of the boys were sentenced to death (the ninth boy's case was declared a mistrial). The decision of the Alabama court was twice appealed to the Supreme Court, which declared in 1935 that the constitutional rights of the Scottsboro boys had been violated, and that there would have to be a retrial. A compromise was worked out; four of the defendants were given sentences equivalent to life imprisonment, and the rape charges against the other boys were dropped. In the thirties, the Scottsboro case became the subject of several literary works, most notably John Wexley's *They Shall Not Die*, Langston Hughes' *Scottsboro Limited*, and the poem by Muriel Rukeyser which we have reprinted. Miss Rukeyser's "The Trial" was published in her first collection of verse. *Theory of Flight*, which was the 1935 volume in the Yale Series of Younger Poets. The editor of the series, Stephen Vincent Benét, wrote in his introduction that although Miss Rukeyser was politically a revolutionary, when she "speaks her politics—and she speaks with sincerity and fire—she does so like a poet, not like a slightly worn phonograph record, and she does so in poetic form."

Joe Hill Listens to the Praying

BY KENNETH PATCHEN

Look at the steady rifles, Joe.
It's all over now—"Murder, first degree,"
The jury said. It's too late now
To go back. Listen Joe, the chaplain is reading:

Lord Jesus Christ who didst
So mercifully promise heaven
To the thief that humbly confessed
His injustice
             throw back your head

Joe; remember that song of yours
We used to sing in jails all over
These United States—tell it to him:
"I'll introduce to you
A man that is a credit to our Red, White
and Blue,
His head is made of lumber and solid as
a rock;
He is a Christian Father and his name is
Mr. Block."
                   Remember, Joe—

"You take the cake,
You make me ache,
Tie a rock on your block and jump
in the lake,
Kindly do that for Liberty's sake."

Behold me, I beseech Thee, with
The same eyes of mercy that
                                on the other
Hand we're driftin' into Jungles
From Kansas to the coast, wrapped
                round brake beams on a thousand
                freights; San Joaquin and Omaha
                brush under the wheels—"God made the summer
                for the hobo and the bummer"—we've been
                everywhere, seen everything.
Winning the West for the good citizens;
Driving golden spikes into the U. P.;
Harvest hands, lumbermen drifting—
                now Iowa, now Oregon—
God, how clean the sky; the lovely wine
Of coffee in a can. This land
                is our lover. How greenly beautiful
Her hair; her great pure breasts
                that are
The Rockies on a day of mist and rain.

We love this land of corn and cotton,
                Virginia and Ohio, sleeping on
With our love, with our love—
O burst of Alabama loveliness, sleeping on
In the strength of our love; O Mississippi flowing
Through our nights, a giant mother.

Pardon, and in the end
                How green is her hair,
                how pure are her breasts; the little farms
                nuzzling into her flanks
                drawing forth life, big rich life
Under the deep chant of her skies
And rivers—but we, we're driftin'
Into trouble from Kansas to the coast, clapped
                into the stink and rot of country jails
                and clubbed by dicks and cops
Because we didn't give a damn—
                                remember Joe
How little we cared, how we sang
                the nights away in their filthy jails;

                                    and how, when
We got wind of a guy called Marx
                we sang less, just talked
And talked. "Blanket-stiffs" we were
·But we could talk, they couldn't jail us
For that—but they did—
                        remember Joe
Of my life be strengthened
                        One Big Union:
                our convention in Chi; the Red Cards,
                leaflets; sleeping in the parks,
                the Boul' Mich; "wobblies" now, cheering
                the guys that spoke our lingo, singing
                down the others. "Hear that train blow,
Boys, hear that train blow."

Now confessing my crimes, I may obtain

Millions of stars, Joe—millions of miles.

                        Remember Vincent St. John
In the Goldfield strike; the timid little squirt
                with the funny voice, getting onto the platform
                and slinging words at us that rolled
                down our chins and into our hearts,
                like boulders hell-bent down a mountain side.
And Orchard, angel of peace
                —with a stick of dynamite in either hand.
                Pettibone and Moyer: "The strike
Is your weapon, to hell with politics."
                        Big Bill—remember him—
At Boise—great red eye rolling like a lame bull
                through the furniture and men
                of the courtroom—"This bastard,
His Honor."

                Hobo Convention:
(Millions of stars, Joe—millions of miles.)
"Hallelujah, I'm a bum,
Hallelujah, I'm a bum." His Honor,
                the sonofabitch!
One Big Strike, Lawrence, Mass—
                23,000 strong, from every neck

of every woods in America, 23,000,
Joe, remember. "We don't need
                a leader. We'll fix things up
                among ourselves."
"Blackie" Ford and "Double-nose" Suhr in
Wheatland—"I. W. W.'s don't destroy
                property"—and they got life. "I've counted
The stars, boys, counted a million of these prison bars."

                San Diego, soap boxes,
Hundreds of them! And always
                their jail shutting out the sky,
                the clean rhythm of the wheels
                on a fast freight; disinfectant getting
                into the lung-pits, spitting blood
But singing—Christ, how we sang,
                                remember the singing
Joe, One Big Union,
                One Big
                    hope to be
With Thee

What do they matter, Joe, these rifles.
They can't reach the towns, the skies, the songs,
                that now are part of more
                than any of us—we were
The homeless, the drifters, but, our songs
                had hair and blood on them.
There are no soap boxes in the sky.
We won't eat pie, now, or ever
                when we die,
                                but Joe
We had something they didn't have:
                our love for these States
                was real and deep;
                                to be with Thee
In heaven. Amen.
                (How steady are
the rifles.) We had slept
                naked on this earth on the coldest nights
                listening to the words of a guy named Marx.
Let them burn us, hang us, shoot us,

Joe Hill,

For at the last we had what it takes
to make songs with.

Stone Face

BY LOLA RIDGE

They have carved you into a stone face, Tom Mooney,
You, there lifted high in California
Over the salt wash of the Pacific,
With your eyes . . . crying in many tongues,
Goading, innumerable eyes of the multitudes,
Holding in them all hopes, fears, persecutions,
Forever straining one way.

Even in the Sunday papers,
        and your face tight-bitten like a pierced fist,
The eyes have a transfixed gleam
        as they had glimpsed some vision and there hung
Impaled as on a bright lance.

Too much lip-foam has dripped on you, too many
And disparate signatures are scrawled on your stone face that all
Have set some finger on, to say who made you for the years
To mouth as waves mouth rock . . . you, a rough man,
Rude-nurtured, casually shouldering
Through a May-day crowd in San Francisco,
To be cast up out of the dark mass—terribly gestating, swarming
        without feature,
And raised with torsion to identity.

Now they—who wrote you plain, with Sacco and the fishmonger,
High on the scroll of the Republic—
Look up with a muddled irritation at your clenched face,
It set up in full sight under the long
Gaze of the generations—to be there
Haggard in the sunrise, when San Quentin
Prison shall be caved in and its steel ribs
Food for the ant-rust . . . and Governor Rolph
A fleck of dust among the archives.

August 22, 1927

BY DAVID WOLFF

From Ellis Island, over the guarded fence,
what grasp against the smoky bay,
index electric for the immigrant,
bright as the panes where Wall St. lifts the sky?

—Of Liberty, the Statue. And of her golden land
draped like a mother in the neon veils,
two men asked innocently food. Bruised
mouth they got at the iron nipples.

Then Boston: a hawker of fish; in the last alley
his pennies stank in the twilight.
August; the fire escapes a-heave with sleepers;
a cobbler clops in his shop till midnight.

Chained are the days, fatigue and blistered rooms,
stuporous nightfall on the bodies chained.
"Workmen, unite! Nothing to lose but chains—,"
under the harsh bulb, fishman and cobbler read;

And sang them with living fist in the mill streets,
for which they were framed into the cynical bars
7 years, watching approach the electric gavel.
Now burn them for murder, said the murderers.

While U.S.S.R. brightens with Lenin's voltage,
socialist engines suckling the cemented river;
long past such playthings, capital restrains
Niagara to electrify a chair.

Thayer has shaved Nicola Sacco's skull;
Lowell on Vanzetti fits the wet iron.
Morgan, Mellon, Ford, and Rockefeller
at the copper switch twice clamp death down.

You, masters of New England! land and wheel
squeeze in your perfumed thumbs, but on your

cuff is the stink of burning skin;
class toward class, we name you murderer.

SACCO: VANZETTI: twice in that hour,
twice our banners were branded. Now when mills hush
in Massachusetts, moves our ruddy storm
from whose first height the deadly truth must flash.

The Trial

BY MURIEL RUKEYSER

The South is green with coming spring; revival
flourishes in the fields of Alabama. Spongy with rain,
plantations breathe April: carwheels suck mud in the roads,
the town expands warm in the afternoons. At night the black boy
teeters no-handed on a bicycle, whistling The St. Louis Blues,
blood beating, and hot South. A red brick courthouse
is vicious with men inviting death. Array your judges; call your jurors,
        come,
here is your justice, come out of the crazy jail.
Grass is green now in Alabama; Birmingham dusks are quiet
relaxed and soft in the park, stern at the yards:
a hundred boxcars shunted off to sidings, and the hoboes
gathering grains of sleep in forbidden corners.
In all the yards: Atlanta, Chattanooga,
Memphis, and New Orleans, the cars, and no jobs.

Every night the mail-planes burrow the sky,
carrying postcards to laughing girls in Texas,
passionate letters to the Charleston virgins,
words through the South: and no reprieve,
no pardon, no release.
A blinded statue attends before the courthouse,
bronze and black men lie on the grass, waiting,
the khaki dapper National Guard leans on its bayonets.
But the air is populous beyond our vision:
all the people's anger finds its vortex here
as the mythic lips of justice open, and speak.

Hammers and sickles are carried in a wave of strength, fire-tipped,
swinging passionately ninefold to a shore.

Answer the back-thrown Negro face of the lynched, the flat forehead
    knotted,
the eyes showing a wild iris, the mouth a welter of blood,
answer the broken shoulders and these twisted arms.
John Brown, Nat Turner, Toussaint stand in this courtroom,
Dred Scott wrestles for freedom there in the dark corner,
all our celebrated shambles are repeated here: now again
Sacco and Vanzetti walk to a chair, to the straps and rivets
and the switch spitting death and Massachusetts' will.
Wreaths are brought out of history
here are the well-nourished flowers of France, grown strong on blood,
Caesar twisting his thin throat toward conquest,
               turning north from the Roman laurels,
the Istrian galleys slide again to sea.
How they waded through bloody Godfrey's Jerusalem!
How the fires broke through Europe, and the rich
and the tall jails battened on revolution!
The fastidious Louis', cousins to the sun, stamping
those ribboned heels on Calas, on the people;
the lynched five thousand of America.
Tom Mooney from San Quentin, Herndon: here
is an army for audience
             all resolved
to a gobbet of tobacco, spat, and the empanelled hundred,
a jury of vengeance, the cheap pressed lips, the narrow eyes like hard-
    ware;
the judge, his eye-sockets and cheeks dark and immutably secret,
the twisting mouth of the prosecuting attorney.

Nine dark boys spread their breasts against Alabama,
schooled in the cells, fathered by want.
      Mother: one writes: they treat us bad. If they send
us back to Kilby jail, I think I shall kill myself.
I think I must hang myself by my overalls.

Alabama and the South are soft with spring;
in the North, the seasons change, sweet April, December and the air
loaded with snow. There is time for meetings
during the years, they remaining in prison.

               In the square
a crowd listens, carrying banners.

Overhead, boring through the speaker's voice, a plane
circles with a snoring of motors revolving in the sky,
drowning the single voice. It does not touch
the crowd's silence. It circles. The name stands:
Scottsboro.

The Scottsboro boys with attorney Samuel Leibowitz.

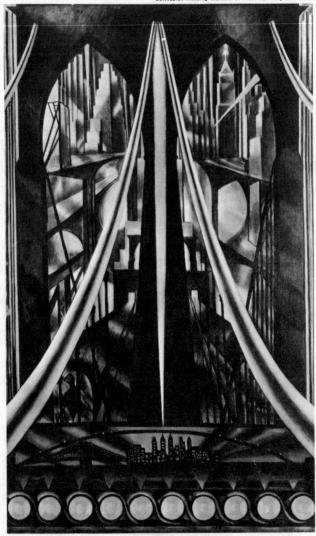

"The Brooklyn Bridge: Variation on an Old Theme" by Joseph Stella.

A Blazing Sun

For me the sun had ceased to exist;
I had myself become a blazing sun.

HENRY MILLER

THERE has never been a period in American history, as Malcolm Cowley observed in *The New Republic* on November 8, 1939, "when literary events followed so closely on the flying coat-tails of social events" as they did in the thirties. And because of this, "thirties literature" has come to mean literature of social protest. For the most part, this socially-oriented literature was identified with such left-wing journals as *New Masses, Partisan Review, Dynamo, Blast,* and *Anvil.* But the thirties were also the time when *Ballyhoo* and *Life* were inaugurated and the *New Yorker* was in its prime; it was the decade which saw the establishment and quick demise of such short-lived "little magazines" as William Carlos Williams' *Contact* (published in the belief that "Good writing stands by humanity in its joys and sorrows because under all it is—and just because it is—so many words") and *Americana,* edited by Alexander King, George Grosz, and Gilbert Seldes (who declared in their opening editorial in November 1932 that they were neither Republicans, Democrats, Socialists, nor Communists, but simply "Americans who believe that our civilization exudes a miasmic stench . . .").

Despite the impact of the political and social struggles on America in the 1930's, many writers would not lend themselves to a communal cause. Their individual liberty was not to be sacrificed; their art was not to be restricted to the immediacy of the class war. This was so not only of those writers who aligned themselves with the Humanists and Agrarians, but also of those who refused to be identified with any cause other than their own being. At the same time, there were those writers —William Carlos Williams and Henry Roth, for example—who, despite their sympathy for the Left, were unable to keep their art within the framework of a proletarian literature. There were many writers, in short, who although actively engaged in their craft, did not become involved in the main current of thirties literature; and the selections in this concluding chapter are intended to be but a sampling of their work.

Henry Miller, E. E. Cummings, and Robinson Jeffers were perhaps the three outstanding literary individualists of the period: Miller, in self-exile in Paris, writing with an intensity of introspection that makes his "I" a blazing sun; Cummings attacking both Communist and capitalist with a syntax that in itself becomes an attack on all that denied individualism; and Jeffers, isolating himself in Carmel, California, awaiting the destruction of civilization and saddened only by the fact that "it will not be in our time, alas, my dear, it will not be in our time."

Both William Carlos Williams and William Saroyan were at one time or another sympathetic to the Communist cause, but neither responded artistically, as had been hoped. Although "The Dawn of Another Day" originally appeared in *Blast* and is intended to be a "proletarian" story, from the point of view of a revolutionary critic Williams' vision is muddled; even when he apparently wanted to, Williams could not force his art into the proletarian mold. Saroyan did not even try. Writing in *The New Republic* on August 29, 1934, Saroyan commented: "I have the idea that the Communists now being held in jail here are rather fine Americans and perhaps the most genuinely patriotic individuals in the city. I'm not sure, though, and I wouldn't be willing to go to jail for the theory, because I have a lot of writing to do and don't like writing in jail." Whether it was Communism or the NRA, Saroyan went his own way.

The three final selections are by writers who, although their output was restricted to the thirties, received little recognition at the time. Nathanael West and Henry Roth wrote nothing before or after the decade; and Daniel Fuchs, discouraged by the poor sales of his serious novels, went to Hollywood. All three have been rediscovered—and acclaimed—in recent years. Their works have been reissued in both cloth and paperback editions, with the unexpected success of *Call It Sleep* in particular playing a major role in the revival of interest in the fiction of the thirties.

Peace! It's Wonderful!

BY HENRY MILLER

IT was only the other night while entertaining an American writer who had come to visit France after a long absence that I realized poignantly what has happened to me since I left my native land. Like all my compatriots who come to see me he asked quite naturally what it was that had kept me here so long. (It is seven years since I am living in Paris.) I felt that it was useless to answer him in words. I suggested instead that we take a stroll through the streets. We started out from the corner of the Rue de la Gaîté and the Avenue du Maine where we had been sitting; I walked him down the Rue de l'Ouest to the Rue du Château, then over the railroad bridge back of the Gare Montparnasse down the Boulevard Pasteur to the Avenue de Breteuil and thence to a little café facing the Invalides where we sat in silence for a long while. Perhaps that silence which one finds in the streets of Paris at night, perhaps that alone was a sufficient answer to his query. It is something difficult to find in a big American city.

At any rate, it was not chance which had directed my footsteps. Walking with my friend through the deserted streets I was reliving my first days in Paris, for it was in the Rue de Vanves that my new life really began. Night after night without money, without friends, without a language I had walked these streets in despair and anguish. The streets were everything to me, as they must be to every man who is lost

---

No one writing during the thirties was more opposed, either in temperament or belief, to the proletarian ideals than Henry Miller. At a time when the expatriates of the twenties were returning to their country and involving themselves in social and political struggles, Miller remained in Paris, except for two brief and unhappy visits to New York in 1935 and 1936, boasting that he was "free of this country, that I have no need of it . . . her problems leave me unaffected. It is not hatred of it . . . but indifference." His reckless optimism and commitment to total freedom, as well as his insistent "irresponsibility," caused him to be virtually ignored in America during the thirties. Yet it was during this period that Miller published his most important works: *Tropic of Cancer* (1934), *Black Spring* (1936), and *Tropic of Capricorn* (1939). "Peace! It's Wonderful!" is the first selection in *The Cosmological Eye* (1939), and is one of Henry Miller's most concise and pointed personal manifestoes.

in a big city. Walking through them again with my countryman I congratulated myself silently that I had begun my life in Paris behind the scenes, as it were. If I *had* led a Bohemian life, as some imagine, it was through bitter necessity. *A Bohemian life!* What a strange phrase that is when you think of it! There is so little that is Bohemian about it. In any case, the important thing is that in the Rue de Vanves I touched bottom. Like it or not, I was obliged to create a new life for myself. And this new life I feel is mine, absolutely mine, to use or to smash, as I see fit. In this life I am God, and like God I am indifferent to my own fate. I am everything there is—so why worry?

Just as a piece of matter detaches itself from the sun to live as a wholly new creation so I have come to feel about my detachment from America. Once the separation is made a new orbit is established, and there is no turning back. For me the sun had ceased to exist; I had myself become a blazing sun. And like all the other suns of the universe I had to nourish myself *from within*. I speak in cosmological terms because it seems to me that is the only possible way to think if one is truly alive. I think this way also because it is just the opposite of the way I thought a few years back when I had what is called hopes. Hope is a bad thing. It means that you are not what you want to be. It means that part of you is dead, if not *all* of you. It means that you entertain illusions. It's a sort of spiritual clap, I should say.

Before this inward change came about I used to think that we were living in extraordinarily difficult times. Like most men I thought that *our* time was the worst possible time. And no doubt it is—for those, I mean, who still say "our time." As for myself, I've thrown away the calendar by which one reckons the lean and the fat years. For me it is all gravy, one continuous, marvellous stream of time without beginning or end. Yes, the times are bad, permanently bad—unless one becomes immune, *becomes God*. Since I have become God I go the whole hog always. I am absolutely indifferent to the fate of the world: I have my own world and my own private fate. I make no reservations and no compromises. I accept. *I am*—and that is all.

That is why, perhaps, when I sit at my typewriter I always face East. No backward glances over the shoulder. The orbit over which I am travelling leads me farther and farther away from the dead sun which gave me birth. Once I was confronted with a choice—either to remain a satellite of that dead thing or create a new world of my own, with my own satellites. I made my choice. Having made it there is no standing still. One becomes more and more alive, or more and more dead. To get a piqûre is useless; a blood transfusion is useless. A new man is made out of the whole cloth, by a change of heart which alters every

living cell of the body. Anything less than a change of heart is sure
catastrophe. Which, if you follow the reasoning, explains why the
times are always bad. For, unless there be a change of heart there can
be no act of will. There may be a show of will, with tremendous activity
accompanying it (wars, revolutions, etc.), but that will not change the
times. Things are apt to grow worse, in fact.

Over many centuries of time a few men have appeared who, to my
way of thinking, really understood why the times are permanently bad.
They proved, through their own unique way of living, that this sad
"fact" is one of man's delusions. But nobody, apparently, understands
them. And it is eminently right that it should be thus. If we want to
lead a creative life it is absolutely just that we should be responsible for
our own destiny. To imagine a way of life that could be patched is to
think of the cosmos as a vast plumbing affair. To expect others to do
what we are unable to do ourselves is truly to believe in miracles,
miracles that no Christ would dream of performing. The whole social-
political scheme of existence is crazy—because it is based on vicarious
living. A real man has no need of governments, of laws, of moral or
ethical codes, to say nothing of battleships, police clubs, high-powered
bombers and such things. Of course a real man is hard to find, but
that's the only kind of man worth talking about. Why talk about trash?
It is the great mass of mankind, the mob, the people, who create the
permanently bad times. The world is only the mirror of ourselves. If
it's something to make one puke, why then puke, me lads, it's your
own sick mugs you're looking at!

Sometimes it almost seems that the writer takes a perverse delight in
finding the times out of joint, finding everything awrack and awry.
Perhaps the artist is nothing more than the personification of this
universal maladjustment, this universal disequilibrium. Perhaps that
explains why in the neutral, sterilized countries (Scandinavia, Holland,
Switzerland), so little art is forthcoming, or why in the countries
undergoing profound social and political changes (Russia, Germany,
Italy), the art products are of negligible value. But, whether there is
little art or bad art, art, it should be understood, is only a makeshift, a
substitute for the real thing. There is only one art which, if we practiced
it, would destroy what is called "art." With every line I write I kill off
the "artist" in me. With every line it is either murder in the first degree
or suicide. I do not want to give hope to others, nor to inspire others. If
we knew what it meant to be inspired we would not inspire. We would
simply *be*. As it is we neither inspire nor aid one another: we deal
out of cold justice. For myself I want none of this stinking cold justice;
I want either warm-hearted magnanimity or absolute neglect. To be

honest, I want something more than any man can give me. I want everything! I want everything—or nothing. It's crazy, I know, but that's what I mean.

Is it good here in France? It's wonderful. Marvellous. For *me* it's marvellous, because it's the only place in the world I know of where I can go on with my murder-and-suicide business—until I strike a new zodiacal realm. For a French writer it may be bad here, but then I am not a French writer. I should hate to be a French or a German or a Russian or an American writer. It must be hell. I am a cosmological writer, and when I open my trap I broadcast to the whole world at once. (Like Father Divine: *Peace! It's Wonderful!*) Acting as I do I am apt to get it in the neck. I am apt to get sucked good and proper, and I know it. But that's my temperament, and I'll stand or fall by it. Eventually I shan't even bother to be a cosmological writer: *I shall be just a man.* But first there's a lot of slaughtering to be done.

Every man who aspires to be a good French writer (or a bad one), or a (good or bad) German writer, or a (good or bad) Russian writer, any man, I mean, who hopes to make a living by giving regular doses of medicine to his sick countrymen, helps to perpetuate a farce which has been going on since the beginning of history. Such writers, and they are practically all we have, it seems, are the lice which keep us from knowing Paradise or Hell. They keep us in a perpetual Purgatory where we scratch without let. Whereas even the earth wobbles on its axis, or will change its axis from time to time, these blokes keep us forever on an even keel. In every great figure who has flashed across the horizon there is, or was, a large element of treachery, or hatred, or love, or disgust. We have had traitors to race, country, religion, but we have not yet bred any real traitors, *traitors to the human race,* which is what we need. The chances are slim, I know. I mention it merely to show how the wind blows.

As I say, one needs either a heaven or a hell in which to flourish—until one arrives at the Paradise of his own creation, that middle realm which is not a bread-and-butter Utopia of which the masses dream but an interstellar realm in which one rolls along his orbit with sublime indifference. Dante was the best cartographer of the soul which Europe ever produced, everything clear as a whistle and etched in black and white; but since his time not only Europe, but the whole universe, has moved into new spiritual dimensions. Man is still the center of the cosmos, but having stretched the cosmos almost to the bursting point— the scientists actually predict that the universe will explode!—man himself is practically invisible. Artificial wings won't help, nor artificial eyes, nor escalators, nor pemmican. The whole damned universe has to be taken apart, brick by brick, and reconstructed. Every atom has to be rearranged. Perhaps just to sit quiet and take deep breathing exercises would be better than popping one another off with slugs of dynamite. Because the strange thing is that just doing nothing, just taking it easy, loafing, meditating, things tend to right themselves. As it is we are all terrified by the thought of losing our freedom. And yet it is freedom, *the idea of freedom,* which is what we dread most. Freedom means the strict inner precision of a Swiss watch—combined with absolute recklessness. Whence gayety and indifference, at present non-existent. Of course only lunatics dream of such a condition. And so we all remain sane and bite into one another like lice. And the lousier it gets the more progress we make. *Peace! It's Wonderful!*

I should say that ever since the dawn of history—all through the great civilizations, that is to say—we have been living like lice. Once every thousand years or so a man arises who is not a louse—and then there is even more hell to pay. When a MAN appears he seems to get a stranglehold on the world which it takes centuries to break. The sane people are cunning enough to find these men "psychopathic." These sane ones seem to be more interested in the technique of the stranglehold than in applying it. That's a curious phenomenon, one that puzzles me, to be frank. It's like learning the art of wrestling in order to have the pleasure of letting someone pin you to the mat.

What do I mean to infer? Just this—that art, the art of living, involves the act of creation. The work of art is nothing. It is only the tangible, visible evidence of a way of life, which, if it is not crazy is certainly *different* from the accepted way of life. The difference lies in the act, in the assertion of a will, and individuality. For the artist to attach himself to his work, or identify himself with it, is suicidal. An artist should be able not only to spit on his predecessor's art, or on all works of art, but on his own too. He should be able to be an artist all the time, and finally not be an artist at all, but a piece of art.

In addition to the deep breathing exercises perhaps mercurial inunctions ought also to be recommended—*for the time being.*

Two Speeches

BY E. E. CUMMINGS

SPEECH FROM A FORTHCOMING PLAY: I

SOLELY as an experiment: stop thinking. Forget, nobly and purely, everything. Undo, graciously relax, break yourselves out of a thousand pieces, and come together. Can you feel (proudly or minutely, humbly or enormously feel) what's coming into this world? Not anything unknown—someone, everyone, even an economizing politician with his life at the end of a leadpencil and his arse on the clouds, can predict that. Not something dreamed—no one, anyone, can guess that; even a physicing mathematician with his hand on the square root of minus one and his mind at the back of his own neck. O no; what's arriving is as unlike meaning, or anything I and somebody and you and everybody didn't dream and nobody knows, as a child's breathing is like geography; form never was where, between them air is; I say it. I say it; which does not tell you. Give a woman's eyes the right man and they'll tell you; rhythm invents when—what's coming is not to compare and include and discuss. What's coming is not to tremble at, to stand up and scream about, to gasp one's heart out for and vomit all over the new rug about. Don't worry; don't try to imagine, the stars know; and the trees even when bursting with buds, sometimes if bending under snow. Wave your voice, make people die, hide in the nonexistence of an

---

In 1931, E. E. Cummings briefly visited the Soviet Union, where he translated "The Red Front," a long revolutionary poem by his friend Louis Aragon. But those who thought that this was a sign of Cummings' sympathy for the Communist cause were quickly disillusioned by the publication in 1933 of *Eimi*, Cummings' "diary" of his trip to Russia, which was a scathing attack of the Soviet system (and contained an unfavorable analysis of Aragon's poem). Two years later Cummings again attacked Communism in a volume of poems entitled *No Thanks*. At the same time that he was voicing his opposition to the "kumrads," Cummings was also criticizing the capitalistic system, which in his view, seemed bent on destroying the individual. Among his most effective denunciations were the two speeches here reprinted. "Speech from a Forthcoming Play: I" first appeared in *The New American Caravan* in 1936, and "Speech from a Forthcoming Play: II" appeared in the March 1938 issue of *Partisan Review*.

atom, get the garbage concession tovarich—that makes no difference; only flowers understand. O little, O most very little civilization, pull your eyes in and kiss all your beautiful machines goodnight; yesterday was another day, which doesn't matter—roses are roses. I swear to you by my immortal head: if sunsets are magnificent (though leaves fall, smiles pass) there shall arrive a whisper—but after the whisper, wonder; and next, death; then laughter (O, all the world will laugh—you never smelled such a world): finally, beginning a bird beyond every bird, oceans young like mountains, universe absurdly beyond opening universe opening, freedom, function of impossibility, the philo-psycho-socialistico-losophers curl up; you die, I melt—only we may happen, suddenly who by disappearing perfectly into destiny are fatally alive. Be alive therefore; generously explode and be born, be like the sea, resemble mountains, dance; it shall not be forgiven you—open your soul as if it were a window and with a not visible cry bravely (through this immeasurable intensely how silent yesterday) fall upon the skilful thunderously and small awful unmeaning and the joy and upon the new inexcusably tomorrowing immensity of flowers.

SPEECH FROM A FORTHCOMING PLAY: II

by virtue of by virtue, I
by hereby virtue of the hereby powers vested in hereby me, do hereby
    declare and say that in the opinion of this court you are completely
    guilty of any crime or crimes of which you are absolutely innocent;
and in the name of this great hypocrisy,
which, as you hereby know, can do no wrong,
being a society based upon the equality of importunity, irrespective of
    andsoforth andsoforth or andsoforth, with liberty and justice for all,
I hereby affirm that to the best of my knowledge and belief you have
    been conclusively proved,
in flagranti delicto, with full benefit of testimony,
to have committed a foul degenerate heinous and inhuman offense
    against your innocent and unsuspecting fellowcitizens, not to mention
    their lives their fortunes and their sacred andsoforth,
namely and to wit,
that hereby you were black in color at the time of your hereby birth.
In consideration of which, I,
by hereby virtue of andsoforth,
do hereby extend to hereby you, on behalf of the government of the
    Benighted States of Hysterica, that glorious andsoforth alternative
    which is the illustrious andsoforth prerogative of every andsoforth

citizen; and which is in accordance with the dictates of justice and of mercy, as revealed to our forefathers in the Declaration of Interdependence; and which, in the ultraenlightened opinion of the super-civilized majority of the hyperhuman andsoforth race, constitutes a glowing andsoforth nucleus andsoforth of radiant andsoforth andsoforth:

e pluribus eunuch, or to make a long story brief,

I give you the choice of either being dead or of not being alive, nolens volens, whichever you prefer.

And in the sacred name of commonsense, I,

by hereby virtue and by hereby andsoforth and by hereby whathaveyou,

do hereby pronounce and decree that hereby you shall be punished for said crime or crimes according to that unwritten law which, according to all rightthinking people, governs the actions of all rightthinking people;

namely and to wit,

that you shall have your right eye suitably excised with a very dull penknife, and placed in your mouth which has previously been opened with a hatchet;

that you shall be soaked with gasoline,

hanged with a rope,

lighted with a match,

cut down while you are alive,

slit up the middle by good women,

stamped on by little children,

and made to kiss the flag by strong men.

Finally: it is the irrevocable verdict of this impeccable court, in due session assembled, that your organ of generation, having been suitably tinged and bedewed with the liquid and solid excrement of all law-abiding citizens in general and of all patriotic persons in particular, shall be forcefully proffered to your own mother, who shall immediately and joyfully eat thereof under penalty of death.

In Hoke signo:

God save the people From the people!

God save All of the people for Some of the people!

God save Some of the people All of the time, and all of the people will take care of themselves.

AMEN.

Night Without Sleep

BY ROBINSON JEFFERS

The world's as the world is; the nations rearm and prepare to change;
the age of tyrants returns;
The greatest civilization that has ever existed builds itself higher towers
on breaking foundations.
Recurrent episodes; they were determined when the ape's children first
ran in packs, chipped flint to an edge.

I lie and hear
dark rain beat the roof, and the blind wind.

In the morning perhaps
I shall find strength again
To value the immense beauty of this time of the world, the flowers
of decay their pitiful loveliness, the fever-dream
Tapestries that back the drama and are called the future. This ebb of
vitality feels the ignoble and cruel
Incidents, not the vast abstract order.
I lie and hear dark rain beat the roof,
and the night-blind wind.
In the Ventana country darkness and rain and the roar of waters
fill the deep mountain-throats.

In the late twenties and early thirties, Robinson Jeffers' reputation was at its
height. Despite the starkness of his poetry, and his bitter denunciations of
western civilization, Jeffers' popularity had reached the point where his manuscripts and first editions were commanding a higher price than those of any contemporary poet. But by the mid-thirties Jeffers' reputation began to decline; his
obsession with what he believed to be the emptiness of human existence, as well
as his prophecies of the destruction of mankind, had little appeal to those struggling through the depression. It has only been within recent years that his reputation has once again begun to rise. * * * Jeffers was no more interested in social
protest than he was in being "modern": "I did not want to become slight and
fantastic," he wrote in 1935, "abstract and unintelligible." Rather he voiced
his asocial philosophy in a verse form which was almost as uncommon to
the thirties as was his philosophy. "Night Without Sleep" appeared in the 1937
collection of poems *Such Counsels You Gave Me and Other Poems*, and was
one of the few poems from this volume to be reprinted in *The Selected Poems
of Robinson Jeffers*, which was published the following year.

The creekside shelf of sand where we lay last August under a slip of
    stars,
And firelight played on the leaning gorge-walls, is drowned and lost.
    The deer of the country huddle on a ridge
In a close herd under madrone-trees; they tremble when a rockslide
    goes down, they open great darkness-
Drinking eyes and press closer.

                          Cataracts of rock
Rain down the mountain from cliff to cliff and torment the stream-bed.
    The stream deals with them. The laurels are wounded,
Redwoods go down with their earth and lie thwart the gorge. I hear
    the torrent boulders battering each other,
I feel the flesh of the mountain move on its bones in the wet darkness.

                                Is this more beautiful
Than man's disasters? These wounds will heal in their time; so will
    humanity's. This is more beautiful . . . at night . . .

"Off Cape Split, Maine" by John Marin, 1938.

The Dawn of Another Day

BY WILLIAM CARLOS WILLIAMS

THERE were a coupla guys prowling around here this morning but when they seen me they beat it.

Thanks.

Any luck?

No. Not with these hands.

What are you gonna do, hang around this tub all winter? And say, where the hell do you keep the key to that booze, anyway? I bet it's around your neck. Scotch.

You said it, with a tank like you on board. Did Pauline come with the laundry?

Yeah, she brought it.

Did she take the dirty stuff?

No. She wouldn't come aboard when she found out you weren't here. Said she'd come back later.

The men looked at each other and the owner of the boat smiled broadly. The other, in an old slouch hat and a seared, sour face under it, didn't change his expression.

Why don't you stick to booze and leave the girls alone?

Any objections if I don't?

These coons are loaded up with gonorrhoea and everything else,

---

In *How To Write A Poem,* William Carlos Williams spoke of his short stories which were collected in 1932 and 1938 as stories about the people he knew: "I was impressed by the picture of the times, depression years, the plight of the poor . . . I wrote it down as I saw it . . . without technical tricks." *Life Along the Passaic,* the second volume of short stories, contained "The Dawn of Another Day," which originally appeared in *Blast: Proletarian Short Stories* (Vol. 1 Number 3). In reviewing the stories for *Partisan Review,* Waldo Tell spoke of "The Dawn of Another Day" as a "significant story about a penniless young man," but noted that, as proletarian literature, it was a failure: "The story is pictorially effective, and makes use of conversation in a manner which very few American writers, least of all revolutionary writers, have mastered. But the disparity between the satisfying prose and the amorphous, unclear ideological approach makes this story a failure, if we are to take *Blast's* subtitle, 'proletarian short stories' seriously."

you damn fool. Go on home and get to bed or the misses'll think you fell in the river or something.

To hell with her. Are you holding out on me with that liquor? What you doing, saving it to celebrate the end of Prohibition? Get it out.

The main motor highway ran along the opposite side of the river toward the city, three miles farther down. As it had already begun to grow dark you could see the first lights of the cars going back and forth intermittently beyond the two or three broken down houses on that shore, old houses occupied by negroes, in whose windows also dim lights appeared.

The younger man had gone forward into the store room of his craft where you could hear him unlock a door. After a moment he came back into the small saloon and put an unopened bottle of bourbon whisky on the table. His companion had already got out glasses and a cork screw.

Will you take it straight or shall I pour it down your neck, you old sweetheart?

You act as if you was lending your wife to your best friend. How much more you got of it in there?

None of your damned business.

Is that so? Well, suppose I don't accept your offer and don't accept—

Go on, your tongue's sticking to the roof of your mouth already so you can't talk straight. Do you want it or shall I chuck it into the river?

No! for Christ's sake, Ed, don't do a thing like that, said the older man turning pale and getting up suddenly.

The other let out a roar of laughter so that his friend sank down again sourly and rested his arms on the little table. You'd leave me here by myself to die of cold and starvation gladly if I ever did run out of it, said Ed pretending seriousness.

Pour it out before you drop it. The men each had three fingers of it. The older man reached for the bottle at once and wanted to fill his friend's glass again.

No thanks, not tonight.

What's the matter? Thinking of your Mama and Papa in Miami? Maybe.

Does that mean I gotta quit too?

The other didn't answer so Ed took the bottle and filled up once more.

Watch it, kid.

Listen here, Ed. What the hell's the matter with you? Sore at somebody or something? Why don't you take this lousy yacht of yours down to the yard and let them drag it out?

I'm broke, you nut. Broke. Can you understand that. No money, Get it? I'm tied up here for the winter, free. Get it? Free. So drink up and get the hell home out of here so you can come back some time when I need you.

If *you're* broke, so's the King of England. Sell the rotten tub . . .

Did you ever try to sell a yacht second hand these days? The trouble with you, Fred, is you've never seen fifty dollars all at once in your life so you still think the stork brings it.

Oh yeah? Well, boy, I made more money and lost it before you was born than you'll ever see.

Cheating at cards?

Maybe it was, maybe it wasn't. What's that to you? I ain't got it now. If I had I wouldn't be taking guff from a spoiled baby like you pouting and sulking because Papa won't buy him another nice new seat on the Exchange so he can skin hell out of another bunch of suckers. Listen baby, close this dump up and go south to your family.

You don't get it, Fred. Listen. Get all your brains together. Now, try hard and let it sink through that thick skull of yours: I'm broke. Broke. No money. You know, money, What you use to buy things with. And my old man's going to commit suicide tomorrow. The whole family's broke. Stoney. Flat. The servants are keeping them, bringing in food.

Maybe you're right, kid. Maybe you're right. Doing your laundry free, eh! Just 'cause they like you. Some guy. A liar like you never should go wanting in this little world.

O.K., boy. Have it your way.

I bet she'll be back inside an hour. Mind if I stay?

Stay all night if you like, kid. I'm going to get supper.

The place was heated by an ordinary coal range which had been rigged up with an iron pipe through the temporary woodwork of old lumber enclosing the original cabin. Ed took the pan from inside the oven door, lifted the stove lid, put the pan on and dropped a lump of butter into it. The butter began at once to melt and run down to the edge of the pan. Ed poked it thoughtfully with a fork and watched it melt.

Did you ever read Das Kapital, Ed? asked the man who was still drinking at the table.

What! Say that again.

You heard me the first time. Did you ever read it? You think I'm a drunken bum, don't you. Just because of the face I got on me—

You're drunk.

Smart guy. You know everything, don't you? Well, if you should ever grow up and be old enough to let your own pants down without askin' your mother to do it for you you'll find out I ain't drunk. And that you ain't half as smart as you think you are.

You got me wrong, Fred. I don't think I'm smart. But I'm smart enough to pull out of this hole on my own. You wait and see if I don't.

Don't need nobody, huh? Just a chance to use your brains. Big business, huh? Self reliant, rugged Americanism . . .

And I'm lucky too. Lucky to have a place I can bunk in without rent. And lucky I got you to keep me from drinking myself to death on expensive booze. It didn't take you long, Senator, to smell it out after I tied up here. How do you want your eggs?

Turn 'em over. You know I was a great reader at one time.

How long were you up for?

—and I'll tell you one thing: I'm a Communist. I tell you I'm a Communist and I'm gonna take that black baby of yours right out from under your runny nose. You're too God damned thick to know your—

Come on, come on. Pick the threads off your vest, Rosenblatt. Pull up the table and tell us how to run the world to hell and gone into the slime—

Now listen to me, young fellah, said the one called Fred getting upon his dignity and eyeing his friend with a glassy look. My father was an Irishman and my mother was German and I'm telling you they're the two finest races on earth. But I'm a Democrat— Now wait a minute. Wait a minute. You'll not be taking me for a fool. I been to college too. Maybe you wouldn't think it but it's true. I played on the ball team. I'm a Democrat and I'm a Communist. You didn't know I could talk and read German. I was over there when I was twenty and read that book. And I'm telling you everything that God damned Kike said in it is coming true. I took my knocks and I've lived rough but I never been a four flusher like the kind of people you come from.

Do you mean that?

Christ no, I don't mean it. What would I do without you, Ed? But by Christ I do mean it! in one way.

Eat your eggs and lay off that booze; you'll be in a hell of a fine condition to take Pauline when she gets here, you old cripple.

Will you let me try it?

What do you want me to do, jump overboard? Be yourself. Why she could tie you into knots, you poor simp. Did you ever look at her arms?

Did you ever look at her legs, my boy, you know—from behind? And what a behind! while we're speaking of it, Eddie, I don't understand this generation. You're all shot with the tea and ginger ale sloshing around in your guts.

So you're a Communist.

I believe in the Revolution. It's here. It's got to be here. I read that whole God damned book three times, in German. Would you believe that?

No.

I read that lousy book till I damned near knew it by heart. And the old bugger is right. To hell with the Capitalists that enslave the resources of the nation. You know yourself 5% of the people of the United States own 95% of the money. And 95% of the people own only 5% of the money. Now that's not right. We got to have a revolution and take it away from them.

You don't need any fancy theory of a revolution by the proletariat to do that. Be yourself, Fred. We're not back in the last century. Russia was. More power to her then. I'm for Russia. We'd be rotten sports if we didn't help their game. Let 'em work it out. But they're nothing but a lot of monkeys, a lot of thick heads. That sort of thing can never happen in America. We're not that thick. You don't need anything but brains. Looka here. You want to break up the game of the Capitalists? You want to know how to do it?

Sure, Bright Eyes, tell us.

Just stop inheritances. Redistribute everything a man has accumulated at the end of his life.

Yeah? And how you gonna do it? You'll have to start by castrating every guy that passes his bar examination seven days after they admit him. If you think that's bright it's no wonder you're living on a discarded yacht for the winter—if you can stand it. Better go back to your wife and kids and graft on your wealthy Ma-in-law. She still has it. Am I right?

Yes, you're right.

And you're broke. Ain't you?

You said it. But I'm not going to stay broke. Take that from me.

Oh you're not aren't you. The resources of the country are limitless! You're going to rise from your ashes like the Phoenix on the revenue stamps and make another fortune by skinning the life out of suckers like me.

No. But if you're an American and keep your nerve you don't need Capitalism—I don't care what you call it. Communism. Your damned Revolution—

Go on. Go on. Did you ever read the book?

I thought you were drunk?

That's what you thought. Did you ever read the book? Answer me that. Well, if you haven't, get it and read it. And don't read just Chapter 14 like the rest of the soap-box orators shootin' their mouths off nowadays. Read the whole thing. And you won't talk like such a damned fool. Why that's a masterpiece of calculation. How in hell are you gonna take inheritances away? Christ man, they'll have the army and the navy and every God damned cop in the country chasin' you for a public enemy and shooting you so full of holes that— Come here with that bottle. What is this, a cheap joint? Put up your glass if you don't want me to finish it alone. Come on now. Be a man.

O.K. Pour me another—to keep you from having it run over into your lungs and drowning you to death.

I can take it. Yes sir, began Fred again—

Aw shut up. I'm going up on deck for a smoke. It's too stinking hot in here, he continued, banking the stove, with all you lousy Communists sweating and farting around the place. Here, have a cigar. I still got a few left. And don't get the wrong end in your mouth. Here, pull! he said holding a match. Then taking the cigar out of his friend's mouth again, he added, You damn fool, do I even have to bite the end of it off for you too.

Ed opened the cabin door letting in a cool blast of air from the outside and went on deck. It was a cloudy November night. The man pulled his coat tightly around him and it being high tide hopped over the boat-side two feet down to the edge of the old wharf where the yacht was made fast.

He turned and looked down between the boat and the old planks of the wharf wondering how she'd take it if they had much ice that winter.

It being coolish he walked toward the road puffing at his cigar and thinking. He stopped, thinking he saw someone turn back from the entrance to the littered area between the river bank and the roadway.

Is that you, Pauline?

Who's that? came back the woman's voice.

It's all right, called back the man knowing she'd recognize his voice. You can come ahead.

He watched her coming stepping carefully along the indistinct path toward the water. She was no girl but a rather short well built woman of about thirty.

Gee, I'm glad to see you. I pretty near lost my nerve. Is that guy still here?

Yes, he's inside. Thanks, Pauline, for bringing my laundry this afternoon. I forgot to tell you I'd be away.

The only reason I come tonight is I'm washing tomorrow early and say why do you have a guy like that hanging around you here. You ain't used to that.

He's a great convenience to me. You know, Pauline, it's damned nice of you to take this interest in me.

Say, you need some new shirts. I darned your socks but I can't fix those cuffs any more, you'll have to do something about it. Go on, get that dirty wash, I got to get home to my husband.

Wish you could have picked it up this afternoon. You would have saved yourself a trip.

Not with him there.

He's not such a bad egg. Wait a minute, I'll get the stuff.

The last streak of orange light had faded out of the west beyond the bare trees as the man and woman stood talking at the edge of the bulwark of the moored yacht. Ed stepped up onto the boat again and opening the cabin door went inside. He left the door open as he did so, deliberately. The young colored woman went curiously up to the wharf edge and tried to peer inside. In the intense stillness of this isolated spot, above the faint lapping of the water somewhere down under her feet, she could hear the slow, heavy breathing of a man drunk and asleep. As Ed came up again with the small parcel of wash tied about with the arms of the shirt which acted as the container, she was laughing softly.

Let me look down in there.

Sure. Go ahead.

Ain't that a pretty sight! The big souse. Why don't he go home and take care of his family, at his age. I don't see how you let a man like that hang around you. All he wants is the whisky you got stowed away down there somewhere. The face on him's enough. I know him, don't worry. And he's ugly. And I mean ugly. Ugh! And she pulled back shivering.

You got him wrong, Pauline. You'd be surprised. He's an educated man.

He don't look it.

No, he doesn't look it. That's right.

How are you making out? It's getting pretty cold these nights. Do you think you're going to be able to stick it?

Hope so.

What's the idea of you hanging around here for anyway? There must be some places you can go. It just don't seem good sense to me. I don't know what you're going to do when it gets real winter.

To tell you the truth, Pauline, neither do I. Forget it. I'm pretty low tonight, just don't like to talk about it.

I wish there was some way I could take care of you.

You wouldn't be any use to me, Pauline, with the mugs there are hanging around here.

But you ain't used to this. You're used to having women round you, looking after you. You're going to get sick.

Well thanks, Pauline, for coming for the wash at this late hour and everything else. I'll walk out to the road with you.

It's nice out tonight, isn't it, said the woman walking at his side. When they got to the roadway they stood a moment awkwardly, she swinging the laundry back and forth like a child and he just standing there.

Well, I gotta go, she said finally. Take care of yourself.

Wait a minute.

What you want.

Just hate to see you go somehow. Stick around a little while and talk to me.

What are we going to talk about?

I'm pretty low tonight, Pauline. Pretty low. I just feel like starting out straight from here and running all night, straight ahead and never coming back.

You can't do that. You got too many good things back there.

I feel pretty cowardly tonight. I'd like a good comfortable chair, a warm room, light, a good book to read—

I don't blame you.

And a nice warm, comfortable bed.

The woman giggled to herself. Well, I gotta get going, she said after a moment.

Stick around a while longer. You don't have to go yet.

Say listen boy. When you begin to talk about nice, comfortable warm beds, you give me the shivers. And it don't come from no cold weather neither. I gotta go.

What do you mean?

You know what I mean. I gotta get going.

Wait a minute. Wait a minute. You're miles ahead of me. Listen, Pauline . . .

No sir. I'm not listening to nobody. Not even you. I gotta go.

Come on back on board with me.

With that man sleeping down there? Not me.

He won't wake up. Why he's got almost a quart of whisky into him. He won't wake up till noon tomorrow. You couldn't wake him with a gun. Come on.

Wait a minute, boy. You're going awful fast.

O.K., said the man letting go of her, maybe you're right, maybe

I am getting a little ahead of myself. I'm sorry Pauline. No disrespect intended.

I suppose you got the idea I'm all burned up to go back there with you, said the woman watching him.

Never gave it a thought, he answered her. Just needing company. Real company. And hating to be alone tonight.

Neither spoke for several moments. You don't want me, she said finally.

Plenty, was all he answered her this time.

She grinned. That sounds good to me.

Good girl. Come on. And he turned abruptly toward the boat.

Hey, what about that guy?

We'll get by him. They started again toward the boat walking far apart and he a little ahead of her. No further word was spoken till they got to the wharf edge.

Wait here a minute, he cautioned her.

No, I want to see too.

Ed stepped up to the boat's deck and gave his hand to Pauline who took a big step up after him. She had a small powerful hand and gave a little puff and smothered grunt as she came up to the deck. He opened the cabin door and looked in while she behind him put one hand on his shoulder and stared down curiously also.

Fred was sprawled out on the cushion seat along the side wall opposite. Ed went in and shook him, taking a chance. Hey, wake up you bum!

Not a stir.

So he disappeared forward and after a moment came back with a blanket and a pillow. Straightening his friend out he shoved the pillow under his head, covered him with the blanket and then, turning, came over and reached up his hand to the woman to help her down the two steps into the boat's small saloon.

Ed led her around the center table to the door opening forward to the staterooms. Pauline was biting her lower lip and stepping carefully. He closed the door behind them then led her another step or two in the dark to another door through which they passed and which he closed also. There was no light except that from the night outside coming in at the porthole which opened off shore. Across the river were the same glares of passing autos and the duller lights in the windows of the old houses backed down toward the water. It was chilly and damp in the room.

Not much room in here, is there? whispered the woman.

More than we'll need. Listen, Pauline, before we go any further with this, are you all right? You know what I mean.

You got nothing to worry about.

She stripped and Ed put a blanket around her. She was a tight, muscular woman with fine arms and the velvety skin of her race. Hurry up, hurry up, she said, don't keep me waiting here in this cold place.

Why didn't you ever go on the stage with such a body as you have woman. You'd have made a hit.

Not for me. Not that kind of life. I don't want to end up in a ditch with a knife sticking in my back. They never leave you alone. Come on boy. Love me! She coaxed, urging him to hurry.

There wasn't much room but they made themselves comfortable finally as best they could. Then, after a while, Ed fell into a gentle sleep. When he wakened Pauline was holding him in her arms. He did not move.

Do you know, Pauline, he began quietly, it takes emotion, and deep emotion, to change the thoughts and habits of a lifetime. And danger—the way I've been feeling recently.

Hey, shut up! Not so loud.

He won't hear us. You've done something to me tonight—right out of nothing. Something I never could have believed possible. You're marvelous.

You're not so bad yourself, boy.

Do you know where I feel it most? Ed went on slowly. In the head. She chuckled and moved against him. Something just went that way, deep down inside me: pow!

Say what kind of crazy talk is this?

Class consciousness. Something I've been fooling around with for a long time not knowing what it was all about.

Come on, love me.

Now listen, lay off a minute. I got to tell this to somebody and you've got to listen to me.

Say, listen yourself, I got to be getting home to my old man or he'll kill me. Come on.

When they had dressed and were on their way out Pauline was all curiosity to look once more at Fred lying in drunken sleep where his friend had stretched him. I don't see how you can stand him, said the woman. Then, turning, she caught sight of a small clock set into the saloon wall. Is that right? she turned to Ed. Eleven o'clock?

Yes, I try to keep it fairly accurate.

You mean that short little while we were back there is almost two hours! Oh boy!

Is it all right?

Oh he won't know where I been. Good night! I'm going. What a bum! she turned again to the man still breathing heavily asleep on the wall seat.

I'll walk down to the bridge with you, Ed said to her when they were again on the wharf in the darkness.

Will you?

Certainly.

The sky had become entirely clear and you could see the Pleiades over in the east. They walked out to the road in silence and turned left on the deserted, unlit roadway to the bridge, its scattered red lights ahead of them. Why don't you kick that dirty bum out, she asked Ed finally.

Can't do it, Pauline.

He isn't in your class. They kept on walking side by side in the darkness toward the bridge.

Pauline, there are some things you don't know a thing about. That's the funny part of it . . .

All I know is, that guy makes me sick. He don't belong to you. I can't stand him. How old is he, anyhow? He ought to know better.

Forget it, woman. That man means a lot to me. And he never meant more to me than right now. For a little while before I saw you tonight I was about ready to be an awful backslider. But you did something to me tonight I'll never forget, Sister. I never quite got what it was all about till what you did for me tonight.

Did you like it?

Maybe you don't get me, Pauline. I liked it fine. I can't tell you how much I did like it. But . . .

Well, what?

You got me all turned over inside. Something kind of snapped inside my head. Come here a minute. I want to kiss you.

Say, are you crazy for sure? Somebody's likely to see you—out here near these lights.

Come here. And he kissed her lovingly on the mouth.

Are you gonna quit and run like you said you were this evening?

Wait and see.

But I can't come back there and see you if that guy's hanging around there all day and night. Can't you drive him out?

Listen, sister. I'm not getting rid of that guy. That's final. So long.

O.K., brother. She went toward the bridge while he turned back through the starry night toward the boat.

Aspirin is a Member of the N.R.A.

BY WILLIAM SAROYAN

REMEMBER above all things the blood, remember that man is flesh, that flesh suffers pain, and that the mind being caught in flesh suffers with it. Remember that the spirit is a form of the flesh, and the soul its shadow. Above all things humor and intelligence, and truth as the only beginning: not what is said or done, not obviousness: the truth of silences, the intelligence of nothing said, nothing done. The piety Faces. Memory, our memory of the earth, this one and the other, the one which is now this and the one that was once another, what we saw, and the sun. It is our life and we have no other. Remember God, the multitudinous God.

Remember laughter.

There were nights, in New York, when my hair would freeze on my head, and I would awaken from sleeplessness and remember. I would remember stalking through print, the quiet oratory of some forgotten name, a quiet man who put something down on paper: *yea* and *yea* and *yea*. Something wordless but precise, my hair frozen, and the small attic room in the heart of Manhattan, across the street from the Paramount Building, and myself in the room, in the darkness, alone, waiting for morning. I used to leave my bed sometimes and smoke a cigarette in the darkness. The light I disliked, so I used to sit in the darkness, remembering.

"Aspirin Is a Member of the NRA" was originally published in the *American Mercury* in May, 1934; and the same year, it was reprinted in Saroyan's most famous collection of stories, *The Daring Young Man on the Flying Trapeze* (whose title story, first published in 1932, made Saroyan one of the best known writers in America). During the thirties, Saroyan published eleven other volumes, including *The Time of Your Life,* for which he was awarded the Pulitzer Prize in 1940 and which he refused because, as he wrote to the Pulitzer committee: "I do not believe in prizes or awards in the realm of art, and have always been particularly opposed to material or official patronage of the arts by government, organization, or individual, a naive and innocent style of behavior which, nevertheless, I believe, vitiates and embarrasses art at its source."

One or two faces I saw coming across the Continent: the boy with a bad dose, riding in the bus, going home to his mother, taking a bad dose with him from a South American resort, talking about the girl, just a young kid and very beautiful, and God, what a pain, every moment and nothing to do about it. He was eighteen or nineteen, and he had gone down to South America to sleep with a girl, and now he had got it, where it hurt most, and he was drinking whisky and swallowing aspirin, to keep him going, to deaden the pain. York, Pennsylvania, a good town, and his people living there. Everything, he said, everything will be all right the minute I get home. And the sick girl, going back to Chicago, talking in her sleep. The language of fear, the articulation of death, no grammar, exclamations, one after another, the midnight grief, children emerging from the grown girl, talking.

And the faces of people in the streets, in the large cities and in the small towns, the sameness.

I used to get up in the middle of the night and remember. It was no use trying to sleep, because I was in a place that did not know me, and whenever I tried to sleep the room would declare its strangeness and I would sit up in bed and look into the darkness.

Sometimes the room would hear me laughing softly. I could never cry, because I was doing what I wanted to do, so I couldn't help laughing once in a while, and I would always feel the room listening. Strange fellow, this fellow, I would hear the room say; in this agony, he gets up, with his hair frozen, in the middle of the night, and he laughs.

There was enough pain everywhere, in everyone who lived. If you tried to live a godly life, it didn't make any difference, and in the end you came up with a dull pain in your body and a soul burning with a low fire, eating its substance slowly. I used to think about the pain and in the end all I could do was laugh. If there had been a war, it would have been much easier, more reasonable. The pain would have been explicable. We are fighting for high ideals, we are protecting our homes, we are protecting civilization, and all that. A tangible enemy, a reasonable opposition, and swift pain, so that you couldn't have time enough to think about it much: either it got you all the way, carrying you over into death and calm, or it didn't get you. Also, something tangible to hate, a precise enemy. But without a war it was different. You might try hating God, but in the end you couldn't do it. In the end you laughed softly or you prayed, using pious and blasphemous language.

I used to sit in the dark room, waiting for morning and the fellowship of passengers of the subway. The room had great strength. It belonged. It was part of the place. Fellows like me could come and go, they could die and be born again, but the room was steady and static, always there. I used to feel its indifference toward me, but I could never feel unfriendly toward it. It was part of the scheme, a small attic room in the heart of Manhattan, without an outside window, four dollars a week: me or the next fellow, any of us, it didn't matter. But whenever I laughed, the room would be puzzled, a bit annoyed. It would wonder what there was for me to laugh about, my hair frozen, and my spirit unable to rest.

Sometimes, during the day, shaving, I used to look into the small mirror and see the room in my face, trying to understand me. I would be laughing, looking at the room in the mirror, and it would be annoyed, wondering how I could laugh, what I saw in my life that was amusing.

It was the secrecy that amused me, the fact of my being one of the six million people in the city, living there, waiting to die. I could die in this room, I used to say to myself, and no one would ever understand what had happened, no one would ever say, Do you know that boy from California, the fellow who is studying the subway? Well, he died in a little room on Forty-fourth Street the other night, alone. They found him in the little room, dead. No one would be able to say anything about me if I died, no one knew I was from California and that I was studying the subway, making notes about the people riding in the subway. My presence in Manhattan was not known, so if I came to vanish, my vanishing would not be known. It was a secret, and it amused me. I used to get up in the middle of the night and laugh about it quietly, disturbing the room.

I used to make the room very angry, laughing, and one night it said to me, You are in a hurry but I am not: I shall witness your disintegration, but when you are destroyed I shall be standing here quietly. You will see.

It made me laugh. I knew it was the truth, but it was amusing to me. I couldn't help laughing at the room wanting to see me go down.

But there was an armistice: what happened was this: I moved away. I rented another room. It was a war without a victor. I packed my things and moved to the Mills Hotel.

But it isn't so easy to escape a war. A war has a way of following a man around, and my room in the Mills Hotel was even more malicious than the other. It was smaller and therefore its eloquence was considerably louder. Its walls used to fall in upon me, with the whiteness of madness, but I went on laughing. In the middle of the night I used to hear my neighbors, old and young men. I used to hear them speaking out against life from their sleep. I used to hear much weeping. That year many men were weeping from their sleep. I used to laugh about this. It was such a startling thing that I used to laugh. The worst that can happen to any of us, I used to laugh, is death. It is a small thing. Why are you men weeping?

It was because of remembrance, I suppose. Death is always in a man, but sometimes life is in him so strongly that it makes a sad remembrance and comes out in the form of weeping through sleep.

And it was because of the pain. Everybody was in pain. I was studying the subway and I could see the pain in the faces of everybody. I looked everywhere for one face that was not the mask of a pained life, but I did not find such a face. It was this that made my study of the subway so fascinating. After months of study I reached a decision about all of us in Manhattan. It was this: the subway is death, all of us are riding to death. No catastrophe, no horrible accident: only slow death, emerging from life. It was such a terrific fact that I had to laugh about it.

I lived in many rooms in many sections of the city, East Side, West Side, downtown, uptown, Harlem, the Bronx, Brooklyn, all over the place. It was the same everywhere, my hair frozen at night, alien walls around me, and the smile of death in my eyes.

But I didn't mind. It was what I had wanted to do. I was a clerk in one of thousands of offices of a great national enterprise, doing my part to make America the most prosperous nation on earth, more millionaires per square inch than all the other nations put together, etc. I was paying cash for my sleeplessness, for the privilege of riding in the subway. I was eating in the Automats, renting vacant rooms all over the place, buying clothes, newspapers, aspirin.

I do not intend to leave aspirin out of this document. It is too important to leave out. It is the hero of this story, all of us six million people in New York, swallowing it, day after day. All of us in pain, needing it. Aspirin is an evasion. But so is life. The way we live it. You take aspirin in order to keep going. It deadens pain. It helps you to sleep. It keeps you aboard the subway. It is a substitute for the sun, for strong blood. It stifles remembrance, silences weeping.

It does not harm the heart. That is what the manufacturers say. They say it is absolutely harmless. Maybe it is. Death does not harm the heart either. Death is just as harmless as aspirin. I expect casket manufacturers to make this announcement in the near future. I expect to see a full page advertisement in the *Saturday Evening Post,* making a slogan on behalf of death. *Do not be deceived . . . die and see your*

*dreams come true . . . death does not harm the heart . . . it is ab-
solutely harmless . . . doctors everywhere recommend it . . .* and so
on.

You hear a lot of sad talk about all the young men who died in the
Great War. Well, what about this war? Is it less real because it destroys
with less violence, with a ghastlier shock, with a more sustained pain?

The coming of snow in Manhattan is lovely. All the ugliness is soft-
ened by the pious whiteness. But with the snow comes the deadly cold.
With the snow death comes a little closer to everyone. If you are pretty
rich, it doesn't bother you much: you don't have to get up in the morning in a cold room and rush out to an Automat for a cup of coffee and
then dive into the subway. If you are rich, the snow is only beautiful
to you. You get up when you please, and there is nothing to do but
sit in warm rooms and talk with other rich people. But if you aren't
rich, if you are working to make America a nation of prosperous millionaires, then the snow is both beautiful and ghastly. And when the
cold of the snow gets into your bones you are apt to forget that it is
beautiful; you are apt to notice only that it is ghastly.

A few evenings ago I was listening to the radio, out here in San
Francisco. Aspirin days are over for me. I depend on the sun these
days. I was listening to a very good program, sponsored by one of
America's most prosperous manufacturers of aspirin. You know the
name. I do not intend to advertise the company. It does enough advertising of its own. The radio announcer said the cold and sore throat
season had come, and of course it had. I could see snow falling over
Manhattan, increasing the sales of aspirin all over the city. Then the
announcer said, Aspirin is a member of the N.R.A.

It made me laugh to hear that. But it is the truth. Aspirin *is* a member of the N.R.A. It *is* helping everyone to evade fundamentals, it *is*
helping to keep people going to work. Aspirin *is* helping to bring back
prosperity. It *is* doing its part. It *is* sending millions of half-dead people to their jobs. It *is* doing a great deal to keep the spirit of this nation
from disintegrating. It *is* deadening pain everywhere. It *isn't* preventing anything, but it is deadening pain.

What about the N.R.A.? Well, I leave that to you. Maybe the N.R.A
is a member of aspirin. Anyhow, together they make a pretty slick
team. They are deadening a lot of pain, but they aren't preventing
any pain. Everything is the same everywhere.

All I know is this: that if you keep on taking aspirin long enough
it will cease to deaden pain.

And that is when the fun begins. That is when you begin to notice that snow isn't beautiful at all. That is when your hair begins to freeze and you begin to get up in the middle of the night, laughing quietly, waiting for the worst, remembering all the pain and not wanting to evade it any longer, not wanting any longer to be half-dead, wanting full death or full life. That is when you begin to be mad about the way things are going in this country, the way things are with life, with man. That is when, weak as you are, something old and savage and defiant in you comes up bitterly out of your illness and starts to smash things, making a path for you to the sun, destroying cities, wrecking subways, pushing you into the sun, getting you away from evasions, dragging you by your neck to life.

It made me laugh, the way I used to laugh in New York, when I heard that radio announcer say that aspirin was a member of the N.R.A., and it made me remember. It made me want to say what I knew about aspirin.

"In Fourteenth Street" by Reginald Marsh, 1934.

Miss Lonelyhearts and the Dead Pan

BY NATHANAEL WEST

ONLY my leader was finished: "Life *is* worthwhile, for it is full of dreams and peace, gentleness and ecstasy, and faith that burns like a clear white flame on a grim dark altar." Although the dead line was but a few minutes away, I sat watching the rain turn the dusty tar roofs below me into shiny patent leather. I had found it impossible to continue. You can't go on finding the same joke funny thirty times a day for months on end. And on most days I received more than thirty letters, all of them alike, as though stamped from the dough of suffering with a heart-shaped cookie knife.

I turned from the window to re-read Broad-shoulders' letter.

Dear Miss Lonelyhearts—

Being an admirer of your column because you give such good advice to people in trouble as that is what I am in also I would appreciate very much if you can advise me what to do after I tell you my troubles.

During the war I was told if I wanted to do my bit I should marry the man I was engaged to as he was going away to help Uncle Sam

Ever since his tragic death on December 22, 1940, Nathanael West's reputation has grown steadily. Not only has he become the subject of several book-length studies and Ph.D. dissertations, but at least two of his novels—*Miss Lonelyhearts* and *The Day of the Locusts*—are regarded as minor classics. Although all of West's work was published in the thirties, it took a new generation to accept his harsh and surrealistic view of contemporary life. * * * "Miss Lonelyhearts and the Dead Pan" appeared in *Contact* in 1932; the following year the draft, heavily revised, became part of the completed novel.

and to make a long story short I was married to him. After the war was over he still had to remain in the army for one more year as he signed an agreement and I went to busines as while doing this patriotic stunt he had only $18 dollars to his name. I worked for three years steady and then had to stay home because I became a mother and in the meantime of those years my husband would get a job and then he would tire of it or wanted to roam. It was all right before the baby came because when I was working bills were paid but when I stopped everything went sliding backward. Then two years went by and a baby boy was added to our union. My girl will be eight and my boy six years of age.

I made up my mind after I had the second child that in spite of my health as I was hit by an auto while carrying the first I would get some work to do but debts collected so rapidly it almost took a derik to lift them let alone a sick woman. I went to work evenings when my husband would be home so as somebody could watch the baby and I did this until the baby was three years old when I suggested taking in a man who had been boarding with his sister as she moved to Rochester and he had to look for a new place. Well my husband agreed as he figured the $15 per he paid us would make it easier for him as this man was a widower with two children and as my husband knew him for twelve years being real pals going out together etc. After the boarder was with us for about a year my husband didn't come home one night and then two nights etc. I listed him in the missing persons and after two and a half months I was told to go to Grove St. which I did and he was arrested on the charge of desertion because he refused to support me and my kids. When he served three months of the six the judge gave him he begged me to give him another chance which like a fool I did and when he got home he beat me up so I had to spend over $30 in the dentist afterwards.

He got a pension from the army and naturaly I was the one to take it to the store and cash it as he was so lazy I always had to sign his name and of course put per my name and through wanting to pay the landlord because he wanted to put us out I signed his check as usual but forgot to put per my name and for this to get even with me because he did three months time he sent to Washington for the copy of the check so I could be arrested for forgery but as the butcher knew about me signing the checks etc nothing was done to me.

He threatened my life many times saying no one solved the Mrs. Mills murder and the same will happen to you and many times when making beds I would find under his pillow a hammer, scissors, knife, stone lifter etc and when I asked him what the idea was he would make believe he knew nothing about it or say the children put them there and then a few months went by and I was going to my work as usual as the boarder had to stay home that day due to the fact that the material for his boss did not arrive which prevented him from going to work as he is a piece worker. I always made a habit of setting the breakfast table and preparing the food the night before so I could stay in bed until seven as at that time my son was in the Kings County hospital with a disease which my husband gave me that he got while fighting for Uncle Sam and I had to be at the clinic for the needle to. So while I was in bed unbeknown to me my husband sent the boarder out for a paper and when he came back my husband was gone. So later when I came from my room I was told that my husband had gone out. I fixed the childs breakfast and ate my own then went to the washtub to do the weeks wash and while the boarder was reading the paper at twelve o'clock noon my mother came over to mind the baby for the afternoon as I had a chance to go out and make a little money doing house work. Things were a little out of order beds not dressed and articles out of place and a little sweeping had to be done as I was washing all morning and I did not have a chance to do it so I thought I'd do it then while my mother was in the house with her to help me so that I could finish quickly. Hurrying at break neck speed to get finished I swept through the rooms to make sure everything was spick and span so when my husband came home he couldn't have anything to say. We had three beds and I was on the last which was a double bed when stooping to put the broom under the bed to get at the lint and the dust when lo and behold I saw a face like the mask of a devil with only the whites of the eyes showing and hands clenched to choke anyone and then I saw it move and I was so frighted that almost till night time I was histerical and I was paralized from my waist down. I thought I would never be able to walk again. A doctor was called for me by my mother and he said the man ought to be put away to do a thing like that. It was my husband lieing under the bed from seven in the morning until almost half past one o'clock lieing in his own dirt instead of going to the bath room when he had to he dirtied himself waiting to frighten me.

So as I could not trust him I would not sleep with him and as I told the boarder to find a new place because I thought maybe he was jealous of something I slept in the boarders bed in an other room. Some nights I would wake up and find him standing by my bed laughing like a crazy man or walking around stripped etc.

I bought a new sowing machine as I do some sowing for other people to make both ends meet and one night while I was out delivering my work I got back to find the house cleaned out and he had pawned my sowing machine and also all the other pawnables in the house. Ever since he frightened me I have been so nervous during the night when I get up for the children he would be standing behind a curtain and either jump out at me or put his hand on me before I could light the light. Well as I had to see that I could not make him work steady and that I had to be mother and housekeeper and wage earner etc and I could not let my nerves get the best of me as I lost a good job once on account of having bad nerves I simply moved away from him and anyway there was nothing much left in the house. But he pleaded with me for another chance so I thought seeing as he is the father of my children I will and then he did more crazy things to numerous to mention and I left him again. Four times we got together and four times I left. Please Miss Lonelyhearts believe me just for the childrens sake is the bunk and pardon me because I dont know what your sircumstanses are but I know from experience that in over three years I got $200 from him altogether.

About four months ago I handed him a warrant for his arrest for non support and he tore it up and left the house and I havent seen him since and as I had newmonia and my little girl had the flu I was put in financial embarasment with the doctor and we had to go to the ward and when we came out of the hospital I had to ask the boarder to come to live with us again as he was a sure $15 a week and if anything happened to me he would be there to take care of the children. But he tries to make me be bad and as there is nobody in the house when he comes home drunk on Saturday night I dont know what to do but so far I didnt let him. Where my husband is I dont know but I received a vile letter from him where he even accused his inocent children of things and sarcasticaley asked about the star boarder.

Dear Miss Lonelyhearts please dont be angry at me for writing such a long letter and taking up so much of your precisious time in reading it but if I ever write all the things which happened to me living with him it would fill a book and please forgive me for saying some nasty things as I had to give you an idea of what is going on in my home. Every woman is intitiled to a home isnt she? So Miss Lonelyhearts please put a few lines in your column when you refer to this letter so as I will know you are helping me. Shall I take my husband back? How can I support my children?

Thank you for anything you can advise me in I remain yours truly

Broad-shoulders

P.S. Dear Miss Lonelyhearts dont think I am broad shouldered but that is the way I feel about life and me I mean.

* * *

IT was Broad-shoulders, Broken-hearted, Unfortunate-cripple, Disillusioned-with-tubercular-husband and my many other communicants who finally drove me to Christ. But don't misunderstand me. My Christ has nothing to do with love.

Even before I became Miss Lonelyhearts, my world was moribund. I lived on a deserted stairway, among steel engravings of ornate machinery. I wrote my first love letters on a typewriter. When I opened a door, I was a criminal returning to the scene of his crime or a famous inventor revisiting the humble shack of his birth.

The joke of suffering and the joke of comforting killed this world. The stairway flattened into a desert, and when I opened a letter addressed to Miss Lonelyhearts, two stones touched.

I turned to Christ as the most familiar and natural of excitants. I wanted him to destroy this hypnosis. He alone could make the rock of sensation bleed and the stick of thought flower.

While sitting in my room, working at this Christ business, I became frightened and decided to go to Delehanty's speakeasy for a drink. As I lifted my glass, Shrike, the feature editor, caught my arm. "Ah, Miss Lonelyhearts," he said, "brooding again, eh? You're morbid, my young friend, morbid."

Shrike practiced a trick used much by moving picture comedians— the dead pan. No matter how fantastic or elaborate his speech, he never changed his expression. Under the shining white globe of his brow, his features huddled together in a grey triangle.

He lifted his glass with a flourish. "I give you the renaissance," he shouted. "Forget the crucifixion, remember the renaissance. There were no brooders then. What a period! What pageantry! Drunken popes . . . Beautiful courtezans . . . Illegitimate children . . ."

How had he discovered my preoccupation? I don't know. But I felt sure that it wasn't an accident. If I had been thinking of the South Seas, he would have said, "Like Gauguin, eh?"

After some pantomime suggesting colorful pageantry, he began again: " 'Brown Greek manuscripts and mistresses with great smooth marbly limbs . . .' But that reminds me, I'm expecting one of my admirers—a cow-eyed girl of great intelligence." He illustrated the word intelligence by carving two enormous breasts in the air. "She works in a bookstore, but wait until you see her behind."

I made the mistake of showing my annoyance.

"So you don't care for women. J. C. is your only sweetheart, eh? the King of Kings, the Miss Lonelyhearts of Miss Lonelyhearts . . ."

At this moment, a young woman came up to the bar and Shrike turned on her. She had long legs, thick ankles, big hands, a powerful body, a slender neck and a childish face made tiny by a man's haircut.

"Miss Farkis," he said, making her bow as a ventriloquist does his doll, "Miss Farkis, I want you to meet Miss Lonelyhearts. Show him, please, the same respect you show me. He too is a comforter of the poor in spirit, and a lover of God."

She acknowledged the introduction with a masculine handshake.

"Miss Farkis," Shrike said to me, "Miss Farkis works in a bookstore and writes on the side." He patted her rump.

"What were you talking about?" she asked.

"Religion."

"Get me a drink, and please continue. I'm very much interested in the new thomistic synthesis."

"St. Thomas!" Shrike shouted, as though terribly insulted. "What do you take us for, stinking intellectuals? We're not fake Europeans. We were discussing Christ, the Miss Lonelyhearts of Miss Lonely-hearts. America has her own religions, and, if you need a synthesis, here is the material for it." He took a clipping from his wallet and slapped it on the bar.

"ADDING MACHINE USED IN RITUAL OF WESTERN SECT . . . *Figures Will be Used for Prayers for Condemned Slayer of Aged Recluse* . . . DENVER, COL., April 2 (A. P.) Frank H. Rice, Supreme Pontiff of the Liberal Church of America, has announced he will carry out his plans for a 'goat and adding machine' ritual for William Moya, condemned slayer, despite objection to his program by a Cardinal of the sect. Rice declared the goat would be used as part of a 'sackcloth and ashes' service shortly before and after Moya's execution, set for the week of June 20. Prayers for the condemned man's soul will be offered on an adding machine. Numbers, he explained, constitute the only universal language. Moya killed Joseph Zemp, an aged recluse, in an argument over a small amount of money."

Miss Farkis laughed and Shrike looked as though he were going to punch her. His actions shocked the bartender who hurriedly asked us to go into the back room. I didn't want to go with them, but they insisted and I was too tired to argue. We seated ourselves at a table inside one of the booths. Shrike again raised his fist, but when she drew back he slipped his hand inside the neck of her dress. The trick worked. She gave in to his hand until he became too daring, then pushed him away.

"I am a great saint," he shouted. "I can walk on my own water. Haven't you ever heard of Shrike's Passion in the Luncheonette, or the Agony in the Soda Fountain? Then I compared the wounds in Christ's body to the mouths of a miraculous purse in which we deposit the small change of our sins. It is indeed an excellent conceit. But now let us consider the holes in our own bodies, and into what these congenital wounds open. Under the skin of a man is a wonderous jungle where veins like lush tropical growths hang along over-ripe organs and weed-like entrails writhe in squirming tangles of red and yellow. In this jungle, flitting from rock-grey lungs to golden intestine, from liver to lights and back to liver again, lives a bird called the soul. The Catholic hunts this bird with bread and wine, the Hebrew with a golden ruler, the Protestant on leaden feet with leaden words, the Buddhist with a string of beads, the Negro with blood. I spit on them all. Phooh! And I call upon you to spit. Phooh! Do you stuff birds? That's the question. Do you stuff birds? No, my dears, taxidermy is not religion. No! A thousand times no. Better, I say unto you, better a live bird in the jungle of the body than two stuffed birds on the library table."

His caresses kept pace with the sermon, and when he reached the end, he buried his thin grey face like the blade of a hatchet in her neck.

"Seeing the New Year In" by Paul Cadmus.

Pioneers! O Pioneers!

BY DANIEL FUCHS

THE next day Papravel in a double-breasted suit, tab collar and derby, walked into the Silver Eagle bus station. Behind him were a heavy-jowled Irishman called Gilhooley, and Gitler, a dapper, stringy fellow who looked like James Cagney. He had resplendent black hair, plastered down. Hands in pockets, these leaned against the walls of the narrow store, surveyed the streamers advertising round trips to city points, and waited. Behind the ticket counter a stumpy man in suspenders had been talking to a customer but he stopped and looked at the three anxiously, for their brisk entrance had been something of a sensation.

Papravel rapped his fist on the ticket counter with deliberation. "Who is the boss here, please?"

"Yes?" said the stumpy individual. "Yes?"

"Are you Mr. Pomerantz?"

"Morand. My name is Morand. What can I do for you, gentlemen?"

"I'm a representative of the Brownsville Business Board," said Papravel, and thereupon began the comedy. "What we try to do always is not only help business in Brownsville but to help the business

In the early thirties, Daniel Fuchs submitted an account of his childhood in the Williamsburg section of Brooklyn to *The New Republic*, who printed part of it and suggested that Fuchs expand it into a novel. Fuchs set to work, and the result was *Summer in Williamsburg* (1934), which was followed in 1936 by *Homage to Blenholt*, and in 1937 by *Low Company*. Because the novels received little critical attention and did not sell, Fuchs undertook to write a story for the *Saturday Evening Post*. When the story was accepted, Fuchs gave up the idea of writing serious fiction, and began to contribute regularly to the *Post* and *Colliers;* he now writes for Hollywood and ladies' magazines. * * * "Pioneers! Oh Pioneers!" appeared in *Story* magazine in December, 1933 and explores the same material as the Williamsburg trilogy.

man too. Because we always say if the Brownsville business man loses, Brownsville business loses. That's a slogan."

"Yes?" said Mr. Morand, sweating a little. "Yes?"

"When the business man loses, Brownsville's business loses. And now, Mr. Morantz, I don't like to say it, but you made a mistake. Everyone makes a mistake sometimes and what we try to do is to hurry up and help out before it's too late. If you catch it in time, you don't lose everything, and while you still got a shirt on your back, listen to me, Morantz, I know what I'm saying, get out of Brownsville because you can't make money here."

Morand went white. He stared at Gilhooley and Gitler against the wall and then back again to Papravel. The customer to whom he had been talking grew worried and wondered whether the man wasn't going to have a stroke.

"Who sent you?" Morand said very quietly.

"Who sent me? Listen, Morantz, you don't understand my meaning. I'm your best friend. I mean only to help you. All I'm saying is you'll lose less if you get out of Brownsville now before it's too late."

"Never mind," Morand said rapidly. He drew himself up to indicate that he comprehended the situation and was able to handle it. "I know who sent you and I know who you are. It was Rubin of the Empire Lines who told you to stick your nose in here and your name is Papravel. But listen to me because I mean every word of it. So long as Rubin does an honest business I'll do business honest too, but if he fights with fire I'll strike with fire also. And listen, Papravel, remember, you're not the only louse, the only snot-nose, the only low-life in Brownsville, for every one like you there's a hundred more bumming the streets. And you can tell Rubin for me, you can tell him I said he will burn like in hell before I get out!"

Morand stopped, almost bouncing from the nervous excitement. The customer touched his arm to quiet him. Gitler at the wall stood erect alertly. Gilhooley's eyes absorbed the scene but he continued to lean back. It was a climax and no one could think of anything to say.

"Listen, my friend," began the customer timidly. His voice was very thin. "I don't like to go where I don't belong but let me tell you something. What I say is a man can't be successful unless he's got a warm heart and is willing to give the other fellow a chance."

"Well, what am I saying?" Papravel almost wept at him. "I come to this man like the best friend in the world and I tell him what's good for him. I don't mean harm, all I want is to help. And he gives me a roar like a lion and insults me left and right."

"See," the customer went on with a little more conviction, "I've traveled everywhere, Paraguay, Chile, Peru, Argentina, Brazil, Mexico, everywhere. I always say I don't like to go where I don't belong but maybe I can tell you something and if you like it, take it, and if you don't, just leave it alone and we're still friends."

Gitler now came up. "Mister," he said, taking him by the elbow, "I think your wife wants you outside." Papravel wiped his nose in two movements and returned to Morand.

"Listen, Mr. Morantz, let there be no hard feeling. I wish you all the luck and all the money in the world. Only, if business goes bad, remember, Morantz, I gave you advice and you wouldn't take it."

"Never mind," Mr. Morand said coldly. "Never mind."

"All right," said Papravel, and they went out.

Two Jews, one Negro and three Italians besides Gitler and Gilhooley were the actors in the sequel. As they barged into the Silver Eagle bus station, Gitler walked up to Morand immediately.

"Listen, Morand, and shut up. All you have to do is stay where you are and not make a move. What we will do here, we'll do and it's no good to worry about it. Just stay and wait, but above all things, Morand, keep quiet." He nodded to Gilhooley and returned to the business on hand. The Irishman took his place near Morand.

"Open your yap," he said with seriousness, "and I will knock out every tooth one after the other."

Morand stood as though paralyzed.

The six men proceeded to strip the place bare. They worked with a methodical nonchalance, a business-like coolness, that was particularly disheartening. One of the Italians went behind the counter and with one rip of his monkey wrench unhinged the ticket box. Like a confetti cascade, the blue and pink slips showered to the floor. He smacked the cash register four or five times, wrenched the counter from its supports and took a running swipe at the wall mirrors.

The Negro, elegantly named Fleurie O'Johnson, made a sudden leap for the chandelier. He swung like a monkey the length of the room until it gave, dropping him on the floor with a loud boom. O'Johnson rubbed his behind and looked up ruefully at the hole in the ceiling. Gitler, supervising the job from the side, laughed in amusement.

"That reminds me," he reflected pleasantly, "did you ever go to the zoo? Once I saw a baboon and he had no hair on his can at all."

"Why?" Gilhooley wanted to know, perplexed. What was the point?

"Why?" repeated Gitler, discountenanced with the failure of his effort. "Why? Kiss my tail, why. How should I know?"

The Italian with the monkey wrench, in the meantime, was walking around cracking windows, wall fixtures and signs. Morand's hands moved once but Gilhooley caught his eyes and he returned to frozen attention. But when they started to rip the rich, red carpet on the floor, Morand could contain himself no longer. He opened his mouth to protest but simultaneously the Irishman brought up his palm stiffly against it. Gilhooley slapped his face repeatedly and he did it with passion. "Enough," Gitler finally called out. "How long, how long, you dumb Irisher?" In the recess Morand drew in his breath, broke down completely and cried with extravagance. There is something ugly about physical violence in addition to its other displeasing qualities.

The Italian with the monkey wrench paused and wiped his forehead.

Like a thread of chewing gum a child stretches from her mouth in idle play, the state road dipped its dainty way through the hills. The morning sun beamed down in yellow brightness cheering the countryside. Through the quiet roared the huge Empire Lines bus on its way to Havers Falls. Nature and power. God's majesty and Rubin's.

"Already," said Rubin, speaking almost poetically, "the railroads are giving in. Yesterday they cut their rates again and still they can't touch Empire fares."

Papravel lay contentedly against the over-upholstered cushions. Expansively he smoked a cigar because it always gave him a sensation of opulence even though it frequently made him sick in the stomach.

"It's America," he said softly, his eyes almost closed. "Where but in America could a man do so well for himself?"

"When we began," Rubin continued, full of honest enthusiasm, "the railroads, they said we were a bunch of snot-noses, we would be thrown on our behinds in six months. You should have heard them, Papravel. Big speeches. Big shots. Big bellies with cigars all the time stuck in their faces. 'Transportation is the backbone of the Nation.' 'American industry and American imagination will find no serious rival in foreign competition.' Now they come to me and give me Mr. Rubin, Mr. Rubin, until I tell Louie, Louie throw these bums out, they're taking up my time." Rubin laughed. In harmony, Papravel smiled pleasantly.

"Listen to me, Papravel, and I'll show you how a man can work himself up in this country. Four years ago I was a jobber in candy. I made fifty dollars a week, sometimes sixty, sometimes seventy, it all depends. I worked like a nigger but I thought I was rich like Herbert Hoover and Charlie Schwab. And now look at me, knock wood, President, Empire Lines, Inc., with regular service to the mountains five times a day in the summer and twice daily in the winter with a connection in a coast-to-coast hook-up. Fourteen Superba buses, seven Nashes and four Buicks, four offices and a pay-roll of sixty-six. And it is just the beginning.

"Four lines there are to Havers Falls: The Empire, The Green Hawk, The Excellent and The Silver Eagle. The Green Hawk is a fancy outfit operated by goyish dopes, catering to Gentiles strictly and tell me, Papravel, how many Gentiles come to the mountains? They'll go out of business the first bad summer but it's all the same to me. As for the Excellent, did you ever hear what happened? It's a funny story. Moss and Reinhardt were partners until one day Moss says he's got enough, he wants to get out. And who buys him out, Papravel? So all that's left is the Silver Eagle and now with God's will and your help they will move out of Brownsville and without a station in Brownsville they, too, can't hurt me."

Rubin stopped. It was a long speech but he had relished every word of it. His cigar had gone out and now Rubin took time to relight it with the importance that this operation alone makes possible.

"Yes, yes," said Papravel, awakening from his mild slumber. "Did you hear what happened to the Silver Eagle, Rubin? Eight bandits, eight bums, eight low-lifes, the rottenest kind of people in the world, you and I should never have anything to do with them, they walked into the bus station. With no pity, no heart, they knock down the furniture, rip the carpets and smash up the place. And poor Morantz, he comes running to me. I swear to him, Morantz, I'm no roughneck, it isn't my business, why should he come to me? I think he will have to get out of Brownsville after all."

Rubin looked sideways at the innocence of Papravel. They rocked gently with the motion of the bus. It was a pleasant sensation.

"Poor Morantz," Rubin sighed. He leaned back, grew lost in thought while the smoke rose and circled in the bus. With the Excellent crippled and the Silver Eagle out of Brownsville a man could make in the summer, let me see, eight hundred, nine hundred dollars a day. Maybe a thousand. Rubin crossed his legs. One thousand dollars! If God would only be good.

Through the window could be seen the lifting dew now rising in mist from the fields. A vari-colored cow, taking no time from her chewing and looking no less stupid for it, stared dumbly at the speeding bus. What hath God wrought? The hills extending upwards on either side revealed squares of blue, green and yellow acres. Now the sun had grown richer, resembling the yolk of an egg medium-boiled. Far off came the shrill whistle of a speeding train. Rubin awoke abruptly from his revery. "Hey, Mike!" he commanded the driver. "Press the button!" Through the still air in answer sounded the soft melodious note of the bus horn and it floated above the car like a plume. . . .

The arrival at Havers Falls was like cold water. The news greeted them from Brownsville that Morand, determined to fight, had reopened with the help of a Detroit combination. Rubin was stunned. He had begun to regard the business as finished. After all, he had a wife and four children.

"Listen, Rubin," Papravel said, speaking carefully and slowly, "trust me and everything will be all right. Don't cry like a baby. Your place in Brownsville I guarantee they won't touch. Every day I'll have three men to watch it with more waiting near a telephone. And as for Morantz's place, leave that to me. Not in a month did I learn my business and only God knows how many ways there are to make trouble. Import! Let Morantz import gangsters from today until tomorrow. What difference does it make if a bum comes from Detroit, Chicago or New York? He's still a stinker and let there be an end to it."

Half way between Middletown and Utseck they stopped the screaming Silver Eagle bus. Two Jews, one Negro, three Italians. The driver, a big man with long arms that went down to his knees, leaped out ready for a fight but stopped short when he saw the guns.

"All right," he said. "What's the game?"

"Shut your mouth," Gilhooley said and the first thing he did was to pull down the driver's pants so that he couldn't move his legs. In the early morning the cool air struck him disagreeably and the driver protested. "Shut your mouth!" Gilhooley said.

It was an early mid-week trip and there were few passengers. However Gitler went through the car to calm them. "Gentlemen," he announced, "everything is all right, keep your seats and stay quiet. Because if anyone makes noise it will certainly go hard with him." He sat down in the driver's seat, one eye on the passengers, the other surveying the work his men were doing. . . .

Neatly and rapidly they slashed the big expensive shoes, knocked holes in the gasoline tank, lifted the shift cover and smashed the teeth of the gears, raised the hood and crumpled the fan, ripped the wires from their places, wrenched the spark-plugs and banged the magneto. Then they dropped everything, piled back into the Nashes and rode off. As they went down the road the driver with the long arms, still dazed by their speed, forgot to pull up his pants but looked after them. "The dirty bastards," he said quietly, in a sort of astonishment recollected in tranquillity. "The dirty bastards."

In the evening Papravel got Morand on the long distance telephone.

"Morantz," he said, "this is from a friend. You know what happened a week ago in Brownsville. About this morning with the bus I don't have to tell you. Listen to me, I'm talking like a father, get out of Brownsville because it's no good for you."

"Who's talking? Who's talking?" Morand's cracked voice came through the earpiece.

"What difference does it make who's talking, Morantz? It's the best friend you got in the world. Listen to me, get out and get out in a hurry. Because all that's happened already is only the beginning and if you keep on being stubborn, may Heaven help you."

"I know who it is, you cut-throat!" the voice screamed. "I want you to know this and I'll say it with the last breath in my body. I'm no ninny, I'm not afraid. I'll fight you and Rubin with my last penny and I'll fight you until I'm in my grave, may you rot in hell. May your bones be twisted in their sockets, may your eyes be screwed to the back of your skull, may God strike you with a bolt of lightning! Till I'm dead and buried in my grave will I fight you, and tell Rubin for me, tell him may his belly foster cancers and ulcers, may his tongue grow swollen and hang from his mouth like a beard, may a subway train run over his stinking body, goddammit!"

From the other end came the sharp click. Papravel hung up. "Goddammit yourself!" he bellowed at the telephone, and then it was he first began to grow angry with Morand.

Moreover, Morand meant what he said, for that night his men broke into the Empire Havers Falls' office. They wrecked it with a thoroughness and regard for detail that equalled in every respect the work of Papravel. Rubin howled. He was tremendously scared. Papravel brushed him aside impatiently.

"I'm busy," he said. "Don't worry. In the end everything will be all right." Papravel wired instructions home, left Gitler and Gilhooley in the mountains and drove to Brownsville.

Gitler and Gilhooley drove through the mountains looking for trouble. Two Jews, one Negro and three Italians. By this time Morand was sending a Detroit gunman with every bus and they had to work carefully because Papravel's orders were to stay clear of the cops. Gitler's boys had to pick their spots, swiftly punching holes in gas tanks or slashing shoes, and then they had to duck out immediately. Morand's help retaliated in kind so that Gitler was compelled to split his men, half protecting, half attacking. He sent telegrams home asking for more men and he got them.

From Brownsville came great news. Papravel had managed one

night to get into the garage where Morand kept his buses. With the dispatch and completeness that were the trade-mark of Papravel's organization, his men put the big cars out of commission. So skilfully did they work that for a day and a half Morand had no cars on the road and his schedule was thrown awry for a week. The damage to Morand was terrific but he held on.

Through it all Rubin groaned. He was frightened to his marrow and cursed the hot day he had begun with Papravel. Papravel pointed to his swelling army and called for more money, more money.

"You're sucking me dry," Rubin wept. "I ask you for one little job and you grow on me like a wife. There is finally a limit. A man can't go on like this forever."

"Give in," Papravel argued relentlessly. "You can't afford to back out now. They'll walk off with your pants if you quit now in the middle. Give in." Papravel got his money, for it was true Rubin could not get out at this stage. Mrs. Van Curen alone was overjoyed. She was the shriveled little lady who owned the place where Papravel boarded the boys in the mountains. She was a pious old woman, but that is natural for people her age. Nevertheless, when Papravel had offered her twenty dollars a day for the men, she thought the sky had fallen out of the heavens. So Mrs. Van Curen alone was overjoyed because for every new man Papravel sent up she got an additional two dollars. He was her benefactor, a straight stalwart man who honestly paid his bills and would never cheat an old woman. Even though he was a Jew, it would be hard to find a better man.

It was as abrupt as that. In mid-August Gilhooley failed to restrain himself, forgot Papravel's strict orders and ended up by seriously wounding a state trooper. With him hooliganism was no colorless business adjunct but a career appropriate to a sporting temperament. Gitler found him at the Van Curen house, surrounded by the other boys who silently gazed at the Irishman now weakly proclaiming his courage and defiance. Gitler smelled the odor of gin and wanted to slap his face right then and there.

"When Papravel gave you a gun," he said coldly, "he meant you should only use it to scare. But if you had to shoot somebody, why, Gilhooley, why did you have to pick a state trooper?"

Gilhooley, heavy with drunkenness, nevertheless had begun to comprehend the seriousness of the situation. The blustering expression on his face had been cracking and revealing his fear. Gitler considered and he considered hard. The proper move for him was to get away before he was mixed into the mess. But Papravel, Papravel. . . .

Through the darkness came the gleam of Papravel for a consolation.

"Say something," Gilhooley commanded and glared around at the men. But everyone remained mute. "Say something," he pleaded. Slowly as a shadow comes, his face filled with sadness and self-pity. "Say something," Gilhooley begged. "Say something!" And in another moment he was crying broken-heartedly. . . .

It was in this crisis that the true quality of Papravel was revealed. A lesser man might have been inclined, like Gitler, to clear out, but to Papravel the emergency presented a challenge to his energy and resourcefulness, and if Papravel had anything it was a vast confidence in himself. Besides, it was alien to his nature to leave Gilhooley stuck, for Papravel was essentially a simple man.

Nevertheless he roundly bawled out the Irishman for his want of business sense. Gilhooley, who resembled in the excitement a man with a heavy nose-cold, stared dumbly, accepting abuse and asking monotonously, "What'll I do? What'll I do?" In disgust Papravel sent him back to Brownsville to get him out of sight while he sounded the situation.

He went directly to Rubin. "Remember, Rubin," he said gingerly, "remember long ago I told you sometimes mistakes happen? Well, a terrible mistake happened, and now we've got to help."

"No!" said Rubin with finality. He was blown up with resentment. "No! Once for all I made my mind up. No! For two months you've bled me until I'm sucked dry. Let Morantz have his bus station in Brownsville. It's cheaper."

"The bus station is all finished, Rubin," Papravel said impatiently. "The Silver Eagle won't be there another month. About this, I told you, I'm positive. Don't be stubborn now, because if you wanted to be stubborn this is the worst time you could pick."

"No!" Rubin's voice rose to a wail from persecution. "Every night I ask myself, why did I ever get mixed up with you? You've never done me any good, you've been like a leech on my flesh. Not another cent will I give, Papravel, and you can know it right now. These things can't go on forever and let there be an end to it!"

In the face of this unexpected resistance, Papravel sharply changed his tactics.

"An end?" he repeated, with terrible calm.

"Cut-throat!" screamed Rubin. He was enormously afraid. "Get out, you robber! I'm an honest business man and won't have dealings with gangsters like you."

"Don't call names," said Papravel imperturbably. "It won't do any good. Besides, have you already forgotten the little business you ran twenty years ago when you told the poor yiddles in the old country what a wonderful place America was? And then when they came over you put them to work in sweat shops for four dollars a week and took a commission on their wages? You even took the dumbbells to board in a railroad flat with no windows and the toilet in the backyard so you could make more money on them. You're no rabbi yourself, Rubin; and from candy-jobbing alone a man doesn't make a fortune. But what will be, will be. Only, listen Rubin, there is no end yet because I'm coming back."

"Get out, blood-sucker!" screamed Rubin. But already his whole body was wet with the sweat of fear.

However, in this time of stress, Papravel's first concern was for Gilhooley. From Brownsville appeared Anschele B. Sussman, and concerning him as a lawyer the legend was great. He was a stoutish man whose shirt tails were always coming out in folds through his vest, and in some neighborhoods this is a mark of importance. From the way in which he shoved the cloth back into place within his trousers, one could perceive Sussman's satisfaction with himself, his confidence in his ability and his pleasure with his growing fame and fortune. He was an energetic man. Rubin could have chosen none better.

A short time after Sussman's arrival, three nondescript individuals came upon the scene. These were the witnesses who affirmed with the conviction of solid truth behind them that while it was true Gilhooley shot, it was only after the policeman had drawn his own revolver and was on the point of killing the Irishman. Further, the trooper seemed intoxicated, although of course at the time there was no certain way of knowing. And this seemed reasonable, they were ready to swear, for there was no cause for the trooper to become involved with Gilhooley otherwise.

Skilfully, and from experience, Sussman was bringing his case to completion. And it was only when the prospect grew brighter, when the judge who was to preside had been shown the light, when the prosecution had been tactfully approached, it was only then that Papravel returned to Rubin. With inordinate calm Papravel baldly proposed that Rubin resign, accept the position of vice-president, and transfer his office together with two-thirds of the stock to Papravel. Rubin had a stroke.

When he recovered, Papravel presented his inexorable argument.

"Give in, Rubin, while you still have a shirt on your back. You know what I did for Morand and the Silver Eagle, and the same party will be in stock for you if you take it into your head to get nasty. Fourteen

Superba buses, seven Nashes and Buicks, four offices and sixty-six on the pay-roll, all this you will lose like a dream going away in the morning. And from you personally I will make such a sight for all Brownsville to talk about for a month."

Rubin made gasping noises as though he were choking. His face was shot with blood.

"On the other hand," Papravel went on with marvelous presence, even for him, "with me as your partner you'll have nothing to worry about. All your competitors I'll drive away from the mountains and we'll expand. I'll make the railroads give up altogether and make them carry only freight. I'll establish for you routes to all the big cities and I'll chase every other company from the roads. You'll have, with me for a partner, not a stinking small business to the mountains but a coast-to-coast organization. Listen Rubin, you'll be a big man with your picture in the papers every Sunday. You'll be a philanthropist like Warburg and Kahn and you'll go good wholesale. They'll name orphan asylums after you and hospitals, and when you die, Rubin, you'll get a funeral that will never be seen before in America!"

And Papravel won.

Outside, the full-starred sky resembled a huge ceiling in a Brooklyn burlesque house. The summer was already leaving and in the coolness of the mountain air could be discerned that gentle sad quality of autumn. But Mrs. Van Curen had the big living room all alight, the boys half sat, half lay in the chairs, everyone smoked cigars. Peace. Quiet. Contentment.

"Listen, boys," said Papravel from a full heart and with satisfaction, "it's a party. Tonight we celebrate because all that comes, knock wood, is good news. Morantz, he's quit Brownsville and soon I'll have him out altogether, give me a year and God's help. As for Gilhooley, let no one say Papravel doesn't take care of his boys right, for Sussman here has everything fixed. And just this morning the railroad company sent out an announcement they take no more passengers, only freight. And it is the beginning, because there is still a God over America."

Papravel interrupted his monologue long enough to relight the cigar. The boys were by this time almost asleep but Mrs. Van Curen was watching him intently, listening with respect. As he held the match in his fingers Papravel abruptly grew serious.

"America," he proclaimed with profound conviction, through the smoke. "I don't care what anybody says, America is a wonderful country. Seriously, seriously! Look at me, look how I worked myself up in four short years. In America everyone has an equal chance. I don't know how it is in Russia now, God himself doesn't know what goes on there, but even so, where, I want to know, where else could a Jew make such a man of himself as right here in America?"

Papravel stopped, his eyes waiting for an answer. But in the pause Mrs. Van Curen suddenly took it into her head to cry. She was very sleepy and wept noiselessly but with many tears.

"What's the matter?" Papravel asked, concerned. "What's the old lady crying about?"

Mrs. Van Curen looked up sadly. "I'm crying because you're such a fine, upstanding, kind gentleman and yet when you die you won't go to heaven."

"Why?" Papravel asked. "Why should you say a thing like that?"

"You've never been baptized, Mr. Papravel," she wept.

"Oh," said Papravel, with relief. "Don't you worry your little gray head over that." He didn't know whether this was a joke or what. "Just you leave this to me, Mrs. Van Curen, and everything will be all right," Papravel said, and he smiled happily.

"Erecting New Building — East 28th Street" by Ernest Feine, 1930.

Courtesy Midtown Galleries

From **Call It Sleep**

BY HENRY ROTH

INSIDE the Royal Warehouse, located on the East River and Tenth Street, Bill Whitney, an old man with a massive body, short-wind and stiff, rheumatic legs, toiled up the stairway to the first floor. In his left hand, he held a lantern, which in his absentmindedness, he joggled from time to time to hear the gurgle of its fuel. In his right hand, clacking on the bannister at each upward reach of his arm, he held a key—the key he turned the clocks with on every floor of the building —the proof of his watch and wakefulness. As he climbed the swart stairs, stained with every upward step by shallow, rocking lantern-light, he muttered, and this he did not so much to populate the silence with ephemeral, figment selves, but to follow the links of his own, slow thinking, which when he failed to hear, he lost:

"And wut? Haw! Ye looked down—and—sss! By Gawd if there waren't the dirt-rud under ye. And. Ha! Ha! Haw! No wheels. Them pedals were there—now waren't they? Saw 'em as clear—as clear—but

---

Call It Sleep was first published in 1934, and has been Henry Roth's only major work. The novel went through two printings and sold more than 4,000 copies; but the publisher, Robert O. Ballou, was forced out of business by the depression and the book was forgotten. In 1956, both Alfred Kazin and Leslie Fiedler, in a symposium conducted by the *American Scholar*, listed *Call It Sleep* among "The Most Neglected Books of the Past 25 Years"; four years later it was reprinted in cloth, and in 1964 a paperback edition was published. * * * Walter B. Rideout, in *The Radical Novel in the United States*, refers to *Call It Sleep* as "the most distinguished single proletarian novel." But despite its setting, *Call It Sleep* is not proletarian; rather, as Leslie Fiedler has observed: "For the Marxian version of the class struggle, to which Roth was theoretically committed, *Call It Sleep* substitutes a Dickensian one: a view of the "Final Conflict" as taking place between a corrupt adult society and the pure child." * * * The selection here reprinted is Chapter XXI from Book IV, "The Rail."

the wheels gone—nowhere. By Gawd, thinks I—Now by Gawst, ain't it
queer? Old Ruf Gilman a'standin' there, a'standin' and a'gappin'. Jest
a'standin' and a'gappin' as plain— And the whiskers he growed afore
the winter . . . By the well with the white housing. A'savin' his ter-
baccer juice till he had nigh a cupfull . . . Whawmmmmm! Went
plumb through the snaw in the winter . . ."

> *Resounded, surged and resounded, like*
> *ever swelling breakers:*
> *—Double! Double! Double dared me!*
> *Where there's light in the crack,*
> *yuh dared me. Now I gotta.*

In the blue, smoky light of Callahan's beer-saloon, Callahan, the
pale fattish bar-keep jammed the dripping beer-tap closed and leaned
over the bar and snickered. Husky O'Toole—he, the broad-shouldered
one with the sky-blue eyes—dominated those before the bar (among
them, a hunchback on crutches with a surly crimp to his mouth, and
a weazened coal-heaver with a sooty face and bright eye-balls) and
dwarfed them. While he spoke they had listened, grinning avidly. Now
he threw down the last finger of whiskey, nodded to the bar-tender,
thinned his thin lips and looked about.

"Priddy wise mug!" Callahan prompted filling his glass.

"Well." O'Toole puffed out his chest. "He comes up fer air, see? He's
troo. Now, I says, now I'll tell yuh sompt'n about cunt— He's still stan-
nin' by de fawge, see, wit' his wrench in his han'. An I says, yuh like
udder t'ings, dontcha? Waddayuh mean, he says. Well, I says, yuh got
religion, aintcha? Yea, he says. An' I says, yuh play de ponies, dontcha?
Yea, he says. An' yuh like yer booze, dontcha? Sure, he says. Well I
says, none o' dem fer me! Waddayuh mean, he says. Well, I says, yuh
c'n keep yer religion, I says. Shit on de pope, I says— I wuz jis' makin' it hot—an' t'hell witcher ponies I says— I bets on a good one sometimes, but I wuzn' tellin' him—an' w'en it comes t' booze I says, shove
it up yer ass! Cunt fer me, ev'ytime I says. See, ev'ytime!"

They guffawed. "Yer a card!" said the coal heaver. "Yer a good
lad!—"

> *As though he had struck the enormous bell*
> *of the very heart of silence, he*
> *stared round in horror.*

"Gaw blimy, mate!" Jim Haig, oiler on the British tramp Eastern
Greyhound (now opposite the Cherry Street pier), leaned over the port
rail to spit. "I ain't 'ed any fish 'n' chips since the day I left 'ome.
W'y ain't a critter thought of openin' a 'omely place in New York—
Coney Island fer instance. Loads o' prawfit. Taik a big cod now—"

Now! Now I gotta. In the crack,
remember. In the crack be born.

"Harrh! There's nights I'd take my bible-oath, these stairs uz higher."
On the first floor, Bill Whitney stopped, gazed out of the window that
faced the East River. "Stinkin' heap out there!" And lifting eyes above
the stove-in, enameled pots, cracked washtubs, urinals that glimmered
in the black snarl, stared at the dark river striped by the gliding lights
of a boat, shifted his gaze to the farther shore where scattered, lighted
windows in factories, mills were caught like sparks in blocks of soot,
and moved his eyes again to the south-east, to the beaded bridge. Over
momentary, purple blossoms, down the soft incline, the far train slid
like a trickle of gold. Behind and before, sparse auto-head lights, belated or heralding dew on the bough of the night. "And George a'gappin' and me a'hollerin' and a'techin the ground with the toe of my boot
and no wheels under me. Ha! Ha! Mmm! Wut cain't a man dream of
in his sleep . . . A wheel . . . A bike . . ." He turned away seeking the clock. "And I ain't been on one . . . not sence . . . more'n
thirty-five . . . forty years. Not since I uz a little shaver . . ."

> *Clammy fingers traced the sharp edge of*
> *the dipper's scoop. Before his eyes*
> *the glitter on the car tracks whisked . . .*
> *reversed . . . whisked . . .*

"Say, listen O'Toole dere's a couple o' coozies in de back." The bar-
keep pointed with the beer knife. "Jist yer speed!"

"Balls!" Terse O'Toole retorted. "Wudjah tink I jist took de bull-
durham sack off me pecker fer—nuttin'? I twisted all de pipes I wanna w'en I'm pissin'!"

"No splinters in dese boxes, dough. Honest, O'Toole! Real clean—"

"Let 'im finish, will ye!" the hunchback interrupted sourly. "O'Toole
don' have to buy his gash."

"Well, he says, yea. An' I says yea. An' all de time dere wuz Steve
an' Kelly unner de goiders belly-achin'— Hey trow us a rivet. An' I
sez—"

> *—Nobody's commin'!*

Klang! Klang! Klang! Klang! Klang!

The flat buniony foot of Dan MacIntyre the motorman pounded the
bell. Directly in front of the clamorous car and in the tracks, the ven-
dor of halvah, candied-peanuts, leechee nuts, jellied fruits, dawdled,
pushing his push-cart leisurely. Dan MacIntyre was enraged. Wasn't
he blocks and blocks behind his leader? Hadn't his conductor been
slow as shit on the bell? Wouldn't he get a hell of a bawling out from
Jerry, the starter on Avenue A? And here was this lousy dago blocking

traffic. He'd like to smack the piss out of him, he would. He pounded the bell instead.

Leisurely, leisurely, the Armenian pedlar steered his cart out of the way. But before he cleared the tracks, he lifted up his clenched fist, high and pleasantly. In the tight crotch of his forefingers, a dirty thumb peeped out. A fig for you, O MacIntyre.

"God damm yuh!" He roared as he passed. "God blast yuh!"

> —So go! So go! So go!
> But he stood as still and rigid as
> if frozen to the wall, frozen fingers
> clutching the dipper.

"An' hawnest t'Gawd, Mimi, darlin' " The Family Entrance to Callahan's lay through a wide alley way lit by a red lamp in the rear. Within, under the branching, tendriled chandelier of alum-bronze, alone before a table beside a pink wall with roach-brown mouldings, Mary, the crockery-cheeked, humid-eyed swayed and spoke, her voice being maudlin, soused and reedy. Mimi, the crockery-cheeked, crockery-eyed, a smudged blonde with straw-colored hair like a subway seat, slumped and listened. "I was that young an' innercent, an' hawnest t' Gawd, that straight, I brought it t' the cashier, I did. And, Eeee! she screams and ducks under the registee, Eeee! Throw it away, yuh boob! But what wuz I t'know—I wuz on'y fifteen w'en I wuz a bus-goil. They left it on a plate—waa, the mugs there is in de woild—an' I thought it wuz one o' them things yuh put on yer finger w'en ye git a cut—"

"A cut, didja say, Mary, dea'?" The crockery cheeks cracked into lines.

"Yea a cut— a cu— Wee! Hee! Hee! Hee! Hee! Mimi, darlin' you're comical! Wee! Hee! Hee! Hee! But I wuz that young an' innercent till he come along. Wee! Hee! Hee! Hawnes' t' Gawd I wuz. I could piss troo a beer-bottle then—"

> Out of the shadows now, out on the dimlit, vacant
> street, he stepped down from the broken
> curb-stone to the cobbles. For all
> his peering, listening, starting, he
> was blind as a sleep-walker, he was
> deaf. Only the steely glitter on the
> tracks was in his eyes, fixed there like
> a brand, drawing him with cables as
> tough as steel. A few steps more and
> he was there, standing between the
> tracks, straddling the sunken rail.

He braced his legs to spring, held
his breath. And now the wavering point
of the dipper's handle found the long,
dark, grinning lips, scraped, and
like a sword in a scabbard—

"Oy, Schmaihe, goy! Vot luck! Vot luck! You should only croak!"

"Cha! Cha! Cha! Dot's how I play mit cods!"

"Bitt him vit a flush! Ai, yi, yi!"

"I bet he vuz mit a niggerteh last night!"

"He rode a dock t' luzno maw jock—jeck I shidda said. Cha! Cha!"

"He's a poet, dis guy!"

"A putz!"

"Vus dere a hura mezda, Morr's?"

"Sharrop, bummer! Mine Clara is insite!"

Plunged! And he was running! Running!

"Nutt'n'? No, I says, nutt'n'. But every time I sees a pretty cunt come walkin' up de street, I says, wit' a mean shaft an' a sweet pair o' knockers, Jesus, O'Toole, I says, dere's a mare I'd radder lay den lay on. See wot I mean? Git a bed under den a bet on. Git me?"

"Haw! Haw! Haw! Bejeeziz!"

"Ya! Ha! He tella him, you know? He lika de fica stretta!"

They looked down at the lime-streaked, overalled wop condescendingly, and—

"Aw, bulloney," he says, "Yea, I says. An' booze, I says, my booze is wut I c'n suck out of a nice tit, I says. Lallal'mmm, I says. An' w'en it comes t' prayin', I says, c'n yuh tell me anyt'ing bedder t' pray over den over dat one!" O'Toole hastily topped the laugh with a wave of his hand. "Yer an at'eist, yuh fuck, he hollers. A fuckin' at'eist I says— An' all de time dere wuz Steve and Kelly unner de goiders hollerin', hey throw us a riv—"

Running! But no light overtook him,
no blaze of intolerable flame. Only
in his ears, the hollow click of iron
lingered. Hollow, vain. Almost within
the saloon-light, he slowed down, sobbed
aloud, looked behind him—

"But who'd a thunk it?" Bill Whitney mounted the stairs again. "By Gawd, who'd a thunk it? The weeks I'd held that spike for 'im . . . Weeks . . . And he druv and never a miss . . . Drunk? Naw, he warn't drunk that mornin'. Sober as a parson. Sober. A'swingin of the twelve pound like a clock. Mebbe it was me that nudged it, mebbe it war me . . . By Gawd, I knowed it. A feelin' I had seein' that black sledge in the air. Afore it come down, I knowed it. A hull damned country-side it might of slid into. And it had to be me . . . Wut? It wuz to be? That cast around my leg? A pig's tit! It wuz to—"

> Like a dipped metal flag or a gro-
> tesque armored head scrutinizing the
> cobbles, the dull-gleaming dipper's
> scoop stuck out from between the rail,
> leaning sideways.
> —Didn't. Didn't go in. Ain't lit. Go back.
> He turned—slowly.
> —No—body's—look—

"Bawl? Say, did I bawl? Wot else'd a kid've done w'en her mont'ly don' show up—Say! But I'll get even with you, I said, I'll make a prick out of you too, like you done t' me. You wait! You can't get away with that. G'wan, he said, ye little free-hole, he called me. Wott're ye after? Some dough? Well, I ain't got it. That's all! Now quit hangin' aroun' me or I'll s-smack ye one! He said."

"Where d'ja get it?"

"I borreed it—it wuzn't much. She called herself a m-mid-wife. I went by m-meself. My old-huhu—my old l-lady n-never—O Jesus!" Tears rilled the glaze.

"Say—toin off de tap, Mary, f'Gawd's sake!"

"Aw! Sh-hu-hu-shut up! Can't I b-bawl if I—I—uh-hu-uh—G-go p-peddle yer h-hump, h-he says—"

"But not hea', Mary, f'r the lova Pete. We all gets knocked up some-times—"

> —Horry op! Horry op back!

"They'll betray us!" Into the Tenth Street Crosstown car, slowing down at Avenue A, the voice of the pale, gilt-spectacled, fanatic face rang out above all other sounds: above the oozy and yearning "Open the door to Jesus" of the Salvation Army singing in the park; above the words of the fat woman swaying in the car as she said, "So the doctor said cut out all meat if you don't want gall-stones. So I cut out all meat, but once in a while I fried a little boloney wih eggs—how I love it!" Above the muttering of the old gray-bearded Jewish peddler (he rocked his baby carriage on which pretzels lay stacked like quoits on the upright sticks) "Founder of the universe, why have you tethered me to this machine? Founder of the universe, will I ever earn more than water for my buckwheat? Founder of the universe!" Above the even enthusiasm of the kindly faced American woman: "And do you know, you can go all the way up inside her for twenty-five cents. For only twenty-five cents, mind you! Every American man, woman and child ought to go up inside her, it's a thrilling experience. The Statue of Liberty is—"

—He stole up to the dipper warily,
on tip—

"Shet up, down 'ere, yuh bull-faced harps, I says, wait'll I'm troo! Cunt, I says, hot er snotty 'zuh same t' me. Dis gets 'em' hot. Dis gets em hot I sez. One look at me, I says, an yuh c'n put dat rivet in yer ice-box—t'ings 'll keep! Yuh reams 'em out with dat he says— kinda snotty like. Shit no, I says I boins 'em out. W'y dontcha trow it t'dem, he says, dey're yellin' fer a rivet. Aaa, I don' wanna bust de fuckin' goider I says. Yer pretty good, he says. Good, I says, didja ever see dat new tawch boinin' troo a goider er a flange er any fuck'n' hunka iron—de spa'ks wot goes shootin' down—? Didja? Well dat's de way 'I comes. Dey tol' me so. An' all de time dere wuz Steve and Kelly unner de goiders havin' a shit-hemorrage an' yellin' hey, t'row—"

toe, warily, glancing over his
shoulders, on tip-toe, over serried
cobbles, cautious—

"Wuz t' be. And by Gawd it might hev gone out when I went to bed a' suckin' of it. By Gawd it hed no call t' be burnin'. . . . Wuz to be—Meerschaum, genuwine. Thankee I said. Thankee Miz Taylor. And I stood on the backstairs with the ice-tongs. Thankee and thank the Doctor . . . Boston, the year I— Haw, by Gawd. And the hull damn sheet afire. And Kate ascreamin' beside me . . . Gawd damn it! It hadn't ought to 'a' done it . . . A'lookin' at me still now . . . A'stretchin' of her neck in the white room . . . in the hospital—"

As though his own tread might shake the
slanting handle loose from its perch
beneath the ground. And now, and—

"Why not? She asks me. Pullin' loaded dice on Lefty. The rat! He can't get away with that y'know. I know, Mag, I said. It'd do my heart good to see a knife in his lousy guts—only I gotta better idee. What? She asks me. Spill it. Spill it is right, I says t' her. I know a druggist-felleh, I said, good friend o' mine. O yea, she looks at me kinda funny. Croak him with a dose o'— No! I said. No poison. Listen Mag. Throw a racket up at your joint, will ye? Give him an invite. He'll come. And then let me fix him a drink. And I winks at her. Dintcha ever hear o' the Spanish Fly—"

over it now, he crouched,
stretched out a hand to

"They'll betray us!" Above all these voices, the speaker's voice rose. "In 1789, in 1848, in 1871, in 1905, he who has anything to save will enslave us anew! Or if not enslave will desert us when the red cock crows! Only the laboring poor, only the masses embittered, bewildered, betrayed, in the day when the red cock crows, can free us!"

lift the dipper free. A sense almost
palpable, as of a leashed and imminent
and awful force

"You're de woist fuckin' liar I ever seen he sez an' ducks over de goiders."

focused on his hand across the hair-
breadth

"Yuh god mor'n a pair o' sem'ns?"

gap between his fingers and the
scoop. He drew

"It's the snug ones who'll preach it wuz to be."

back, straightened. Carefully bal—

"So I dropped it in when he was dancin'—O hee! Hee! Mimi! A healthy dose I—"

anced on his left, advance—

"Yea. I sez, take your pants off."

ed his right foot—
Crritlkt!
—What?
He stared at the river, sprang away
from the rail and dove into the shad-
ows.

"Didja hear 'im, Mack? De goggle-eyed yid an' his red cock?"

The river? That sound! That sound
had come from there. All his senses
stretched toward the dock, grappled with
the hush and the shadow. Empty . . . ?

"Swell it out well with batter. Mate, it's a bloomin' gold-mine! It's a cert! Christ knows how many chaps can be fed off of one bloody cod—"

Yes . . . empty. Only his hollow nos-
trils sifted out the stir in the
quiet; The wandering river-wind seamed
with thin scent of salt

"An' he near went crazy! Mimi I tell ye, we near bust, watchin—"

decay, flecked with clinging coal-tar—
Crrritlkt!

"Can't, he sez, I got a tin-belly."

—It's—Oh—It's—it's! Papa. Nearly
like. It's—nearly like his teeth.

Nothing . . . A barge on a slack hauser or
a gunwale against the dock chirping
because a

"I'll raise it."

            boat was passing.
            —Papa like nearly.
            Or a door tittering to and fro in the wind.

"Heaz a can-opener fer ye I sez."

            Nothing. He crept back.

"Hemm. These last durn stairs."

            And was there, over the rail. The
            splendor shrouded in the earth, the
            titan, dormant in his lair, disdain-
            ful. And his eyes

"Runnin' hee! hee! hee! Across the lots hee! hee! jerkin' off."

            lifted

"An' I picks up a rivet in de tongs an' I sez—"

            and there was the last crossing of
            Tenth Street, the last cross—

"Heazuh a flowuh fer ye, yeller-belly, shove it up yer ass!"

            ing, and beyond, beyond the elevateds,

"How many times'll your red cock crow, Pete, befaw y' gives up?
T'ree?"

        as in the pit of the west, the last

"Yee! hee! hee! Mary, joikin'—"

        smudge of rose, staining the stem of

"Nawthin' t' do but climb—"

        the trembling, jagged

"Show culluh if yuh god beddeh!"

        chalice of the night-taut stone with

"An' I t'rows de fuck'n' rivet."

            the lees of day. And his toe crooked into
            the dipper as into a stirrup. It
            grated, stirred, slid, and—

"Dere's a star fer yeh! Watch it! T'ree Kings I god. Dey came on
huzzbeck! Yee! Hee! Hee! Mary! Nawthin' to do but wait fer day light
and go home. To a red cock crowin'. Over a statue of. A jerkin'. Cod.
Clang! Clang! Oy! Machine! Liberty! Revolt! Redeem!"

            Power
            Power! Power like a paw, titanic power,
            ripped through the earth and slammed
            against his body and shackled him

where he stood. Power! Incredible,
barbaric power! A blast, a siren of light
within him, rending, quaking, fusing his
brain and blood to a fountain of flame,
vast rockets in a searing spray! Power!
The hawk of radiance raking him with
talons of fire, battering his skull with
a beak of fire, braying his body with
pinions of intolerable light. And he
writhed without motion in the clutch of
a fatal glory, and his brain swelled
and dilated till it dwarfed the galaxies
in a bubble of refulgence—Recoiled, the
last screaming nerve clawing for survival.
He kicked—once. Terrific rams of dark-
ness collided; out of their shock space
toppled into havoc. A thin scream wobbled
through the spirals of oblivion, fell like
a brand on water, his-s-s-s-s-ed—

"W'at?

  "W'ut?

    "Va-at?

      "Gaw blimey!

   "W'atsa da ma'?"

The street paused. Eyes, a myriad of eyes, gay or sunken, rheumy, yellow or clear, slant, blood-shot, hard, boozy or bright swerved from their tasks, their play, from faces, newspapers, dishes, cards, seidels, valves, sewing machines, swerved and converged. While at the foot of Tenth Street, a quaking splendor dissolved the cobbles, the grimy structures, bleary stables, the dump-heap, river and sky into a single cymbal-clash of light. Between the livid jaws of the rail, the dipper twisted and bounced, consumed in roaring radiance, candescent—

    "Hey!"

  "Jesus!"

"Give a look! Id's rain—"

   "Shawt soicit, Mack—"

  "Mary, w'at's goin'—"

   "Schloimee, a blitz like—"

    "Hey mate!"

On Avenue D, a long burst of flame spurted from underground, growled as if the veil of earth were splitting. People were hurrying now, children scooting past them, screeching. On Avenue C, the lights of

the trolley-car waned and wavered. The motorman cursed, feeling the
power drain. In the Royal Warehouse, the blinking watchman tugged
at the jammed and stubborn window. The shriveled coal-heaver leaned
unsteadily from between the swinging door—blinked, squinted in pain,
and—

"Holy Mother O' God! Look! Will yiz!"

"Wot?"

"There's a guy layin' there! Burrhnin'!"

"Naw! Where!"

    "Gawd damn the winder!"

   "It's on Tent' Street! Look!"

"O'Toole!"

The street was filled with running men, faces carved and ghostly in
the fierce light. They shouted hoarsely. The trolley-car crawled forward.
Up above a window slammed open.

"Christ, it's a kid!"

"Yea!"

   "Don't touch 'im!"

  "Who's got a stick!"

      "A stick!"

"A stick, for Jesus sake!"

   "Mike! The shovel! Where's yer fuck'n' shov—"

"Back in Call—"

     "Oy sis a kind—"

      "Get Pete's crutch! Hey Pete!"

"Aaa! Who touched yer hump, yuh gimpty fu—"

     "Do sompt'n! Meester! Meester!"

"Yuh crummy bastard, I saw yuh sneakin'—" The hunchback
whirled, swung away on his crutches. "Fuck yiz!"

   "Oy! Oy vai! Oy vai! Oy vai!"

  "Git a cop!"

     "An embillance—go cull-oy!"

    "Don't touch 'im!"

"Bambino! Madre mia!"

"Mary. It's jus' a kid!"

"Helftz! Helftz! Helftz Yeedin! Rotivit!"

A throng ever thickening had gathered, confused, paralyzed, babbling. They squinted at the light, at the outstretched figure in the heart
of the light, tossed their arms, pointed, clawed at their cheeks, shoved,
shouted, moaned—

"Hi! Hi down there! Hi!" A voice bawled down from the height.
"Look out below! Look out!"

The crowd shrank back from the warehouse.

W-w-whack!

"It's a—"

"You take it!"

"Grab it!"

"Gimme dat fuck'n' broom!"

"Watch yerself, O'Toole!"

"Oy, a good men! Got should—"

"Oooo! De pore little kid, Mimi!"

"He's gonna do it!"

"Look oud!"

"Dunt touch!"

The man in the black shirt, tip-toed guardedly to the rails. His eyes, screwed tight against the awful glare, he squinted over his raised shoulder.

"Shove 'im away!"

"Go easy!"

"Look odda!"

"Atta boy!"

"Oy Gottinyoo!"

The worn, blackened broom-straws wedged between the child's shoulder and the cobbles. A twist of the handle. The child rolled over on his face.

"Give 'im anudder shove!"

"At's it! Git 'im away!"

"Quick! Quick!"

Once more the broom straws rammed the outstretched figure. He slid along the cobbles, cleared the tracks. Someone on the other side grabbed his arm, lifted him, carried him to the curb. The crowd swirled about in a dense, tight eddy.

"Oy! Givalt!"

"Gib'm air!"

"Is 'e boined?"

"Bennee stay by me!"

"*Is* 'e boined! Look at his shoe!"

"Oy, de pooh mama! De pooh mama!"

"Who's kid?"

"Don' know, Mack!"

"Huz pushin' ?"

"Jesus! Take 'im to a drug-store."

"Naa, woik on 'im right here. I woiked in a power house!"

"Do sompt'n! Do sompt'n!"

The writhing dipper was now almost consumed. Before the flaring light, the weird white-lipped, staring faces of the milling throng wheeled from chalk to soot and soot to chalk again—like masks of flame that charred and were rekindled; and all their frantic, gnarling bodies cut a darting splay of huge, impinging shadow, on dump-heap, warehouse, river and street—

Klang! The trolley drew up.

"Oyeee! Ers toit! Ers to-i-t! Oye-e-e-e!" A woman screamed, gagged, fainted.

"Hey! Ketch 'er!"

"Schleps aveck!"

"Wat d' hell'd she do dat fer—"

"Vawdeh!"

They dragged her away on scuffing heels to one side.

"Shit!" The motorman had jumped down from the car and seized the broom—

"Fan 'er vid de het!"

"Git off me feet, you!"

"At's it! Lean on 'im O'Toole! Push 'im down! At's it! At's it! I woiked in a power house—"

And with the broom straws the motorman flipped the mangled metal from the rail. A quake! As if leviathan leaped for the hook and fell back threshing. And darkness.

Darkness!

They grunted, the masses, stood suddenly mute a moment, for a moment silent, stricken, huddled, crushed by the pounce of ten-fold night. And a voice spoke, strained, shrunken, groping—

"Ey, paizon! She 'sa whita yet—lika you looka da slacka lime alla time! You know?"

Someone shrieked. The fainting woman moaned. The crowd muttered, whispered, seething uneasily in the dark, welcomed the loud newcomers who pierced the dense periphery—

"One side! One side!" Croaking with authority, the stone-grim uniformed one shouldered his way through. "One side!"

"De cops!"

"Dun't step on 'im!"

"Back up youz! Back up! Didja hea' me, Moses? Back up! Beat it! G'wan!" They fell back before the perilous arc of the club. "G'wan before I fan yiz! Back up! Let's see sompt'n' in hea'! Move! Move, I say!" Artificial ire flung the spittle on his lips. "Hey George!" He flung at a burly one. "Give us a hand hea', will yiz!"

"Sure! Git back you! Pete! Git that other side!"

The policeman wheeled round, squatted down beside the black-shirted one. "Don' look boined."

"Jist his shoe."

"How long wuz he on?"

"Christ! I don't know. I came ouda Callahan's an' de foist t'ing I know somebody lams a broom out of a winder, an' I grabs it an' shoves 'im off de fuck'n t'ing—"

"Sh! Must a done it himself— Naa! Dat ain't de way! Lemme have 'im." He pushed the other aside, turned the child over on his face. "Foist aid yuh gits 'em hea'." His bulky hands all but encompassed the narrow waist. "Like drownin', see?" He squeezed,

Khir-r-r-r-f! S-s-s-s-.

"I hoid 'im!"

"Yea!"

"He's meckin' him t' breed!"

"See! Gits de air in 'im."

Khir-r-r-r-f! S-s-s-s.

"Looks like he's gone, do. W'ere de hell's dat ambillance?"

"Vee culled id a'reddy, Ufficeh!"

"Arh!"

"Rap 'im on de feet arficer, I woiked in a power—"

Khir-r-r-r-f! S-s-s-s.

"Anybody know 'im? Any o' youz know dis kid?"

The inner and the craning semi-circle muttered blankly. The policeman rested his ear against the child's back.

"Looks like he's done fer, butchuh can't tell—"

Khir-r-r-r-f! S-s-s-s.

"He sez he's dead, Mary."

"Dead!"

"Oy! Toit!"

"Gott sei donk, id's nod mine Elix—"

Khir-r-r-r-f. S-s-s-s.

"Sit im helfin vie a toitin bankis." The squat shirt-sleeved Jew whose tight belt cut his round belly into the letter B turned to the lime-streaked wop—squinted, saw that communication had failed. "It'll help him like cups on a cawps," he translated—and tapped his chest with an ace of spades.

Khi-r-r-r-f. S-s-s-s.

(E-e-e-e. E-e-e-e-.

One ember fanned . . . dulling . . . uncertain)

"Here's the damned thing he threw in, Cap." The motorman shook off the crowd, held up the thinned and twisted metal.

"Yea! Wot is it?"

"Be damned if I know. Hot! Jesus!"

Khir-r-r-f. S-s-s.

(E-e-e-e.

> *Like the red pupil of the eye of darkness, the ember*
> *dilated, spun like a pinwheel, expanding, expanding,*
> *till at the very core, a white flaw rent the scarlet*
> *tissue and spread, engulfed the margin like a stain—)*

"Five hundred an' fifty volts. What a wallop!"

"He's cooked, yuh t'ink?"

"Yea. Jesus! What else!"

"Unh!" The policeman was grunting now with his efforts.

Kh-i-r-r-r-f! S-s-s-s.

> "Hey, Meester, maybe he fell on id—
> De iron—"
>> "Sure, dot's righd!"

"Id's f'om de compeny de fault!"

"Ass, how could he fall on it, fer the love O Jesus!"

The motorman turned on them savagely.

> "He could! Id's easy!"
>> "Id vuz stink—stick—sticken oud!"

"He'll sue, dun' vorry!"

"Back up, youz!"

Khi-r-r-r-f! S-s-s.

> *(Eee-e-e-e*
> *And in the white, frosty light within*
> *the red iris, a small figure slanted*
> *through a desolate street, crack-paved,*
> *rut-guttered, slanted and passed, and*
> *overhead the taut, wintry wires whined*
> *on their crosses—*
> *E-e-e-e-e.*
> *They whined, spanning the earth and sky.*
> *—Go-d-d-b! Go-o-o-ob! Go-o-b! G'bye!* . . .

"Makin' a case fer a shyster. C'n yuh beat it!"

"Ha-a-ha! Hunh!"

> "I'm late. Dere it is." The motorman dropped the gnarled and
blackened dipper beside the curb.

> "An Irisher chuchim!"

"Ain't it a dirty shame—"

> "Noo vud den!"
>> "Wat's happened, chief?"

"Dere give a look!"

"Let's git troo dere!"

"Unh!"

Kh-i-r-r-r-f! S-s-s-s.

> (—G'by-e-e. Mis-s-s-l-e. M-s-ter. Hi-i-i-i.
> Wo-o-o-d.
> And a man in a tugboat, hair under
> arm-pits, hung from a pole among the
> wires, his white undershirt glittering.
> He grinned and whistled and with every
> note yellow birds flew to the roof.)

"T'ink a shot o' sompt'n' 'll do 'im any good?"

"Nuh! Choke 'im if he's alive."

"Yeh! If hiz alife!"

"W'ea's 'e boined?"

"Dey say id's de feet wid de hen's wid eveytingk."

"Unh!"

Khi-r-r-r-f! S-s-s-s.

> (We-e-e-e-
> The man in the wires stirred. The
> Wires twanged brightly. The blithe
> and golden cloud of birds filled the
> sky.)

"Unh!"

> (Klang!
> The milk tray jangled. Leaping he
> neared. From roof-top to roof-top,
> over streets, over alley ways, over
> areas and lots, his father soared with
> a feathery ease. He set the trays
> down, stooped as if searching, paused—)

"Unh!"

> (A hammer! A hammer! He snarled,
> brandished it, it snapped like a whip.
> The birds vanished. Horror thickened
> the air.)

"Unh!"

"He's woikin' hard!"

"Oy! Soll im Gott helfin!"

"He no waka."

> (Around him now, the cobbles stretched
> away. Stretched away in the swirling

> *dark like the faces of a multitude aghast*
> *and frozen—)*

"Unh!"

> *(W-e-e-e-e-p! Wheep! Overhead the*
> *brandished hammer whirred and whistled.*
> *The doors of a hallway slowly opened.*
> *Buoyed up by the dark, a coffin drifted*
> *out, floated down the stoop, and while*
> *confetti rained upon it, bulged and*
> *billowed—)*

"Unh!"

Khi-r-r-r-rf! S-s-s-s-

> *(—Zwank! Zwank! Zwank!*
> *The man in the wires writhed and*
> *groaned, his slimy, purple chicken-*
> *guts slipping through his fingers.*
> *David touched his lips. The soot*
> *came off on his hand. Unclean.*
> *Screaming, he turned to flee, seized*
> *a wagon wheel to climb upon it. There*
> *were no spokes—only cogs like a*
> *clock-wheel. He screamed again, beat*
> *the yellow disk with his fists.)*

"Unh!"

Kh-i-r-r-rf! S-s-s-s.

"Didja see it?"

"See it? Way up on twelft'!"

"I could ivin see id in de houz—on de cods."

"Me? I vas stand in basement—fok t'ing mack blind!"

"Five hundred an' fifty volts."

> *(As if on hinges, blank, enormous*
> *mirrors arose, swung slowly upward*
> *face to face. Within the facing*
> *glass, vast panels deployed, lifted a*
> *steady wink of opaque pages until*
> *an endless corridor dwindled into*
> *night.)*

"Unh! Looks Jewish t' me."

"Yea, map o' Jerusalem, all right."

"Poor bastard! Unh!"

"Couldn't see him at foist!"

"Unh!"

Kh-i-r-r-rf! S-s-s-s.

> *("You!" Above the whine of the*
> *whirling hammer, his father's voice*
> *thundered. "You!"*
> *David wept, approached the glass,*
> *peered in. Not himself was there,*
> *not even in the last and least of*
> *the infinite mirrors, but the cheder*
> *wall, the cheder)*

"Junheezis!"

Kh-i-r-r-rf! S-s-s-s.

> *(Wall sunlit, white-washed. "Chadgodya!"*
> *moaned the man in the wires. "One*
> *kid one only kid." And the wall dwindled*
> *and was a square of pavement with a foot-*
> *print in it—half green, half black,*
> *"I too have trodden there." And*
> *shrank within the mirror, and the*
> *cake of ice melted in the panel be-*
> *yond. "Eternal years," the voice*
> *wailed, "Not even he.")*

"Unh!"

  "Gittin' winded? Want me to try it?"

"Nunh!"

  "Look at 'im sweat!"

      "Vy not? Soch a coat he's god on!"

        "Wot happened, brother?"

        "Cheh! He esks yet!"

    "Back up, you!"

"Unh!"

Kh-i-r-r-r-f! S-s-s-s.

> *(And faded, revealing a shoe box full*
> *of calendar leaves, "the red day must*
> *come.")*

"Unh! Did he move or sumpt'n?"

  "Couldn't see."

> *(which lapsed into a wooden box with*
> *a sliding cover like the chalk-boxes*
> *in school, whereon a fiery figure*
> *sat astride a fish. "G-e-e-e o-o-o d-e-e-e-!"*
> *The voice spelled out. And shrank and was*
> *a cube of sugar gripped be-)*

"Unh!"

Kh-i-r-r-r-f! S-s-s-s.

"Shah! Y'hea id?"

"W'a?"

"Yea! It's commin!"

"Id's commin'!"

"I sees it!"

"Meester Politsman de—"

"Back up, youz!"

A faint jangle seeped through the roar of the crowd.

"Unh!"

> *(tween the softly glowing tongs. "So
> wide we stretch no further—" But when
> he sought to peer beyond, suddenly the
> mirrors shifted, and—*
> *"Go down!" his father's voice thun-*
> *dered, "Go down!" The mirrors lay*
> *beneath him now; what were the groins*
> *now jutted out in stairs, concentric*
> *ogives, bottomless steps. "Go down!*
> *"Go down!" The inexorable voice beat*
> *like a hand upon his back. He*
> *screamed, de—)*

Jangle! Angle! Angle! Angle!

"Dere! It's comin'!"

"Look! Look hod dere!"

"Orficer!"

Angle! Jang!

"Christ's about time!"

The crowd split like water before a prow, reformed in the wake, surged round the ambulance, babbling, squall—

> *(scended. Down! Down into darkness,*
> *darkness that tunneled the heart of*
> *darkness, darkness fathomless. Each*
> *step he took, he shrank, grew smaller*
> *with the unseen panels, the graduate*
> *vise descending, passed from stage*
> *to dwindling stage, dwindling. At*
> *each step shed the husks of being,*
> *and himself tapering always downward*
> *in the funnel of the night. And now*
> *a chip—a step-a flake-a step-a shred.*

> *A mote. A pinpoint. And now the seed*
> *of nothing, and nebulous nothing, and*
> *nothing, And he was not. . . .)*

ing, stabbing the dark with hands. "Ppprrr!" Lips flickered audibly as the blue-coat rose. With one motion, palm wiped brow, dug under sweat-stained collar. Softly bald, the bareheaded, white garbed interne hopped spryly from the ambulance step, black bag swinging in hand, wedged whitely through the milling crowd. Conch-like the mob surrounded, contracted, trailed him within the circle, umbiliform—

"Lectric shot; Doc!"

"De hospital!"

"Knocked him cold!"

"Shock?"

" 'Zee dead?"

"Yea, foolin' aroun' wid de—"

"Shawt soicited it, Doc!"

"Yea, boined!"

"Vee sin id Docteh!"

"Git back, youz!" The officer crouched, snarled, but never sprang. "I'll spit right in yer puss!"

"Mmm!" The interne pinched the crease of his trousers, pulled them up, and kneel—

"Guess yuh better take 'im witchuh, Doc. Couldn't do a goddam t'ing wit—"

"He's gonna hea' de heart! See?"

(But—)

ing beside the beveled curbstone, applied his ear to the narrow breast.

"Shoe's boined. See it, Doc?"

> *(the voice still lashed the nothingness*
> *that was, denying it oblivion. "Now find!*
> *Now find! Now find!" And nothingness*
> *whimpered being dislodged from night,*
> *and would have hidden again. But out*
> *of the darkness, one ember)*

"Take it off, will you, let's have a look at it."

> *(flowered, one ember in a mirr—)*

"Sure!" Blunt, willing fingers ripped the

> *(or, swimming without motion in the*
> *motion of its light.)*

buttons open,

"Hiz gonna look."

> *(In a cellar is)*

dragged the shoes off,
>   *(Coal! In a cellar is)*

tore the stocking down, re—
>   *(Coal! And it was brighter than the*
>   *pith of lightning and milder than pearl,)*

vealing a white puffy ring about the ankle, at
>   *(And made the darkness dark because*
>   *the dark had culled its radiance for*
>   *that jewel. Zwank!)*

>   "Is it boined?"
>   "Can't see, c'n you?"

which the interne glanced while he drew
>   "Waddayuh say, Doc?"

a squat blue vial from his bag, grimaced, un-
>   *(Zwank! Zwank! Nothingness beati-*
>   *fied reached out its hands. Not cold*
>   *the ember was. Not scorching. But as*
>   *if all eternity's caress were fused and*
>   *granted in one instant. Silence)*

corked it, expertly tilted it before
>   *(struck that terrible voice upon the*
>   *height, stilled the whirling hammer.*
>   *Horror and the night fell away. Ex-*
>   *alted, he lifted his head and screamed*
>   *to him among the wires—"Whistle,*
>   *mister! Whistle!)*

the quiet nostrils. The crowd fell silent, tensely watching.
>   "Amonya."
>   "Smells strong!"
>   "Stinks like in de shool on Yom Kippur."
>   *(Mister! Whistle! Whistle! Whistle!*
>   *Whistle, Mister! Yellow birds!)*

On the dark and broken sidewalk, the limp body gasped, quivered. The interne lifted him, said sharply to the officer. "Hold his arms! He'll fight!"
>   "Hey look! Hey look!"
>   "He's kickin'!"
>   (Whistle, mister! WHISTLE!")

"W'at's he sayin' ?"
"There! Hold him now!"
>   (A spiked star of pain of conscious-
>   ness burst within him)

"Mimi! He's awright! He's awright!"

"Yeh?"

"Yea!"

"No kiddin'! No kiddin'!"

"Yea!"

"Yuh!"

"Yeh!"

"Oi, Gott sei dank!"

SELECTED
BIBLIOGRAPHY

GENERAL

Adamic, Louis. *My America, 1928-1938*. New York, 1938. An immigrant's view.

Allen, Frederick L. *Since Yesterday*. New York, 1940. A "popular" chronicle.

Asch, Nathan. *The Road: In Search of America*. New York, 1937. Record of a cross-country journey.

Bagnall, Joseph A., ed. *Depression Dialogue: An Anthology of Representative Political Dialogues of the Depression Decade*. Dubuque, 1965.

Beard, Charles A. and Mary R. Beard. *America in Midpassage*. New York, 1939. A political and economic history of the twenties and thirties.

Bernstein, Irving. *The Lean Years: A History of the American Worker, 1920-1933*. Boston, 1960.

Bird, Caroline. *The Invisible Scar*. New York, 1966. The lasting effects of the depression.

Browder, Earl. *The People's Front*. New York, 1938. Speeches and articles.

Caldwell, Erskine and Margaret Bourke-White. *You Have Seen Their Faces*. New York, 1937. Southern sharecroppers.

Cole, G.D.H. *Socialism and Fascism, 1931-1939*. New York, 1960.

Draper, Theodore. *The Roots of American Communism*. New York, 1957.

Feis, Herbert. *1933: Characters in Crisis*. Boston, 1966.

Galbraith, John Kenneth. *The Great Crash, 1929*. Boston, 1955.

Gilfillan, Lauren. *I Went To Pit College*. New York, 1934. The depression's effect on a mining town in Pennsylvania.

Hoyt, Edwin P. *The Tempering Years*. New York, 1963. Social and political study.

Kempton, Murray. *Part of Our Time: Some Ruins and Monuments of the Thirties*. New York, 1955. Contains portraits of several outstanding figures of the thirties.

Lange, Dorothea & Paul S. Taylor. *An American Exodus: A Record of Human Erosion*. New York, 1939. A pictorial study of the plight of the migratory worker.

Leighton, George. *Five Cities: The Story of Their Youth and Old Age*. New York, 1939.

Lyons, Eugene. *The Red Decade: The Stalinist Penetration of America*. Indianapolis, 1941.

McKenney, Ruth. *Industrial Valley*. New York, 1939. Rubber workers in Akron.

MacLeish, Archibald. *Land of the Free—U.S.A.* New York, 1938. Farm Security Administration photographs "illustrated" by MacLeish's poem.

McWilliams, Carey. *Factories in the Field*. Boston, 1939. An account of the migratory labor problem in the United States.

Mitchell, Broadus. *Depression Decade: From New Era Through New Deal, 1929-1941*. New York, 1947. A standard economic history.

Payne, Robert, ed. *The Civil War in Spain, 1936-1939*. New York, 1962. First-hand accounts of the war.

Romasco, Albert U. *The Poverty of Abundance: Hoover, the Nation, the Depression*. New York, 1965.

Rorty, James. *Where Life Is Better: An Unsentimental American Journey*. New York, 1936. Sees America as "building the stockades of fascism."

Schlesinger, Arthur M., Jr. *The Age of Roosevelt*. 3 Vols. Boston, 1957-1960.

Seldes, Gilbert. *The Years of the Locust (America, 1929-1932)*. Boston, 1933.

Shannon, David A., ed. *The Great Depression*. New Jersey, 1960. A collection of contemporary newspaper accounts, articles, case histories, and essays.

Stearns, Harold E., ed. *America Now: An*

Inquiry into Civilization in the United States by Thirty-six Americans. New York, 1938.

Swing, Raymond. *Forerunners of American Fascism.* New York, 1935. Includes discussions of Coughlin, Long, Townsend, and Hearst.

Thomas, Hugh. *The Spanish Civil War.* New York, 1961. A history.

Tull, Charles J. *Father Coughlin and the New Deal.* Syracuse, 1965.

Warren, Frank. *Liberals and Communism: The "Red Decade" Revisited.* Bloomington, 1966.

Wecter, Dixon. *The Age of the Great Depression, 1929-1941.* New York, 1948. A general history.

Wilson, Edmund. *The American Earthquake: A Documentary of the Jazz Age, the Great Depression, and the New Deal.* New York, 1958.

WPA. *These Are Our Lives: As Told By the People and Written by the Members of the Federal Writers' Project of the Works Progress Administration in North Carolina, Tennessee, and Georgia.* Chapel Hill, 1939.

LITERARY MEMOIRS, STUDIES, AND COLLECTIONS

Aaron, Daniel. *Writers on the Left. Episodes in American Literary Communism.* New York, 1961.

_____ , moderator. "Thirty Years Later: Memories of the First American Writers' Congress," *The American Scholar,* XXXV (Summer, 1966), 495-516. A symposium with Kenneth Burke, Malcolm Cowley, Granville Hicks, and William Philips.

Beach, Joseph Warren. *American Fiction, 1920-1940.* New York, 1942.

Clurman, Harold. *The Fervent Years: The Story of the Group Theater and the Thirties.* New York, 1950.

Cowley, Malcolm. "The Sense of Guilt," *Kenyon Review,* CV (Spring, 1965), 260-274. The best statement of Cowley's present attitude toward the quarrels of the thirties.

Eastman, Max. *Love and Revolution: My Journey Through An Epoch.* New York, 1964.

Filler, Louis, ed. *The Anxious Years: America in the Nineteen Thirties: A*

Collection of Contemporary Writing. New York, 1963.

Flanagan, Hallie. *Arena.* New York, 1940. By the Director of the Federal Theatre Project of the Works Progress Administration.

French, Warren. *The Social Novel at the End of an Era.* Carbondale, 1966.

Frohock, Wilbur M. *The Novel of Violence in America, 1920-1950.* Dallas, 1950.

Geismar, Maxwell. *Writers in Crisis: The American Novel, 1925-1940.* Boston, 1963.

Gurko, Leo. *The Angry Decade.* New York, 1947. Social-literary study.

Hart, Henry, ed. *The American Writers' Congress.* New York, 1935. Speeches delivered at the first American Writers' Congress.

_____ . *The Writer in the Changing World.* New York, 1937. The second American Writers' Congress.

Hicks, Granville. *Part of the Truth: An Autobiography.* New York, 1965.

Hicks, Granville, et. al., eds. *Proletarian Literature in the United States.* New York, 1935. A major anthology of proletarian writing, with an introduction by Joseph Freeman.

Kazin, Alfred. *On Native Grounds: An Interpretation of Modern American Prose Literature.* New York, 1942.

_____ . *Starting Out In the Thirties.* Boston, 1965. Reminiscences.

Phillips, William. "What Happened in the 30's," *Commentary,* XXXIV (September, 1962), 204-212.

Rahv, Philip. "Proletarian Literature: A Political Autopsy," *Southern Review,* IV (Winter, 1939), 616-628.

Rideout, Walter B. *The Radical Novel in the United States: 1900-1954.* Cambridge, Mass., 1956. Contains a list of major proletarian novels.

Swados, Harvey, ed. *The American Writer and the Great Depression.* Indianapolis, 1966. Anthology.

Wilson, Edmund. *The Shores of Light: A Literary Chronicle of the Twenties and Thirties.* New York, 1952.

WPA. *American Stuff: An Anthology of Prose and Verse by Members of the Federal Writers Project.* New York, 1937.